DARWIN'S BLUFF

Darwin's Bluff

The Mystery of the Book Darwin Never Finished

Robert F. Shedinger

Seattle Discovery Institute Press 2024

Description

Tucked away in Charles Darwin's surviving papers is a manuscript of almost 300,000 words that he never completed. It was his sequel to *The Origin of Species*. It was the book he had promised would finally supply solid empirical evidence for the creative power of natural selection, evidence he admitted was absent from the *Origin*, which he repeatedly described as a "mere abstract." Darwin soon abandoned his sequel, though he never revealed that decision to those who awaited its appearance. The mystery of why Darwin didn't finish his sequel has never been satisfactorily resolved. In this fascinating piece of historical detective work, Robert Shedinger draws on Darwin's letters, private notebooks, and the unfinished manuscript itself to piece together the puzzle and reveal an embarrassing truth: Darwin never finished his sequel because in the end he could not deliver the promised goods. His book, begun in earnest, devolved into a bluff.

Copyright Notice

Library Cataloging Data

Darwin's Bluff: The Mystery of the Book Darwin Never Finished

by Robert F. Shedinger

284 pages, 6 x 9 inches

Library of Congress Control Number: 2023952153

ISBN: 978-1-63712-037-8 (Paperback), 978-1-63712-039-2 (Kindle), 978-1-63712-038-5 (EPUB)

BISAC: BIO015000 BIOGRAPHY & AUTOBIOGRAPHY / Science & Technology

BISAC: SCI027000 SCIENCE / Life Sciences / Evolution

BISAC: SCI034000 SCIENCE / History

Publisher Information

Discovery Institute Press, 208 Columbia Street, Seattle, WA 98104

Internet: http://www.discoveryinstitutepress.com/

Published in the United States of America on acid-free paper.

First Edition, February, 2024

Advance Praise

It is a testimony to the mythical status of Charles Darwin that most of his admirers do not know or do not take seriously the fact that *The Origin of Species* was sold as an abstract of a much longer work. Reviewers of the *Origin* took Darwin at his word and cut him considerable slack when evaluating the case for evolution by natural selection. The promised volume would presumably explain the modus operandi of this mysterious process. However, the promised volume never came, though a hefty manuscript survived its author. Robert Shedinger takes a deep dive into Darwin's correspondence, as well as the unfinished follow-up manuscript, and concludes that Darwin abandoned the project simply because he couldn't meet the objections to natural selection made even by broadly sympathetic reviewers of the *Origin*. In addition, Shedinger casts a forensic eye on how scholarly interpretations of Darwin's life have subtly served to obscure this ultimate intellectual failure. The result is nothing short of a demythologization of modern biology's origin story.

—**Steve Fuller**, Auguste Comte Professor of Social Epistemology, University of Warwick, author of *Dissent over Descent*

Darwin's Bluff particularly resonates with me. In 2009, as a card-carrying Darwinist serving as a fossil curator in one of Germany's natural history museums, I mounted an exhibit showing Darwin's famous work outweighing the works of his leading modern detractors. To prepare for hard questions from reporters, I decided to give the naysayer books a quick read, books I had been assured were all froth and foolishness. I soon discovered that I had been misled. The arguments in those pages were neither shallow nor illogical. Instead, I came to see that it was actually modern Darwinism that rested on a carefully constructed bluff.

Robert Shedinger's latest book shows that the bluffing has a long pedigree, stretching back to the master of Down House himself. What emerges from Shedinger's deep dive into Darwin's private writings is a picture of a man wracked by doubts and insecurities about his evolutionary theory, but also a man not above a good bluff, one he sold so artfully that he may even have persuaded himself.

—**Günter Bechly**, former curator for amber and fossil insects in the Department of Paleontology at the State Museum of Natural History (SMNS) in Stuttgart, Germany; Senior Fellow with Discovery Institute's Center for Science and Culture

Robert Shedinger's fascinating book explores a puzzling question about Darwin's career: Why didn't he ever publish a longer book on evolution by natural selection that he had almost completed? Darwin continually promised his contemporaries that his forthcoming work would provide the evidence he was unable to include in his shorter book, *The Origin of Species*, which he called an "abstract" of his theory. Through painstaking historical research, Shedinger sheds light on Darwin's modus operandi and on the shortcomings of his scientific evidence, thus dismantling what Shedinger calls the mythology surrounding Darwin.

—**Richard Weikart**, Professor of History, California State University, Stanislaus; author of *Darwinian Racism: How Darwinism Influenced Hitler, Nazism, and White Nationalism*

Stung by early reviewers' resistance to many unsubstantiated conjectures in which his *Origin of Species* abounds, Charles Darwin announced he would bring out a more detailed sequel to quell the opposition of skeptics. Robert Shedinger shows that this promise was essentially a bluff since the promised book on natural selection never appeared. In the early 1860s, Darwin instead devoted his energies to a botanical study of orchids. He nevertheless hoped that, by describing the exquisite "contrivances" found in orchids, his readers would see in these adaptations the power of natural selection at work. Yet precisely the opposite impression was created. Expressing a common sentiment in a review of the volume, an anonymous reviewer wrote in 1862, "The notion of the origin of species by natural selection, we continue to regard as an ingenious mistake." Worse, Darwin's *Orchids* volume was favorably compared with the Bridgewater Treatises in its supposed contribution to Christian apologetics!

Contextualizing Darwin's own doubts and insecurities by exhaustively researched reference to his correspondence, Shedinger opposes many accretions of Darwinian hagiography. It would be a sensible step forward, Shedinger concludes, to take Darwin at his word when he wrote in a letter to Asa Gray in 1857, "I am quite conscious that my speculations run quite beyond the bounds of true science." This book is particularly to be recommended to those tempted to view Darwin as an unquestionable Victorian sage.

—**Neil Thomas**, Reader emeritus in Modern European Languages, Durham University (GB); author of *Taking Leave of Darwin: A Longtime Agnostic Discovers the Case for Design*

Robert Shedinger's accomplishment deserves much attention within my own primary field of the history of science. Historians of Darwin have largely overlooked what Shedinger here demonstrates: The rhetorical success of Darwin's *Origin of Species* owed much to the early readers imagining mountains of evidence forthcoming in the much larger book that Darwin promised would soon be finalized and published. The evasiveness of this maneuver is well documented in Shedinger's analysis of Darwin's forever unfinished—and evidentially disappointing—"big book" and his collegial correspondence.

—**Michael N. Keas**, author of *Unbelievable: 7 Myths About the History and Future of Science and Religion*

Robert Shedinger's portrait of Darwin is far different from the reverent hagiographies we've come to expect. In accessible, enticing prose—and drawing from more than 260 letters Darwin wrote or received from his contemporaries—Shedinger shows us sides of the man long obscured. Darwin emerges as a striver whose reach exceeded his grasp in his failing to provide ironclad evidence for his famous theory. The candor in his letters peels back the years; we discover a Darwin whose quirks, motivations, and foibles make him recognizably human. Shedinger's meticulously researched and carefully argued volume takes the patina off this Victorian legend, opening Darwin to a most appropriate fresh inspection.

—**Michael A. Jawer**, author of *Sensitive Soul* and co-author of *The Spiritual Anatomy of Emotion* and *Your Emotional Type*

Why did Darwin call *The Origin of Species* an abstract? Anyone interested in Darwin's evolving strategy to roll out his revolutionary ideas in two distinct stages will find here a luscious banquet. Robert Shedinger's *Darwin's Bluff* will shock most readers in every chapter. In my own field of the rhetoric of science, the varied tactics of persuasion employed by Darwin are brought to light. Best of all, as we listen in on his own correspondence, Darwin himself comes alive in ways we never imagined. So, what's the untold story of Darwin's abandoned "big book" project? Carve out a few hours and feast on Shedinger's vivid reconstruction and resolution of this mystery.

—**Tom Woodward**, Research Professor at Trinity College of Florida; author of *Doubts about Darwin: A Rhetorical History of Intelligent Design* and *The Mysterious Epigenome* with ophthalmologist James Gills

The adequacy of natural selection to explain evolution and life has been seriously challenged on a number of fronts—from paleontology, biochemistry, molecular biology, and genetics to theology, philosophy of mind, and the history of religions. In a minutely researched piece of new scholarship, Robert Shedinger shows us that *The Origin of Species* was intended as an abstract of a theory that Darwin could never substantiate, and that, more telling still, the confident scientific naturalism for which Darwin is mythologized today is largely a set of rhetorical devices and dogmatic beliefs that add up to a massive bluff with significant negative consequences, particularly with respect to race, gender, scientific inquiry, religious belief, and intellectual freedom. *Darwin's Bluff* is the history of science and the study of religion at their best, brought together toward a more nuanced future.

—**Jeffrey J. Kripal**, J. Newton Rayzor Professor of Religion at Rice University; author of *The Flip: Epiphanies of Mind and the Future of Knowledge*

ACKNOWLEDGMENTS

The road toward this book began several years ago when I quite accidently noticed that my undergraduate library had, back in the 1980s, begun collecting Cambridge University Press's publication of the Darwinian correspondence. It was out of sheer curiosity that I decided one day to pick up the first volume and start to essentially read Darwin's mail. I was quickly hooked and entranced by the Victorian drama of life, loss, and discovery playing out in these letters, thus beginning the long journey to the present publication. I would like to thank the long-since-retired biology professors whose interest in Charles Darwin prompted the library to begin investing in this collection. I would never have even thought about reading this material without this ease of access.

I would also like to thank the Luther College interlibrary loan staff who so efficiently tracked down many obscure references and sources. Thanks also to Tyler Anderson, a Facebook friend whom I have never met but who provided me unintentionally with an important lead by posting about an article by Janet Browne that I had not previously seen. This article opened up several important avenues of research that have made this book richer. Score one for social media!

Much of the research for this book was done during the Covid era, making travel impossible. Until recently, serious primary source research into Charles Darwin required a trip to Cambridge University. But due to the recent development of the Darwin Online project, much of this archival material is now available at the touch of a button. Many thanks are due to John van Wyhe and all those who have worked to make this invaluable resource possible. I could not have written this book without it.

Thanks also to John West at Discovery Institute for his interest in my work and encouragement to submit my manuscript to Discovery

Institute Press. And thanks to Jonathan Witt for his thoughtful and thorough editing, which has strengthened this book in innumerable ways and saved me from some embarrassing errors. Any remaining errors are, of course, my responsibility.

Finally, thanks to Tina, Amey, and Tyler for their patience with my Darwin obsession and their continuing support of all my scholarly endeavors.

Contents

Introduction

Does the world need another book about Charles Darwin? What can anyone say that has not already been said about this seminal figure, considering the wealth of literature written about him? The simple answer is yes, we do need another book about Charles Darwin, for there are aspects of his life and work that have surprisingly continued to evade the attention of his many biographers and interpreters.

The very human Charles Darwin has grown into a mythological figure—the paradigmatic example of a true scientist—without whom nothing in biology would make sense, in the words of Theodosius Dobzhansky. Unfortunately, this mythological figure would be scarcely recognizable to Darwin's own contemporaries.

Happily for the present enterprise, the flesh-and-blood Charles Darwin is considerably more interesting than the two-dimensional Darwin of the hagiographies.

The state of his scientific legacy is also more intriguing than those same hagiographies would allow—intriguing because it is embattled in ways confessed to in some of the peer-reviewed literature and at high-level scientific conferences but rarely acknowledged beyond these specialized contexts.

Modern scientific advances in fields like molecular biology, genomics, epigenetics, paleontology, developmental biology, and more are raising significant questions about the power of the Darwinian mechanism of variation and natural selection to account for the evolutionary history of life on Earth. Some are calling for an extended evolutionary synthesis while others believe the entire Darwinian edifice needs to be overhauled. It is no longer clear that Darwin can be said to have answered the question of the origin of species. There is thus no reason to begin an investigation into his life and work with the assumption that he did.

One effect of Darwinian mythology has been to downplay the nineteenth-century Englishman's own characterization of *The Origin of Species* as a mere abstract of his species theory, a summary lacking much of the facts, evidence, and authorities he promised would follow in a later work. The *Origin* is usually treated as Darwin's magnum opus, a characterization in keeping with Darwinian mythology but out of step with Darwin's own view of his work. In truth, *The Origin of Species* was an abstract of a much larger book on species that Darwin was working on (and that was three-quarters complete) before events forced him to put the larger book aside and instead publish a mere abstract of it.

Once the *Origin* was in circulation, Darwin's many correspondents anticipated that he would quickly follow up with the publication of his big book on species so they could better evaluate the argument for natural selection made in the *Origin*. Indeed, Darwin himself created this expectation both in the *Origin* and in his correspondence. Even early reviewers of the *Origin* noted the lack of empirical evidence for natural selection but gave Darwin the benefit of the doubt since the *Origin* was a mere abstract and therefore could not be expected to provide all the evidence. Given the anticipation among Darwin's readers for the big book on species, anticipation that Darwin himself repeatedly stoked, why did he never publish the big book? This question is rarely asked.

A rough, handwritten manuscript of Darwin's big book, titled *Natural Selection*, survived among his papers and was published by Cambridge University Press in 1975.[1] Yet despite the easy access scholars now have to this work (I bought a copy on Amazon), there has been little detailed engagement with its contents or comparison of this work with its abstracted form in the *Origin*. Such a comparison proves enlightening, for it serves to highlight the secondary nature of the *Origin* as a hastily written abstract rather than a finely honed scientific treatise, thus challenging the iconic status of the *Origin* as the foundational text of the modern biological sciences. This, of course, may be precisely why the big book gets overlooked.

Another reason the big book has been largely ignored, I hope to show, is that it does not deliver the promised goods. This, I will also argue, is the best explanation for why Darwin never brought the book to print. It wasn't, as one might suppose, that he had made little headway on it and simply lacked the time or energy to produce it. Abstracts are usually distillations of longer works already in existence. So, if the *Origin*, as Darwin constantly repeats, is only an abstract, it would suggest the big book on species already existed in some substantial form prior to 1859. And in fact, this was the case. The manuscript contained nine chapters and was close to 300,000 words in length. It would likely have been around 400,000 words complete. Given that this book was nearly three-quarters complete, why did Darwin never publish it? And why did he instead turn to the study of orchids as a follow-up to the *Origin*? Because, as will become clear, he came to see that it did not answer some key criticisms that the *Origin* had elicited. So, he abandoned the project, even as he allowed anticipation of its publication to persist for many years.

To be sure, Darwin's orchid book, which he called "a flank movement on the enemy,"[2] did attempt to provide some of the evidence for natural selection missing from the *Origin* (and, as it turns out, missing from the big book as well). He tried to outflank his opponents by putting before them an entirely new work on the numerous contrivances (Darwin's word) found among orchid flowers to ensure their cross-fertilization by insects. Surely this would impress his readers with the power of natural selection to evolve all these exquisite contrivances.

But Darwin's strategy failed. Reviewers of his orchid book read it as providing evidence for natural theology, not natural selection. And surprisingly, even Darwin himself in one place likened his orchid book to the Bridgewater Treatises, a series of writings designed to extol the power of God manifest in nature! Could anything be more ironic than that Charles Darwin, the poster child for the triumph of scientific naturalism in biology, actually advanced the cause of natural theology in his day? This is an aspect of his life and work that has been entirely erased by the prevailing mythological Darwinian narrative.

For all these reasons, a more nuanced assessment of Darwin's evolutionary writings is warranted.

In my engagement with Darwin, I will give pride of place to his voluminous correspondence as the evidentiary basis of this more critical portrait of a truly enigmatic Victorian figure. The argument that lies ahead cites more than 250 letters written by and to Darwin up to the year 1863, some never cited in Darwinian biographies. These letters represent Darwin's engagement with more than seventy friends, family members, and scientific correspondents. I have elected to adorn the book with many direct quotations from these letters, since I think it is crucial for readers to hear Darwin's own voice on the page as much as possible to truly encounter the thought patterns and rhetorical style of this fascinating individual.

Many of Darwin's biographers take the reverse approach—providing their own paraphrases of Darwin's words—which has the effect of subordinating Darwin to the mythological figure the biography exists to perpetuate. I have also elected, for authenticity's sake, to retain Darwin's spelling and punctuation rather than correct them to modern standards. We need to let Darwin speak for himself. It turns out that Darwin, given the opportunity, is quite capable of dismantling his own mythology.

Who Was the Real Charles Darwin?

In searching for this more authentic Darwin, we will pay particular attention to the many letters he wrote and received up through the year 1863. Unless otherwise noted, all letters mentioned in this book are taken from Frederick Burkhardt et al., eds., *The Correspondence of Charles Darwin* (Cambridge University Press) and can easily be located based on the date and addressee of the letter.[3] In addition, an index of letters cited, arranged chronologically, appears in the back matter of the book. (Many of these letters are, as of this writing, freely available online at the Darwin Correspondence Project.)

Chapter 1 will limn the mythological Darwin found in many of his biographies, show how even mainstream biographers have begun calling that portrait into question, and begin to show how Darwin himself contributed to the mythology. The opening chapter will pay particular attention to one rhetorical technique Darwin employed almost obsessively, involving his health.

Chapter 2 considers Darwin as a geologist. Long before he turned to questions about the diversity of living organisms, his main interest was geology. While aboard the *Beagle*, Darwin read Charles Lyell's *Principles of Geology*. Lyell had replaced the geological theory of catastrophism with the principle of uniformitarianism. Catastrophism taught that the Earth's geological features resulted from sudden cataclysmic events (like a global flood) while uniformitarianism taught that the Earth's geological features could be explained by slow, gradual change brought about by the more mundane processes of wind and water erosion, earthquakes, and volcanic eruptions acting over enormous spans of time. Darwin was convinced by Lyell's theory and spent much of his time in South America seeking evidence for it.

After the voyage, Darwin continued his interest in geology, developing a theory on the origin of the parallel roads of Glen Roy in Scotland as well as a theory about coral reefs. Why is Darwin's early interest in geology relevant to his more famous biological work? First, because it challenges the commonly accepted notion that the *Beagle* voyage was absolutely formative for Darwin's species work, and second, because some of Darwin's geological theories turned out to be wrong, shining a light on some of his weaknesses as a scientist.

Of course, Darwin did eventually turn to the species question and began trying to accumulate evidence for it. This involved running various experiments. Chapter 3 focuses on this side of Darwin. He had little formal training in science, his only university degree being the general Bachelor of Arts degree from Cambridge. Did it show in the way he conducted his experiments? What kinds of experiments did he run, and what did he think about the results? Do his letters describing these efforts suggest the competence of a professional experimenter, or is the portrait that emerges more that of a plucky amateur? And if the latter, what light does this shed on the *Origin*?

Chapters 4 and 5 focus on the writing and publishing of the *Origin*, and the responses to the book. What was Darwin's thought process as he wrote his abstract? Why did he encourage his readers to view it as only an abstract? How did people respond to the book? How did Darwin respond to his critics? And just how confident was Darwin that he had solved the problem of the origin of species?

Chapter 6 turns to Darwin's big book. Darwin drafted most of it, repeatedly promised that he would finish and publish it, but ultimately declined to do so. Happily for contemporary scholars, the unfinished manuscript was published a century later. The work has received surprisingly little attention, given that it is Darwin's big, promised book. After all, it was supposed to provide the crucial evidence for the miraculous creative powers of natural selection, evidence that he conceded was largely absent from his "mere abstract," *The Origin of Species*. In this chapter we will give it the attention it deserves, explore the question of why Darwin left it unfinished and unpublished, and see what the book can teach us about Darwin the man and his theory of evolution.

Chapter 7 turns to the curious fact that Darwin, immediately after publishing the *Origin*, immersed himself in the study of orchids and the many ways they were structured to ensure their cross-fertilization by insects. The readers of the *Origin* were awaiting the appearance of Darwin's promised big book on natural selection so that they could better evaluate the arguments presented in Darwin's abstract. So why did Darwin put aside the big book and turn to botany, something he referred to as a mere hobbyhorse? I have suggested an answer above, but there is much more to be said on the matter.

In a final chapter, I will consider several ways that Darwinian mythology obscures other aspects of Darwin and his work. For example, while it is true that Darwin came from abolitionist roots and himself detested slavery, what were his real views on race and racism? To what extent, if any, was Darwin himself partly responsible for the development of later scientific racism and the eugenics movement that drew on his work?

Likewise, what about his views on gender roles and sexuality? Darwin's sexual selection theory has recently come under the microscope of scientifically informed feminist theorists. Are Darwin's arguments for sexual selection as an important driver of evolutionary change merely unfashionable politically, or are gender theorists and other critics of the idea pointing up significant evidential and logical problems with the idea?

Finally, if Darwin and the *Origin* have been mythologized, what about the modern version of his theory? Is there a bluff here as well? Or, as is regularly claimed, is the present state of the evidence for modern evolutionary theory truly overwhelming?

In general, a detailed engagement with Darwin's correspondence will paint a picture of a very insecure amateur naturalist desperate to make a mark in science but acutely aware of his limitations. Though a prodigious collector and cataloger of facts and observations, and as someone who made real scientific contributions to the description of organisms like barnacles and orchids, Darwin knew that he had fallen well short of cinching the case for the evolution of all life via natural selection, and he knew that his critics also knew this. But unable or unwilling to admit this, Darwin hid behind a variety of rhetorical devices that allowed him to keep up the appearance that he had indeed solved the "mystery of mysteries," as he called it.[4]

This more critical appraisal of Darwin's work should not be viewed in a purely negative light. Wading through the Darwinian correspondence over these last several years has brought me to a place of real appreciation for aspects of Darwin's personality and work. I admire his undying devotion to his family and friends and his acute sense of humor. I marvel at his incredible patience and industry in collecting encyclopedic quantities of facts and observations. And I certainly can sympathize with his anxieties over publishing such a revolutionary new theory. If someone ever creates a time machine, I will be first in line with the dials set to Down House to meet the man I feel I already know so intimately through his letters and works. That said,

Darwin was a mere human with foibles and faults like all the rest of us, and he was a product of his times. But this more human Darwin so infrequently emerges from the literature about him that I will do my best to let him emerge here.

1. Piercing the Veil of Darwinian Mythology

Few figures in the history of science lie more hidden behind a veil of mythology than Charles Darwin. Whether it be philosopher Daniel Dennett's famous assertion that Darwin had the best idea anyone has ever had,[1] Janet Browne calling *The Origin of Species* "one of the greatest scientific books ever written,"[2] or Richard Dawkins's indefatigable defense of Darwinian evolution, Darwin continues to be hailed today in both scientific and popular circles as perhaps the most important and influential scientist of all time. In *Darwin's Sacred Cause*, Adrian Desmond and James Moore articulate well the mythological figure Darwin has become:

> Darwin changed the world because he was a tough-minded scientist doing good empirical science. As a young man, he exploited a great research opportunity aboard the HMS *Beagle*. He was shrewd beyond his years, driven by a love of truth. Sailing around the world, he collected exotic facts and specimens—most notably on the Galapagos Islands—and followed the evidence to its conclusion, to evolution. With infinite patience, through grave illness heroically borne, he came up with "the single best idea anyone has ever had" and published it in 1859 in *The Origin of Species*. This was "a dangerous idea"—evolution by "natural selection"—an idea fatal to God and creationism equally, even if Darwin had candy-coated this revolutionary pill with creation-talk to make it more palatable.[3]

Desmond and Moore go on to draw their own highly questionable picture of Darwin, but to their credit they push back against the portrait encapsulated in the above quotation, for it is a caricature so grossly distorted that it would be scarcely recognizable to Darwin's contemporaries.

Some of the historical facts are correct, of course. Darwin did sail on the HMS *Beagle*, he did visit the Galapagos Islands, and he published *The Origin of Species*. But was he really a tough-minded scientist doing good empirical work? Was he in fact shrewd beyond his years? Did he simply follow evidence to the inescapable conclusion of evolution by natural selection? There are good historical reasons to revisit each of these claims.

Even the great Harvard zoologist and tireless defender of Darwin's scientific work, Ernst Mayr, was forced to admit that *The Origin of Species* provided embarrassingly little concrete evidence for some of Darwin's most important ideas, including the idea of natural selection.[4]

Nevertheless, we still get inflated statements from the likes of Michael Ghiselin: "In 1859 there began what ultimately may prove to be the greatest revolution in the history of thought," he writes. "*The Origin of Species*, published in November of that year, effected an immediate and cataclysmic shift in outlook, casting into doubt ideas that had seemed basic to man's conception of the entire universe."[5]

Or consider the opening lines of John Bowlby's *Charles Darwin: A New Life*: "Charles Darwin, whose life spanned much of the nineteenth century, is the most influential biologist to have lived. Not only did he change the course of biological science, but he changed forever how philosophers and theologians conceive of man's place in nature."[6]

Darwin may well have wished that he had sparked such a far-reaching and radical revolution in humanity's understanding of its place in the universe, but as we will see, he was far less sanguine regarding what he had actually accomplished. And we should be as well.

Upon publishing *The Origin of Species* in 1859, Darwin wrote to almost everyone he knew, alerting them to view the *Origin* as only an abstract of a much larger work, a big book on speciation he planned to bring out soon. Since the *Origin* was only an abstract, Darwin wanted to make sure his readers would not evaluate too harshly the lack of empirical evidence for natural selection and reserve judgment on his theory until the big book containing all the evidence and authorities appeared in full. So his readers waited... and waited... and waited.

The substantial size of his 1868 book, *Variation of Animals and Plants under Domestication*, might lend the impression that here was the big, promised book, but it merely expanded on two of the fourteen chapters of the promised book, and as the title makes clear, the focus of the 1868 work was variation *under domestication*. As interesting as the analysis was, no one doubted that variation within a species could and did take place under domesticated breeding programs. What friends and critics alike were waiting for was Darwin's promised work cinching the case for his central and dramatic claim, namely, that variations *under nature* could accumulate so as to give rise to dramatically new biological forms.

Darwin continued to promise the big book after *Variation of Animals and Plants under Domestication* was published. The 1868 book was issued in January, and in a letter the following summer, Darwin told Alphonse de Candolle that he intended to resume work on the big book in a year or so, and offered excuses for the continued delay. There he referred to the promised work as "Variation of Species in a State of Nature."[7]

Darwin's public would never get more than the promissory note. He appears never to have seriously attempted to finish the book, much less bring it to press, despite his showing every capacity to write, research, and publish on subjects scientific in the years that followed.

We can see the effect of Darwinian mythology in the way Darwin's biographers have downplayed Darwin's own characterization of the *Origin* as a mere abstract. According to Janet Browne, "Although he subsequently complained that he had been rushed into *Origin of Species*, that it was nothing but an abstract, that his evidence was truncated, and his footnotes and sources were omitted, the book was undeniably Darwin's masterpiece."[8] But Darwin's characterization of the *Origin* as a mere abstract is repeated so often in his letters to such a large array of correspondents that it is difficult to fathom how Browne can so easily brush off Darwin's own thoughts on the subject and instead dare speak for him.

John Bowlby takes a different tack. He puts the word *abstract* in scare quotes ("abstract"), something Darwin never does, which allows Bowlby to downplay the significance Darwin attached to this word and maintain the illusion that the *Origin* represents Darwin's magnum opus.[9]

And then there is James Costa, who, like Bowlby, puts the word *abstract* in scare quotes only to write on the very next page that the *Origin* "really *was* an abstract of his aborted big book."[10] So was it an abstract or an "abstract"? For Darwin it was the former, but for writers steeped in the pervasive Darwinian mythology, this is an inconvenient fact. Dismissing the fact makes possible the maintenance of the *Origin*'s iconic status as a masterpiece brimming with cogently assembled scientific evidence.

How do we come to know a demythologized Darwin? We might be tempted to simply read one of the many biographies of Darwin adorning library shelves. But here we encounter a problem. Many of these biographies are written from the perspective of someone who knows how the Darwinian story turns out. Biographers know that Darwin would become one of the most famous scientific figures of all time, and this indelibly colors the way Darwin's life story is told. Even Darwin's own brief autobiography, written toward the end of his life, is likely colored by Darwin's own knowledge about how his life turned out.

Biographies are not useless, of course. They provide detailed documentation of many facts of Darwin's life, and I will make use of them in this book. But to truly understand who Darwin was as a person and his own thoughts on his scientific work, we must get behind the influence of the Darwinian mythology that many of these biographies serve. And to do that, to really understand the unfolding in real time of Darwin's thinking, we must comprehensively engage with Darwin's voluminous correspondence.

Darwin wrote and received thousands of letters during his life, and many have been preserved and published. These letters are a gold mine of information about his thinking untinged by the influence of later Darwinian mythology. When Darwin was writing a letter in 1850 to his botanist friend Joseph Dalton Hooker, for example, he could not know that nine years later he would write and publish *The Origin of Species*, let alone that this work would make him a household name. A letter written in 1850 simply documents for us what Darwin was thinking in 1850. Thus do Darwin's letters provide us with real-time insight into what made Darwin tick at different points in his life.

This is not to say that Darwin was always fully transparent in his letters. As we will see, he often employed rhetorical devices to create impressions in the minds of his correspondents that may not always have accorded with reality. Nevertheless, Darwin's correspondence still allows us to document the development of his thinking—including his rhetorical devices—undistorted by the lens of his later scientific fame.

Darwin's many biographers have, of course, mined the Darwinian correspondence as they researched his life. But because these biographies are written from the perspective of Darwin's later scientific fame, the correspondence tends to be mined and interpreted in such a way as to support this preconceived evaluation of Darwin's importance.

This is not a feature only of biographical works. The chief editor of the official collection of Darwin's correspondence published by Cambridge University Press, Frederick Burkhardt, published a small selection of 168 letters written by Darwin between the years 1825 and 1859. Some of these letters do present some of the more dubious aspects of Darwin's personality and work. But at the head of the collection we find, "Charles Darwin stands as a towering figure in the history of science, who changed the direction of modern thought by establishing the basis of evolutionary biology."[11] And in the book's foreword, Stephen Jay Gould intones, "Above all, of course, Charles Darwin changed our intellectual world perhaps more than any other person in the history of science.... For this cardinal reason alone, the wonderfully expressive and richly varied letters of Charles Darwin represent one of the great dramas of western history."[12]

Once a reader has internalized these hyperbolic statements, the letters that follow will be read in their light, and a more nuanced Darwin obscured. Additionally, Burkhardt's collection contains only letters written by Darwin. But letters written to Darwin by his scientific collaborators and friends are also quite revealing of his character, so I will draw on these as well.

In order to uncover this more nuanced portrait, we also must be willing to recognize the prominent biologists today who view Darwin's theory of natural selection as being far too simplistic to account for the evolutionary history of life on earth. This is even true of the updated form of Darwin's theory, neo-Darwinism, which cashes out random variation in terms of random genetic mutations. Contemporary theories in molecular biology, genomics, epigenetic inheritance, evolutionary developmental biology, natural genetic engineering, biological relativity, and other fields increasingly regard the twin mechanism of random genetic mutation and natural selection as incapable of explaining the dizzying complexity of life as we now understand it.

Science journalist Stephen Buranyi summarized the ongoing debate over the status of the neo-Darwinian synthesis in a 2022 *Guardian* article titled, "Do We Need a New Theory of Evolution?"[13] And Nicholas Barton, 2008 winner of the Darwin-Wallace Medal, the highest honor bestowed on an evolutionary biologist, recently stated that "no fundamentally new principles have been established in molecular biology, and, in evolutionary biology, despite sophisticated theoretical advances and abundant data, we still grapple with the same questions as a century ago."[14]

Massimo Pigliucci and Gerd Müller have co-edited a book calling for an extended evolutionary synthesis that goes beyond neo-Darwinism's narrow focus on population genetics as the driver of evolution.[15] And paleontologists Douglas Erwin and James Valentine, in their book analyzing the sudden diversification of animal life in the Cambrian period—a phenomenon that even Darwin saw as potentially fatal to his theory—have written, "One important concern has been whether the microevolutionary patterns commonly studied in modern organisms by evolutionary biologists are sufficient to understand and explain the events of the Cambrian explosion or whether evolutionary theory needs to be expanded to include a more diverse set of macro-evolutionary processes. We strongly hold to the latter position."[16]

Whether it be Cambridge University paleontologist Simon Conway Morris's work on convergent evolution,[17] Oxford University physiologist Denis Noble's theory of biological relativity,[18] or University of Chicago biochemist James Shapiro's idea of natural genetic engineering,[19] or many another line of research, an increasingly common theme in origins biology is that the Darwinian mechanism of evolutionary change—random variation and natural selection—is an evolutionary model in crisis (much more on this in Chapter 8). There is no sense, then, in beginning an investigation into Darwin's life and work by treating him and his theory as sacrosanct. We should instead comprehensively engage with Darwin's correspondence, along with other lines of data, and let this evidence lead us to a more nuanced and historically plausible picture of the man and his work. We must, in short, rescue Darwin and his *Origin of Species* from the grasp of Darwinian mythology.

The official collection of the Darwinian correspondence currently runs to more than thirty volumes. In my research, I have focused primarily on volumes 1 through 11, spanning the years 1830 to 1863, four years past the publication of *The Origin of Species*. Many of these letters have little to do with Darwin's scientific work and contain family gossip and personal reflections (though even these can shed light on Darwin as a person). This still leaves a trove of letters bearing directly on Darwin's scientific work, and a comprehensive engagement with those letters tells a far more ambiguous story about Darwin and his scientific work than we get from the familiar mythology. Given his outsized influence on Western culture, affecting everything from biology and psychology to economics and philosophy, we deserve a more nuanced understanding of this enigmatic Victorian figure than what emerges in much of the voluminous literature about him. In a recent survey article, noted Darwinian biographer Janet Browne observes how the field of Darwinian historiography since the beginning of the publication of the correspondence in 1985 has been moving in the direction of progressively deconstructing Darwin as a key figure in the history of science.[20] The present work should be viewed within the context of that larger movement.

This book is not meant, however, to be another comprehensive biography of Charles Darwin. Its scope is limited to Darwin's species work and engages the question of why Darwin failed to follow up his abstract with his comprehensive volume on speciation by natural selection. The present book can therefore function as a supplement to the many biographies already in existence while providing a more comprehensive look into the Darwinian correspondence through 1863 for those who understandably will not themselves undertake the task of reading those volumes in their entirety.

In reading through those letters, one quickly encounters several rhetorical devices Darwin employed when writing to his scientific collaborators. As a first illustration of what we can learn from a more comprehensive engagement with the correspondence, let's turn now to his use of one of these rhetorical devices, whose relevance will become clear with the accumulation of examples and the accompanying commentary.

The Rhetoric of Illness in Darwin's Correspondence

As we saw above, Desmond and Moore cite Darwin's "grave illness heroically borne" as one aspect of the Darwinian caricature so common today. Indeed, Darwin's struggle against chronic ill health is one of the more recognizable aspects of his biography. But what was the nature of this chronic illness?

Much has been written about Darwin's health without a firm consensus emerging. Some believe Darwin suffered from some type of parasitic disease contracted during his travels through tropical South America—perhaps Chagas disease. Others have argued that Darwin suffered from hereditary illnesses. The most complete assessment of Darwin's health came from the pen of Ralph Colp, a medical doctor with specialization in psychiatry. After a thorough assessment of all the available evidence and the various proposed theories, Colp makes a convincing case that Darwin's symptoms stemmed primarily from stress and anxiety. This does not mean that Darwin did not suffer many of the symptoms he describes, but it does challenge the notion that Darwin was incapacitated by organic disease for long stretches of his life.[21]

Whatever the cause of his symptoms, he was not shy about sharing intimate details regarding them in his correspondence. Indeed, he rehearses his ill health to his scientific correspondents all over the world *ad nauseam*. It was clearly important to him to paint a picture of himself as a chronically ill invalid seriously compromised in his ability to work by a bevy of difficult symptoms such as chronic headaches, vertigo, regular bouts of vomiting, boils, extreme flatulence, depression, insomnia, and skin inflammation. The question becomes why Darwin was so transparent about his ill health, sharing intimate details of his sufferings even with people he hardly knew. What was the purpose of creating this rhetoric of illness?

Before considering this question, it will be helpful to provide some examples of this rhetorical device from his letters.

Darwin's health began to take a turn for the worse within a couple of years of his return from the *Beagle* voyage in 1836. In June of 1838 he reported to his second cousin William Darwin Fox (who had been with Darwin at Cambridge) that he had not been very well of late and would be leaving London earlier than expected to go to Scotland.[22] By January of 1841 he was reporting again to Fox, "I am forced to live, however, very quietly and am able to see scarcely anybody & cannot even talk long with my nearest relations. I was at one time in despair & expected to pass my whole life as a miserable valetudinarian but I have now better hopes for myself."

Darwin may have experienced a reprieve, but by July 4, 1847, he was back complaining to Swiss geologist Bernhard Studer that ill health would prevent him from being able to geologize England.[23]

Later that month, on July 19, 1847, Darwin wrote to his close botanist friend Joseph Dalton Hooker, assistant director of the Royal Gardens at Kew in London: "As it turns out, I cd. not come to you on Saturday, for on Friday one of my boils fiercely reinflamed & all Saturday I was lying on my face on the sofa—a laughable spectacle to anyone, who by experience did not know what pain I was in."

On May 10, 1848, Darwin reported to Hooker the worsening of his stomach problems; and then on May 27, he wrote to his wife, Emma, from his family home where he had gone to visit his father:

> I am weak enough today, but think I am improving. My attack was very sudden: it came on with fiery spokes & dark clouds before my eyes; then sharpish shivery & rather bad not very bad sickness [*sic*]. I got up yesterday about 2, & about 7 I felt rather faint & had a slight shaking fit & little vomiting & then slept too heavily; so today am languid & stomach bad, but do not think I shall have any more shivering & I care for nothing else.

This worsening of symptoms eventually drove Darwin to seek hydropathy treatment at Dr. Gully's water cure establishment at Malvern. He was there from March 10 to June 30, 1849. He appears to have received some relief from this treatment, but it wouldn't last. By September 1852 he was complaining to his naturalist friend George Waterhouse that he could work on his barnacles for only two hours per day and to Fox in October that excitement and fatigue brought on flatulence.

During this period he was clearly living a semi-reclusive existence, leaving his country estate only when necessary to do business in London or to escape disease epidemics in the village. Indeed, in a January 2, 1856, letter, Darwin reported to John Herbert, a county court judge, that he never went far from home.

Things appear to have taken a turn for the worse when Darwin was writing *The Origin of Species.* He wrote to Fox on February 12, 1859, from another hydropathic establishment at Ilkley Wells: "I have been extra bad of late, with old severe vomiting rather often & much distressing swimming of the head; I have been here a week & and shall stay another & and it has already done me good.... My abstract is the cause, I believe of the main part of the ills to which my flesh is heir to."

Later that year (November 13), Darwin apologized to his naturalist friend Leonard Jenyns about his nearly illegible handwriting, blaming it on his doing so poorly that he could hardly sit up. Then three days later he wrote to Fox, "I have had a whole series of calamities; first a sprained ankle, & then badly swollen leg & face, much rash & frightful succession of Boils—4 or 5 at once. I have felt quite ill—& have little faith in this 'unique crisis' as the Doctor calls it, doing me much good. I cannot now walk a step from boil on knee."

Things did not improve much following the publication of the *Origin*. On July 2, 1860, Darwin reported to Hooker that he had been "very poorly with almost continuous bad headache for 48 hours, & I was low enough & thinking what a useless burden I was to myself & all others."

In April of 1862 Darwin wrote to Hooker that he had vomited all night after giving a paper at the Linnean Society and had to crawl home. In May he wrote to Alfred Russel Wallace, the co-developer of the theory of evolution by natural selection, that his health was very poor, calling himself "that miserable animal, a regular valetudinarian."

The litany of ills continued. In June of 1862 Darwin reported to Hooker that he had been extra bad with violent skin inflammation. On October 23 he described to his neighbor John Lubbock how following a reunion visit from three officers from the *Beagle*, a visit that Darwin certainly should have enjoyed, "I took every possible precaution, but it made me very ill with violent shaking & vomiting till the early morning; & Could not even wish them goodbye next morning." In November he reported to his botanist friend Hugh Falconer his desire to come to London to visit Falconer, but said he was afraid to travel because twice recently, merely talking for less than two hours in the evening had brought on violent vomiting and trembling.

Darwin not only constantly narrated the state of his health in his letters, but also frequently blamed his poor health for his not completing aspects of his work in a timely fashion. In the November 13 letter to Jenyns, in which he told his friend to expect a copy of *The Origin of Species* soon, he wrote, "I wish that my health had allowed me to publish in extenso; if I ever get strong enough I will do so, as the greater part is written out; & of which M.S. the present volume is an abstract." On the same day that he wrote to Jenyns, Darwin also penned a letter to Wallace, stating, "God only knows when I will have strength for my bigger book."

Many of Darwin's readers noticed that the *Origin* was missing a historical overview of the subject of evolution to provide a context for Darwin's contribution. Again, Darwin chalked up this omission to his health, writing to Baden Powell, professor of geometry at Oxford, on January 18, 1860: "My health was so poor, whilst I wrote the Book, that I was unwilling to add in the least to my labour; therefore I attempted no history of the subject, nor do I think that I was bound to do so.... I had intended in my larger book to have attempted some such history; but my own catalogue frightens me. I will, however, consult some scientific friends & be guided by their advice."

In May 1860 Darwin reported to Wallace that he was at work on his bigger book but was making slow progress due to ill health and swarms of letters. The progress was slow indeed. Despite having told Jenyns that the greater part of the bigger book was already written, a fact verified by the existence of his handwritten manuscript, Darwin did not actually publish any of it until 1868, and as noted above, then only the modest fraction dealing with variation under domestication. In a footnote to that 1868 book, *Variation of Animals and Plants under Domestication*, Darwin once again blamed the delay in publication on ill health: "To any one who has attentively read my 'Origin of Species' this Introduction will be superfluous. As I stated in that work that I should soon publish the facts on which the conclusions given in it were founded, I here beg permission to remark that the great delay in publishing this first work has been caused by continued ill-health."[24]

So not only did Darwin create a picture of himself as a miserable wretch suffering from a host of physical ailments that incapacitated him for long stretches of time, but he also repeatedly blamed this ill health for his failure to provide the additional facts and evidence on which the arguments of the *Origin* were said to be based, though he leads us to believe he had all those facts at hand. We must, then, raise the question, was Darwin really as incapacitated by illness as he would have us believe? Or is it possible that he exaggerated his level of disability to create a ready excuse for not presenting the promised additional evidence for natural selection's creative powers, likely knowing that the evidence would prove unconvincing to his fellow scientists? And what might this mean for how we should assess the scientific status of *The Origin of Species* today? These are the central questions of this book.

Just How Sick Was Charles Darwin?

In the 1960s Nobel Laureate Peter Medawar, who believed that Darwin was organically ill with Chagas disease, nevertheless suggested that Darwin may have exaggerated the extent of his illness. In Medawar's view, the obscurity of the course of Darwin's illness may have caused him to exaggerate his symptoms in order to convince others and himself that he was truly sick. "Ill people suspected of hypochondria or malingering have to pretend to be iller than they really are and then may get taken in by their own deception," wrote Medawar. "They do this to convince others, but Darwin had also to convince himself, for he had no privileged insight into what was wrong with him."[25]

Janet Browne argues that Darwin's illness may have become a crutch for him:

> He may have come to enjoy the medical attention and the rituals of dietary restrictions, and have been stimulated by the pursuit of one therapy after another as he sought an all-embracing cure, rather in the same manner as he relentlessly pursued botanical or zoological facts. He may have come to rely on being able to shelter behind an illness which allowed him to escape commitments, intellectual and domestic alike.[26]

And escape such commitments he did. In June of 1847 Darwin was at a meeting of the British Association for the Advancement of Science at Oxford when he received an invitation to dine with James Clark Ross, the naval officer who had led a famous expedition to Antarctica (and for whom the Ross ice shelf is today named). Being invited to dine with such a famous explorer should have been a great honor for Darwin, but he declined, writing to Ross, "I fear you will think me very ungrateful & capricious, but such is not the case, when I say that I fear I must decline your kind invitation for tomorrow. The temptation made me break through my rule of dining by myself, but since you asked me, I have not been well, & I am in truth afraid of being knocked up if I dine out anywhere out of my own rooms."

In 1858, Darwin learned that he had been nominated president of the zoology section of the British Association. But again he declined the honor, writing to John Phillips on September 1 that "my health would not permit me to attempt so arduous a duty." The next year, Darwin learned from John Phillips that he was to receive the Wollaston Medal of the Geological Society, an honor that surprised him, leading him to write to Phillips on January 21, 1859:

> It would be superfluous to say how highly I feel the honour which the Council has conferred on me. I am astonished at it, for I am well aware how little I have done for many years for geology, having been incapacitated for any bodily fatigue.—This has been a great misfortune to me, for I honour from the bottom of my soul the noble science & its followers.—I will, of course, attend at the anniversary, if I possibly can, but my health is very uncertain & I never know what I can do the next day.

Alas, two weeks later found Darwin receiving hydropathy treatment at Moor Park, leading him to write to Phillips, "I am sorry, very sorry to say that the Medical man here urges me *most strongly* not to expose myself to the excitement & fatigue of receiving the Medal." Darwin even used health complaints to cancel visits to his own home by his closest friends. On March 5, 1863, he wrote Hooker that he had to cancel a visit from another close friend, Charles Lyell, because "I have been having very bad 10 days with much sickness & weakness."

Cambridge botany professor John Stevens Henslow became an important mentor to Darwin and recommended him for the voyage of the HMS *Beagle*. In 1857, upon hearing that Henslow's wife was quite ill, Darwin wrote to Hooker (Henslow's son-in-law) on November 21, "To the last day of my life I shall feel under what deep obligations I lie to Henslow and Mrs. Henslow for their extraordinary kindness to me at Cambridge." On January 25, 1858, Darwin wrote directly to

Henslow: "Those old days when I used as an undergraduate to be so much at your house were certainly amongst the most happy & best days which I have ever spent. Never shall I forget to [the] end of my life the uniform & very great kindness of poor dear Mrs. Henslow to me."

Darwin's great affection for the Henslows shines through in his correspondence, but Darwin's concerns for his health took priority. Hearing in April of 1861 from Hooker that Henslow was seriously ill, Darwin wrote to Hooker:

> I am much pained to think of poor dear Henslow's state.... I write now only to say that if Henslow, you thought, would really like to see me, I would of course start at once. The thought had once occurred to me to offer, & the sole reason why I did not was that the journey with the agitation would cause me probably to arrive utterly prostrated. I sh^{d}. be certain to have severe vomiting afterwards, but that would not much signify, but I doubt whether I could stand the agitation at the time.

It appears that Darwin never did go to the sickbed of his mentor, and when Henslow died later that year, Darwin declined to attend the funeral. With Darwin, health was always a ready reason to avoid travel and obligations. He created such negative expectations about his health that Janet Browne reports that when Thomas Carlyle, a Scottish historian and mathematician, visited Darwin in 1875, he was astonished to find a jolly, active man when he expected to be greeted by an invalid.[27]

The idea that Darwin sheltered behind his illness to escape certain commitments is certainly well documented in the correspondence. Darwin became a semi-recluse, generally leaving Down House only to escape disease epidemics in the village of Downe, take his sick children to the coast for recuperation, make a quick trip to London, or get hydropathy treatment for his illness. This point is underscored by an exchange of letters with Hooker in June of 1862. Hooker reported that his wife had become ill and frail, and so he was taking her to Switzerland for a change of scenery, prompting this response from Darwin: "It is folly in me to have an opinion; but is not Switzerland too great an exertion? Does not Mrs. Hooker rely too much on it having done her good formerly? It seems to me a frightful thing to go so far as Switzerland."

A man who had circumnavigated the globe on the HMS *Beagle* now viewed Switzerland as too far to travel![28] Likewise, the Harvard botanist, Asa Gray, invited Darwin to visit America and to bring all his sickly ones with him (several of Darwin's children were recovering from bouts of infectious disease). Darwin responded on October 16, 1862, "So we are all [to] come to you next summer! Alas my days for moving anywhere are come to an end."

But was Darwin really so incapacitated? That he may have been exaggerating the extent of his illness for rhetorical effect would seem to be supported by three facts about his life not often considered in this context: his strong constitution and apparently healthy immune system, the prodigious volume of work he produced, and perhaps more humorously, his obviously healthy libido.

The Good Side of Darwin's Health

One might expect a man as wretchedly ill and incapacitated as Darwin would have us believe he was to be somewhat immune-compromised and hence vulnerable to the infectious disease epidemics that often swept through Victorian society. Yet throughout his life, Darwin seems to have been amazingly resistant to such diseases.

Several members of the *Beagle* crew succumbed to tropical diseases, but Darwin seems to have been one of the healthier crew members, suffering only one significant illness in Chile, which he chalked up to drinking bad wine. As an adult, Darwin was often surrounded by sick children but never seems to have caught their diseases. When the Darwins' oldest daughter, Annie, became ill, possibly with tuberculosis or typhus, Darwin took her to Dr. Gully's hydropathy establishment at Malvern for treatment. Emma stayed behind due to being pregnant. In a gut-wrenching series of letters back and forth, Charles provided Emma with constant updates on Annie's condition. It is clear that he was at her bedside during the whole ordeal, even helping to try and feed her, until Annie died. But Charles did not catch her disease. In fact, Darwin's medically trained brother, Erasmus, expressed to

Charles in an April 25, 1851, letter, "I was afraid too that you might become ill at Malvern after all you have gone through."

Along with attending to his sick children, Darwin was always healthy enough to mount up the family and travel to seek medical care or recuperation by the sea for his ailing family.

During her teenage years, the Darwins' daughter Henrietta (or Etty as they called her) became ill more than once, with diphtheria being the likely culprit in one instance. It was bad enough that Charles and Emma thought they might lose her, and the girl's nurses also got sick. "The first nurse became ill with ulcerated throat & quincy & the second is now ill with Scarlet Fever, but thank God recovering," Darwin reported to Hooker on July 5, 1858. "You may imagine how frightened we have been. It has been a most miserable fortnight."

The next day he told Fox that Etty was too weak to even put on clothes. This was clearly a serious and very contagious disease, but Darwin didn't catch it.

In 1862 Leonard Darwin was sent home from boarding school with suspected scarlet fever. "I received several days ago two large packets, but have as yet read only your letter; for we have been in fearful distress & I could attend to nothing," Darwin wrote to Asa Gray on July 23. "Our poor Boy had the rare case of second rash & sore throat, besides mischief in kidneys; & as if this was not enough a most serious attack of erysipelas[29] with typhoid symptoms."

After an initial recovery, the Darwins decided to travel to the seacoast for further recuperation. But on the way, Leonard had a relapse, followed by Emma's contracting scarlet fever. Darwin wrote to Wallace on August 20: "You will not be surprised that I have been slow in answering, when I tell you that my poor boy became frightfully worse after you were at Down, & that during our journey to Bournemouth he had a slight relapse here & my wife took the Scarlet Fever rather severely."

The next day found Darwin writing to Gray:

> We are a wretched family and ought to be exterminated. We slept here to rest our poor Boy on his journey to Bournemouth, & my poor dear wife sickened with Scarlet-fever & has had it pretty

> sharply, but is recovering well. Our boy suffered sadly from the Journey, though we took it on the advice of two Doctors. I fear he will be an invalid for months, if not years—There is no end of trouble in this weary world—I shall not feel safe till we are all at home together, & when that will be I know not.

The Darwins' last child, Charles, died of scarlet fever as a toddler.

Darwin was frequently surrounded by seriously ill children with infectious diseases but seems to have been quite resistant to the diseases. Such a healthy immune system does not seem to comport with the picture Darwin paints of his overall weak constitution.

Moreover, while Darwin frequently used ill health as an excuse for delays in publication and complained repeatedly of his inability to work more than a couple hours a day before needing complete rest, the fact is that Darwin churned out a breathtakingly large amount of work over his lifetime. True, as someone who lived off family inheritance and never held a paying job, he had more time to devote to his scientific work than did many of his scientific friends who were burdened by the demands of academic lecturing and administration. But even taking this into account, Darwin's output is staggering.

The Origin of Species ran to over 150,000 words in its first edition, and Darwin saw it through five more revised and significantly expanded editions. His *Descent of Man and Selection in Relation to Sex* spanned another 250,000 words. The *Variation of Animals and Plants under Domestication* accounted for another nearly 300,000 published words, and the *Beagle* diary around 165,000 words. When we consider Darwin's incomplete and unpublished manuscript on natural selection as well as all his other published works on geology, botany, emotions, and earthworms, a very conservative estimate would put Darwin's published words at close to two million. If we add to this his voluminous correspondence, more than 15,000 letters between 1822 and 1882, Darwin probably wrote well over three million words during his lifetime.

Further, all his published works draw upon facts and observations gleaned from his experimental work and from his voracious reading of books, articles, and letters received from interlocutors all over the world. Darwin was an obsessive collector and cataloger of facts and observations, which he carefully arranged in file drawers and then spilled onto thousands of pages of writing, perhaps in the hope that the sheer volume of facts would overwhelm readers and convince them of the rightness of his theoretical ideas.

Darwin's industriousness is especially apparent following the publication of the *Origin*, when he turned to botany and undertook numerous experiments on plants grown in his garden and hothouse. Darwin first described in minute detail the anatomy of various species of orchid flowers to understand the variety of ways they seemed designed to ensure cross-fertilization by insects. He wrote to correspondents all over the world to send specimens of orchid flowers to Down House for dissection.

Darwin also became fascinated by insect-eating plants and performed all kinds of experiments to understand the mechanisms by which these flowers are signaled to close on unsuspecting prey. He spent an enormous amount of time and energy studying the different forms of flowers that appear on certain plants of the same species. He ran hundreds of experimental crosses and then, opening seed capsules, studied the seeds under a microscope to determine the level of fertility of each cross, some capsules containing hundreds of tiny seeds that Darwin painstakingly counted and tabulated in papers written for the *Linnean* and later published in a 100,000-word monograph, *The Different Forms of Flowers on Plants of the Same Species.*

Darwin's botanical work alone attests to an incredibly industrious man possessing enormous reserves of energy, stamina, and patience. But consider also that he spent eight years slaving over a comprehensive description of all the world's barnacle species.

Reflecting on his working life in his autobiography, even Darwin seems to have been impressed with his output: "When I see the list of books of all kinds which I read and abstracted, including whole series of Journals and Transactions, I am surprised at my industry."[30]

Darwin wrote to his cousin Fox on January 25, 1841, "If you attend at all to Nat. Hist.—I send you this P.S. as a memento, that I continue to collect all kinds of facts, about 'Varieties & Species' for my some-day work to be so entitled." Darwin was such an obsessive collector of facts that he even kept detailed records of the winner of more than 5,000 of his nightly backgammon games with Emma. (Charles had a small edge!)

The time and energy necessary to procure and catalog Darwin's encyclopedic collection of facts and observations and then write and rewrite and revise nearly two million words' worth of published material is a herculean task by any estimation. Are we really to believe that this was all produced by a man so chronically ill and compromised in his ability to work that he labored at his scientific work only two hours a day on a good day?

The third indication of Darwin's overall good health revolves around what appears to have been a healthy, active sex life. Charles and Emma produced ten children, the first nine coming over an eleven-year span during which Emma was almost perpetually pregnant. After birthing nine children in eleven years, an exhausted Emma must have begun avoiding regular sex, prompting Charles to write to his cousin Fox on October 24, 1852, "Emma has been very neglectful of late & we have not had a child for more than one whole year." Referring to Emma as neglectful would seem to convey a certain frustration on Charles's part with diminished sexual activity.

Moreover, Darwin's children were often conceived during periods when Darwin claimed he was very ill. For example, the early years of Darwin's illness spanning the years 1837–1843 were, according to Darwin, particularly acute. In January of 1841, Darwin told Fox, "I grow very tired in the evenings & am not able to go out at that time or hardly receive my nearest relatives." In March of 1845, Darwin wrote to Joseph Dalton Hooker, "I believe I have not had one whole day or rather night, without my stomach having been greatly disordered, during the last three years, & most days great prostration of strength.... many of my friends, I believe, think me a hypochondriac."

Darwin must be exaggerating his condition here, for at least four of his children would have been conceived during this period of daily—and perhaps more importantly, nightly—suffering. There had to have been many nights when Darwin's stomach was ordered enough for him to be interested in sexual activity.

As we saw above, Darwin sought hydropathic treatment at Dr. Gully's water cure establishment at Malvern from March 10 to June 30, 1849. In a March 19, 1849, letter to his sister Susan, he describes in detail his daily regimen, worth repeating in full:

> —¼ before 7 get up, & am scrubbed with rough towel in cold water for 2 or 3 minutes, which after the first few days, made & makes me very like a lobster—I have a Washerman, a very nice person, & he scrubs behind while I scrub in front—Drink a tumbler of water & get my clothes on as quick as possible & walk for 20 minutes—I c[d]. walk further, but I find it tires me afterwards—I like all this very much.—At same time I put on a compress which is a broad wet folded linen covered by mackintosh & which is 'refreshed'—i.e. dipt in cold water every 2 hours after midday dinner.—I don't perceive much effect from this of any kind—After my walk, shave & get my breakfast, which was to have been exclusively toast with meat or egg, but he has allowed me a little milk to sop the *stale* toast in. At no time must I take any sugar, butter, spices tea bacon or anything good.—At 12 o'clock I put my feet for 10 minutes in cold water with a little mustard & they are violently rubbed by my man: the coldness makes my feet ache much, but upon the whole my feet are certainly less cold than formerly.—Walk for 20 minutes & dine at one.—He has relaxed a little about my dinner & says I may try plain pudding, if I am sure it lessens my sickness.—After dinner lie down & try to go to sleep for one hour.—At 5 o'[c]lock feet in cold water—drink cold water & walk as before—Supper same as breakfast at 6 o'clock.—I have had much sickness this week, but certainly have felt much stronger & the sickness has depressed me much less.—Tomorrow I am to be packed at 6 o'clock for 1 & ½ hours in Blanket, with hot bottle to my feet & then rubbed with cold drippings sheet; but I do not know anything about this.

Clearly Darwin was kept busy from early morning until well into the evening. But there is one activity he neglects to report to his sister. Emma accompanied Charles to Malvern, and when we consider that Leonard Darwin was born on January 15, 1850, he must have been conceived about nine months earlier, around April 15, 1849, right in the middle of Darwin's time at the water cure. Darwin even wrote to

Charles Lyell in late June, "Emma has deputed me to write, for she, poor soul, is in her usual wretched state, which to none of our friends requires any further explanation." This is almost certainly a reference to Emma suffering morning sickness, now about seven weeks into her pregnancy. So despite all the water cure activities Darwin was being put through and the reportedly wretched state of his health, he and Emma were obviously sexually active during the earlier stages of the hydropathy treatment. If John Bowlby is correct that Darwin suffered from hyperventilation syndrome, which would cause the autonomic nervous system to overreact to stress or excitement, bringing on his shaking and vomiting symptoms, sexual excitement should certainly have brought on these symptoms as well. But if they had, I doubt Darwin would have fathered ten children!

Darwin's reaction to hydropathy treatment contains a clue that his ills were primarily stress-related and not organic. After spending time at the water cure establishment at Ilkley Wells, Darwin reported to Fox on Christmas Day of 1859: "The last 10 days at Ilkley, I was splendidly well & for the first week at home; but since then I have had as bad a week as man could well have with incessant discomfort, I may say misery.—I have necessarily been very busy during these weeks but not with work which would be any strain to any other mortal man."

Two years earlier, Darwin had sought hydropathy at an establishment at Moor Park, and reported to Hooker on April 29 how much it had helped: "I can walk & eat like a hearty Christian; & even my nights are good.—I cannot in the least understand how hydropathy can act as it certainly does on me. It dulls one's brain splendidly, I have not thought about a single species of any kind, since leaving home."

Darwin hits the nail on the head. Hydropathy took his attention away from his work, but once he returned to work, his symptoms returned. He admitted to Fox on October 30 that while he did well at Moor Park, he fell back into his old state immediately upon returning home. Etty accompanied him to Moor Park for treatment of her illness. According to Darwin, she received much benefit from hydropathy "but can walk very little & is still very feeble." It does not sound like she received much benefit, but one would not expect the water cure to have much effect on infectious disease. That it had such a positive, though temporary, effect on Darwin supports the idea that he was basically quite healthy physically, but emotionally stressed and anxious.

Another characteristic worth noting here is Darwin's keen sense of humor. While he may have been a suffering wretch, he was always quick with a wry comment. September 1860 saw him responding to a sharp criticism of the *Origin*, sent to him by the Irish botanist William Harvey (a criticism we will consider in more detail in Chapter 5). Darwin implored Harvey to reread the *Origin*, but realizing how unlikely this was, added, "I shd. think you would as soon take an emetic as reread any part of my Book." Whether Harvey actually preferred induced vomiting to rereading the *Origin* we know not.

In 1862 Hooker was looking to hire a new cook and asked Darwin for recommendations. Hooker was clear that the cook must be an older woman to prevent her possibly becoming romantically interested in Hooker. Darwin consulted with Emma, who was then away from Down, with no luck. He replied to Hooker on June 11: "I have sent your message about trustworthy oldish cook (to Emma); I fear she cannot help. We might have recommended the very woman; but she is going to marry: I wish to Heaven Nat. Selection had produced 'neuters,' who would not flirt or marry; I am sure that they would be as useful as neuter Bees."

As another final example of Darwinian humor, Darwin caught a typographical error in an announcement about his orchid book. He wrote to John Murray, his publisher, on October 7, 1862: "My eye has just caught sight of a curious misprint in your announcement of my Book, viz., the good effects of *intercussing* for intercrossing. It might do a man good to swear a little occasionally, but a formal treatise on the good effects of intercussing is a novelty."

Darwin was not so far down that he could not see humor in life.

There are good reasons to believe Darwin exaggerated the extent of his illness and created a rhetoric of illness in his letters. A comprehensive assessment of the Darwinian correspondence reveals a man desperate to make a mark in the scientific world but who labored under tremendous insecurity about his ability to do so. This insecurity probably did issue in stress-related symptoms, providing Darwin with a ready excuse for the endless delays in his issuing the big book on species that was to provide the crucial evidence on which the *Origin*'s central thesis was said to rest. Darwin, I want to suggest, knew that he did not have the kind of evidence necessary to prove the theory of natural selection, and his rhetoric of illness provided a ready excuse for his endless delays in presenting the promised evidence to the public.

It was also a ready excuse for his absence from scientific meetings where he might be confronted by critics and have to defend his ideas. The evidence for this conclusion, as I will show, is to be found in a comprehensive engagement with Darwin's correspondence, as well as in a survey of his 300,000-word big book manuscript draft on speciation, published only posthumously in 1975.

2. Darwin the Geologist

Long before Darwin concerned himself with the origin of species, geological subjects were foremost on his mind. Though he collected beetles and showed some interest in the living world fairly early in life, it was in geological subjects that he first developed scientific theories that he hoped would bring him to the attention of the scientific elites of his day. However, before we launch into a detailed engagement with Darwin's geological work, it will be helpful to first provide a brief biographical sketch of his life up to his momentous voyage on the *Beagle*.

Darwin's Early Life

Charles Robert Darwin was born on February 12, 1809, at Shrewsbury, England, to the prominent physician Robert Waring Darwin and Susannah Wedgwood Darwin of the famous pottery family. As such, Charles at birth entered the upper class of Victorian society and would never want for material comfort. In fact, he never needed to hold a paying job; family inheritance was more than enough to provide a life of material ease. Yet things were not always easy. Charles's mother died when he was eight years old, leaving him to be raised by an authoritarian father and three older sisters, Marianne, Caroline, and Susan, the latter two becoming like surrogate mothers. Charles also had an older brother, Erasmus, and a younger sister, Catherine.

As Charles grew, he developed a fondness for the sporting life, riding horses and shooting quail at every opportunity. School work took a back seat to these sporting interests, so much so that Charles still recalled in his old age how his father had castigated him with the words, "You care for nothing but shooting, dogs, and rat-catching, and you will be a disgrace to yourself and all the family."[1] Such a comment from a father whom Charles nearly idolized had to cut deep, and may be what drove Darwin later to try so hard to make a contribution to science. Proving to his father that he would not be a disgrace may have been one of the chief motivating forces in Darwin's life. As Barry Gale has written: "Darwin undoubtedly wanted to make a major contribution to the corpus of scientific knowledge. I do not think that it mattered to Darwin, especially as a young man, where he achieved recognition: in geology, zoology, or evolutionary theory. The important thing was that he achieve some noteworthy place, some 'fair place among scientific men,' as he put it."[2] This desire will explain many aspects of Darwin's scientific work.

Once Charles reached his teenage years, his father sent him off to the University of Edinburgh to study medicine. Charles's grandfather, Erasmus Darwin, had been a prominent physician, and his father was a prominent physician, so it was determined that Charles should be one too. Besides, his older brother, Erasmus, was already studying medicine at Edinburgh. Charles dutifully obeyed his father's orders, but quickly learned that medicine could not be the career for him. Observing surgeries turned his stomach; the screams and blood sickened him. He also found medical lectures boring and began to attend lectures in natural history, which he found much more to his liking. Many of the medical professors at Edinburgh had side interests in natural history. News of Charles's neglect of his medical studies, however, soon reached Shrewsbury, prompting his sister Susan to write to her brother on March 27, 1826, with this warning from their father:

> My reason for writing so soon is, that I have a message from Papa to give you, which I am afraid you won't like; he desires me to say that he thinks your plan of picking & chusing what lectures you like to attend, not at all a good one; and as you cannot have enough information to know what may be of use to you, it is quite necessary for you to bear with a good deal of stupid & dry work: but if

you do not discontinue your present indulgent way, your course of study will be utterly useless.

It is worth noting that warnings like this had to be relayed to Charles via his sisters; the Darwinian correspondence is strikingly devoid of letters written directly between Charles and his father. This might betray a certain aloofness in the father/son relationship, which may also explain much about Darwin's apparent obsession to prove wrong his father's prediction that he would be a disgrace to the family.

Darwin's son, Francis, seems to capture the nature of the father/son relationship in the reminiscences he wrote about his father after his death. Francis reports about his mother, Emma: "She thinks decidedly that Dr. D (Darwin's father) did not like him (Darwin) or understand him or sympathize with him as a boy. He was a fidgety man and the noise & untidiness of a boy were unpleasant to him. Everything in the house had to run in the master's way so that the inmates had not the sense of being free to do just what they liked."[3]

Francis further reported, "My mother thinks that the affection which Dr. D felt for my father sprang up chiefly after the return from the voyage," and that Emma was glad when Darwin's father went off on a long journey and was sorry to see him return. Growing up in Dr. Robert Darwin's household must not have been a particularly pleasant experience for Charles.

As for the paternal warning relayed to Charles by his sister regarding his studies at Edinburgh, he appears to have largely ignored it. He continued to explore natural history at Edinburgh, coming especially under the influence of Robert Grant, who held views about the transmutation of species that undermined the need for a creative intelligence. Darwin, however, could only stay at Edinburgh as long as his brother Erasmus was there. When Erasmus graduated, Charles finally got up the nerve to inform his father that he could not pursue a career in medicine. Needing to find a vocation for his son worthy of the family's social status, his frustrated father sent his wayward son to Cambridge University to do the general bachelor's degree that was a typical path to the ministry. As at Edinburgh so at Cambridge,

Charles found natural history lectures far more stimulating than theology or any of the other subjects (Greek and Roman literature, philosophy, math, and physical science) in his Arts program. Collecting beetles became a favored hobby, and Charles went on many long collecting expeditions with the Cambridge botany professor John Stevens Henslow. Charles eventually graduated from Cambridge, but before becoming ordained and settling down to the life of a country parson he longed to visit the tropics and so began to plan a natural history trip to Tenerife in the Canary Islands.

Charles had become infatuated with the tropics by reading the travels of Alexander von Humboldt, and he was itching to explore the world beyond England. He wrote to his cousin William Darwin Fox on April 7, 1831, "At present, I talk, think, & dream of a scheme I have almost hatched of going to the Canary Islands.—I have long had a wish of seeing Tropical scenery & vegetation; & according to Humboldt Tenerife is a very pretty specimen."

Three weeks later had him writing to his sister, Caroline, that what he liked most about London was the Zoological Gardens. "On a hot day when the beasts look happy and the people gay it is most delightful." Later in the same letter, Charles let his sister in on his plans to visit Tenerife:

> All the while I am writing now my head is running about the Tropics: in the morning I go and gaze at Palm trees in the hot-house and come home and read Humboldt: my enthusiasm is so great that I cannot hardly sit still on my chair. Henslow & other Dons give us great credit for our plan: Henslow promises to cram me in geology.—I never will be easy till I see the peak of Tenerife and the great Dragon tree; sandy, dazzling, plains, and gloomy silent forest are alternately uppermost in my mind.—I am working regularly at Spanish: Erasmus advised me decidedly to give up Italian. I have written myself into a Tropical glow.

While Charles busied himself with planning this tropical excursion, a more dramatic opportunity came his way. The British admiralty was commissioning the HMS *Beagle* for a planned two-year trip to survey the coast of South America under the command of Captain

Robert FitzRoy. This would be FitzRoy's second adventure at sea and he knew first-hand the loneliness attending long months on the open ocean. As captain of the ship he had to maintain distance from the crew members he commanded, leaving him to eat meals at sea alone. So for this new trip, he sought a companion; someone of his own social status who could share meals at the captain's table and engage him in intellectual conversation, thus dispelling the loneliness of the open sea. If this dining companion had some facility in natural history, all the better. George Peacock of the Admiralty contacted Henslow at Cambridge for recommendations, leading Henslow to write to Darwin on August 24, 1831:

> I have been asked by Peacock who will read & forward this to you from London to recommend him a naturalist as companion to Capt Fitzroy employed by Government to survey the S. extremity of America—I have stated that I consider you to be the best qualified person I know of who is likely to undertake such a situation—I state this not on the supposition of your being a *finished* Naturalist, but as amply qualified for collecting, observing, & noting anything worthy to be noted in Natural History. Peacock has the appointment at his disposal & if he can not find a man willing to take the office, the opportunity will probably be lost—Capt. F wants a man (I understand) more as a companion than a mere collector & would not take anyone however good a Naturalist who was not recommended to him likewise as a *gentleman*.

For someone itching to explore the world beyond England, this news must have been like music to Darwin's ears.

But two problems immediately arose. Darwin met with FitzRoy to learn more about the opportunity, but FitzRoy, who was a believer in physiognomy, did not like the shape of Darwin's nose, thinking it portended a lack of the physical vigor necessary for the voyage. In addition, Darwin's father, while not strictly forbidding his son to go, strongly urged against it. Unwilling to cross his father, Darwin reluctantly turned down the opportunity. He went off to Maer Hall, the location of the Wedgwood family, where he told his Uncle Josiah about the *Beagle* excursion. His uncle felt he was turning down the opportunity of a lifetime and wrote to Darwin's father with a long list of reasons why Charles should be encouraged to go. With Josiah Wedgwood's coaxing, Darwin's father relented and gave Darwin permission, though he clearly was not fond of the idea. Darwin thus had to scramble to get word to FitzRoy that he had changed his mind, hoping that the position had not already been filled and hoping FitzRoy would lay aside his concerns about his nose. Lucky for Darwin the position was not yet filled and with FitzRoy relenting about his nose, Darwin sailed for the tropics on December 27, 1831, as FitzRoy's companion and unofficial naturalist of the HMS *Beagle*.

Geology and the *Beagle* Voyage

During the *Beagle* voyage, Darwin wrote many letters to his sisters. While it is clear that he spent much time collecting specimens of all kinds of organisms, living and fossilized, to send back to England to enhance museum collections, he was really enamored with questions of geology. Having read the three volumes of Charles Lyell's *Principles of Geology* while onboard the ship, Darwin sought evidence to support Lyell's uniformitarian theory. Recall that according to Lyell, the Earth's geological features were shaped by the mundane processes occurring in the world today acting over enormous spans of time; processes like wind and water erosion, earthquakes, and volcanic eruptions. The Earth had been largely shaped through such processes, not through major cataclysmic events such as a global flood. Darwin was clearly convinced by Lyell's theory and made many observations about the geology of South America that he later published in his *Journal of Researches*. The problem of accounting for life's diversity seems not to have been at the forefront of his mind.

Around March or April of 1833, Darwin wrote to his sister Caroline:

> I have been very successful in geology; as I have found a number of fossil shells in the very oldest rocks, which ever have organic remains.—This <ha>s long been a great desideratum in geology, viz the comparison of animals of equally remote epocks [*sic*] at different

> stations of the globe.—As for living creatures, these wretched climates are very unfavourable; yet I have the great satisfaction to find my powers of examining & describing them have increased at a great pace.—As for our future plans I know nothing; circumstances alter them daily.—I believe we must have one more trip to the South, before finally going round the Horn, or rather passing the... [Straits] of Magellan, for the Captain had enough of the great sea at the Cape to last all his life.—I am quite astonished, to find that I can endure this life; if it was not for the strong & increasing pleasure from Nat: History I never could.

Though Darwin dreamed of the tropics and certainly got his opportunity to experience them in Brazil, the *Beagle* voyage also entailed sailing through Tierra del Fuego and Cape Horn on the southern tip of South America where the weather was cold and harsh and the seas rough and stormy. This must have been a real hardship for one like Darwin who was prone to seasickness. But Darwin endured through his work in natural history, especially geology, where he cites his great success.

Sometime between May and July 1833, Darwin wrote to his sister Catherine with reasons why he needed to see this voyage through, despite the hopes from his family that he would cut it short and return home. Commenting on the great variety of invertebrate animals inhabiting the intertropical ocean, he wrote:

> If it was not for these & still more for geology—I would in short time make a bolt across the Atlantic to good old Shropshire.—In for penny, in for pound.—I have worked very hard (at least for me) at Nat History & have collected many animals & observed many geological phenomena: & I think it would be a pity having gone so far, not to go on & do all in my power in this my favourite pursuit; & which I am sure, will remain so for the rest of my life.

One wonders if Darwin's parenthetical expression "at least for me" is a mild taunt at his father's view that Darwin lacked industry and focus. Regardless, it is clear that collecting specimens and observing geological formations were now his favorite activities.

Two years later, while the *Beagle* was surveying the west coast of South America, Darwin made an extended excursion high up into the Andes Mountains. About this he wrote to his sister Susan on April 23, 1835, "To a geologist also there are such manifest proofs of excessive violence, the strata of the highest pinnacles are tossed about like the crust of a broken pie." It was also during this period that Darwin witnessed a major earthquake along the coast of Chile, an earthquake that wreaked great havoc on the town of Concepcion and raised the level of the ground by several feet. In his *Journal of Researches*, Darwin writes of the aftermath of the earthquake:

> After viewing Concepcion, I cannot understand how the greater number of inhabitants escaped unhurt. The houses in many parts fell outwards; thus forming in the middle of the streets little hillocks of brickwork and rubbish. Mr. Rouse, the English consul, told us that he was at breakfast when the first movement warned him to run out. He had scarcely reached the middle of the court-yard, when one side of his house came thundering down.[4]

Experiencing firsthand how an earthquake could alter the geological features of the land helped cement Darwin's support for Lyell's uniformitarian geology.

By April 1836, the *Beagle* was on the final leg of a journey that had lasted almost five years and Darwin began thinking about life after the *Beagle*. In a letter to Caroline dated April 29, he admitted to being homesick and reported that he passed the time aboard ship "rearranging old geological notes" and discovering the difficulty of "expressing one's ideas on paper." But he also reported that "I am in high spirits about my geology.—& even aspire to the hope that, my observations will be considered of some utility by real geologists. I see very clearly, it will be necessary to live in London for a year, by which time with hard work, the greater part, I trust, of my materials will be exhausted."

Darwin is aware here of his status as an amateur geologist, but is beginning to think that he might be able to make some kind of significant contribution to geology upon his return home. To this end, he wrote to his Cambridge professor John Stevens Henslow from St. Helena on July 9, 1836: "I am going to ask you to do me a favor. I am very anxious to belong to the Geolog. Society. I do not know, but I suppose, it is necessary to be proposed some time before being balloted for, if such is the case, would you be good enough to take proper preparatory steps."

Even before returning to England, Darwin was laying plans to make his mark in geology despite his lack of professional training in the discipline. Lyellian uniformitarianism was becoming his new religion, a religion that would form the foundation of his species work. Indeed, Darwin would later write to Leonard Horner, on August 29, 1844, "I cannot say how forcibly impressed I am with the infinite superiority of the Lyellian school of Geology over the Continental. I always feel as if my books came half out of Lyell's brains."

Geology after the *Beagle* Voyage

Once back on land, Darwin quickly set about writing up his many observations made during the nearly five-year voyage around the world. This included a volume on the geology of South America that caught the attention of the London scientific elite, including Charles Lyell. By collecting observations that could be understood as supporting Lyell's uniformitarian geology, Darwin quickly became a close scientific associate and friend of Lyell. Darwin's expressed hope that his observations would be useful to real geologists (Darwin knew he was not a real geologist) seemed to be coming true. So was his hope to become a member of the Geological Society in London, a hope that was fulfilled beyond his expectations when Henslow invited him to become Secretary of the Geological Society in the fall of 1837. Darwin initially resisted this appointment, citing in an October 14 letter to Henslow his ignorance of English geology, his ignorance of other languages ("not knowing how to pronounce a *single* word of French"), the time it would take away from his other projects, and his "slow manner of writing." Not surprisingly, Darwin also cited his poor health.

Nevertheless, by 1838, Darwin had become Secretary of the Geological Society, and in an August letter to George Waterhouse, founder of the Entomological Society and the man who had described Darwin's insect specimens from the *Beagle* voyage, he wrote, "I am so determined to make you a geologist that I have taken the liberty of sending you a copy of Lyell, by which means I obtain full right to mal-treat & abuse you till you have read it." It is no overstatement to say that Darwin had developed an almost religious zeal for Lyellian geology.

As Darwin's success in geology continued, he apparently began to wonder if this new-found talent was in his blood. He wrote to his cousin Fox on October 24, 1839:

> My father gave me a curious old ivory box, which belonged to W. Darwin of Cleatham, who died in 1682.— By the way Hensleigh Wedgwood made a curious discovery regarding our august family, which I must tell you, that a W. Darwin my great grandfather is described in the Phil. Transacts for 1719, as a person of curiosity, who discovered the remains of a giant, evidently an Icthyosaurus.— so that *we* have a right of hereditary descent to be naturalists & especially geologists.

Darwin was clearly brimming with enthusiasm about geological ideas. Though he was almost certainly beginning to think about the distribution of living organisms around the world by this time, it seems for the time to have been subordinate to his interest in geology. In any event, it was his geological work that was being noticed and providing Darwin with a sense that he was making a real contribution to science.

Darwin's emphasis on geology would help explain his initial positive attitude toward Louis Agassiz. Agassiz, a Swiss naturalist who came to Harvard University and established the Harvard Museum of Comparative Zoology, had studied glacial activity and published a book on it. Darwin loved the book and expressed his appreciation in a March 1, 1841, letter to Agassiz:

> I take the liberty of sending you a copy of my Journal, published some time since.—I have lately enjoyed the pleasure of reading your

> work on Glaciers, which has filled me with admiration. As I have briefly treated of the boulders of S. America in the accompanying volume I thought you possibly might like to possess a copy; and sending it you is the only means I have of expressing the regret I feel at the manner in which I have alluded to (although probably the fact is unknown and quite indifferent to you) your most valuable labours on the action of Glaciers. I trust you will excuse the liberty I now take simply for my own satisfaction, and I beg to remain with feelings of much respect.

What makes Darwin's great show of respect for Agassiz's work on glaciers noteworthy is that Agassiz was a creationist who believed species represented ideal types created by God that had come into existence in the forms in which we see them today, varying in only small ways from their ideal specific types. Sixteen years later Darwin would write to Thomas Henry Huxley (on September 26, 1857), "I have always suspected Agassiz of superficiality & wretched reasoning powers, but I think such men do immense good in their way."

Darwin's goodwill toward Agassiz was first tested after the publication of *The Origin of Species*. The book did not change the Swiss naturalist's mind, and he became a strong critic of the book. But Darwin was obviously not so suspicious of Agassiz's intellect in 1841 when the issue was glaciers; he only became so as it became increasingly clear that Agassiz would be a formidable opponent of his evolutionary theory.

Having published his geological observations on South America, Darwin then came out in 1842 with a book about coral reefs. The *Beagle* voyage had given Darwin an opportunity to see coral reefs around the world, and based on his observations he developed a theory to explain their origin. While most geologists of the time (including Lyell) thought reefs formed by corals accumulating on the top of volcanoes rising up from the ocean floor, Darwin took the opposite view; coral reefs and coral atolls form as a result of subsidence of the land. As a volcanic island slowly sinks into the ocean, a fringe reef will form around its edge. With further subsidence, the reef will move outward away from the land, resulting in a lagoon with a barrier reef forming around it. Eventually the island would subside entirely under the sea, leaving behind just a coral atoll—a ring of coral surrounding only water. Darwin proposed subsidence as the cause of all three types of coral reefs. Given the fact that coral structures do occasionally appear on land (while coral only grows under water) Darwin further hypothesized that in some areas, uplift must have lifted fringe reefs above the water level. Darwin's theory was simple and elegant, and many geologists initially signed on. But not everyone.

Critics argued that while some reefs may be formed this way, coral reef formation was more complex and Darwin's theory of subsidence could not be generalized to all coral formations.

One such critic was Scottish geologist Charles Maclaren, who reviewed Darwin's coral reef monograph for the *Scotsman* shortly after publication. Maclaren accepted the possibility of Darwin's theory being true, noting that it is consistent with known geological principles. Both subsidence and uplift of islands in the Earth's oceans were well documented. But he did raise three criticisms. First, there are many anomalous facts inconsistent with the theory. Atolls and barrier reefs sometimes occur in areas of uplift rather than subsidence, while fringing reefs and volcanoes can be found in areas of subsidence rather than uplift. Second, in areas of uplift, fringing reefs should occur in a variety of different stages of formation. That is, we should find reefs of different depths with variation in the depths of the lagoon channels that form between the reef and the mainland. Some variety exists but not, in Maclaren's view, to the level predicted by Darwin's theory. Third, and most serious, some reefs are 2,000 to 3,000 feet thick, and given the reality of uplift, there should be the remnants of reefs this size on land, but none had ever been found. Maclaren viewed these anomalous facts as a significant challenge to what he otherwise felt was an interesting and well-designed monograph.[5]

As we will see in the next section on the parallel roads of Glen Roy and later in his species work, Darwin frequently resisted taking anomalous data seriously. When he proposed a grand theory to explain some phenomenon, he stuck to it even in the face of contrary facts, leading him into many errors. Darwin responded to Maclaren's challenges in a three-page letter in December of 1842. Toward the end he wrote, "I do not expect the foregoing view will appear at all satisfactory to anyone besides myself.—I believe, however, there is more in it than special pleading. The case, undoubtedly, is very perplexing; but I have the confidence to think, that the experience explains so well many facts, that I shall hold fast by it, in the face of two or three puzzles, even as good ones as your third objection."

This passage is a rhetorical masterpiece and demonstrates many of the rhetorical devices Darwin would employ in his letters surrounding the *Origin*. He first disarms his critic with a statement of false modesty (no one will believe his theory but him). He then admits that the issue is indeed perplexing, but then passes off valid and substantive criticisms as just "two or three puzzles." But most importantly, he bases his continued confidence in his theory on the grounds that it "explains so well many facts." Philosophers of science have long recognized that the same set of facts can often be explained by more than one theory; this is the problem of underdetermination. If one starts with a theory, then interprets the facts through the lens of that theory, then of course it may look like the facts prove the theory. But this does not prove that this particular theory is correct. The same set of facts might just as well be explained on the basis of a different theory.

For example, it is known that fossils of marine organisms occur on mountaintops. This fact is easily explained by the theory of uplift—that mountaintops were once below sea level and then were uplifted to their present elevation. But this fact alone does not prove the theory of uplift, because the competing theory of a global flood inundating the Earth up to the mountaintops is just as consistent with the existence of marine fossils at great elevations. Other facts might come to light rendering one theory more likely than another (such as the discovery of plate tectonics in the twentieth century, supporting the theory of uplift in this example). But until then, facts that can be viewed as consistent with multiple theories relegate those theories to the status of underdetermination. In the same way, Darwin's coral reef theory was underdetermined and therefore lacking a good empirical foundation.

Darwin would, however, go on to use this same kind of rhetorical argument when defending the *Origin* against its many critics, describing how his species theory could explain so many disparate facts while ignoring the way these facts might just as easily be explained by alternative theories. Clearly, when Darwin proposed a theoretical idea, he was loath to give it up even in the face of contrary evidence, perhaps because he seems to have been motivated more by a desire to make a mark in science and prove himself worthy than by a desire to simply understand the complex workings of the natural world.

As facts accumulated showing that coral reef and coral atoll formation was more complex than Darwin's theory could explain, Darwin was slow to relent. Late in life (on May 5, 1881) he wrote to Alexander Agassiz, Louis's son and a proponent of the bottom-up theory of coral reefs: "Pray—forgive me for troubling you at such length, but it has occurred to me that you might be disposed to give, after your wide experience, your judgment. If I am wrong, the sooner I am knocked on the head and annihilated so much the better. It still seems to me a marvelous thing that there should not have been much and long-contained subsidence in the beds of the great oceans."[6] It seems that Darwin went to his grave still holding to the essential correctness of his coral reef theory.

Unfortunately for Darwin, by the 1930s geologists became aware that ocean levels had undergone significant change in the past due to climatic variations. Ocean levels dropped during periods of glaciation and rose again during the intervening warmer periods. The formation of coral reefs and atolls became attributed to the action of ocean level changes, not the rising and subsiding of the land. Despite this realization, the standard Darwinian story continued to be taught in schools due to the effect of the growing Darwinian mythology.

Recently, however, the *Annual Review of Marine Science* published "The Origin of Modern Atolls: Challenging Darwin's Deeply Ingrained Theory," a paper designed to finally relegate the Darwinian coral reef story to its proper place as an interesting episode in the history of science, but no longer of great scientific value.[7] As the lead author, André Droxler, is quoted as saying about Darwin's coral reef theory in an accompanying *Science Daily* article, "It's so beautiful, so simple, so pleasing that everybody still teaches it."[8] Could the same be said for Darwin's theory of evolution by natural selection? It is deceptively elegant and simple. But is it true?

For Darwin's part, his geological work would run into an even more formidable obstacle when he went to Scotland to study the parallel roads of Glen Roy.

The Parallel Roads of Glen Roy

On June 15, 1838, Darwin wrote to his cousin Fox of his plans for a Scottish holiday during which he intended to spend a week geologizing the parallel roads of Glen Roy, a series of parallel horizontal marks etched into the sides of hills in the area of Glen Roy, Scotland. Charles Lyell had previously studied these strange marks and reports that the first one stands 850 feet above sea level, the next one is about 212 feet higher, with a third another eighty-two feet higher, than the second. At least one of the marks is twenty miles long from east to west. According to Lyell, "Seen at a distance, they appear like ledges, or roads, cut artificially out of the sides of the hills; but when we are upon them, we can scarcely recognize their existence, so uneven is their surface, and so covered with boulders."[9] Much speculation surrounded the origin of these parallel markings, with little consensus emerging. This lack of consensus made room for Darwin to enter his own theory into the debate. The parallel roads, he argued, are ancient sea beaches, markings made by the sea in the distant past as the land was slowly uplifted to its present altitude.

Darwin wrote about Glen Roy to Lyell on August 9, 1838: "It is far the most remarkable area I ever examined.—I have fully convinced myself, (after some doubting at first) that the shelves are sea-beaches,—although I could not find a trace of a shell, & I think I can explain away most, if not all, the difficulties."

If these "sea-beaches" had been originally under the ocean surface, one would expect to find marine fossils, yet Darwin came up empty.[10] Note that he does not tell Lyell that he thinks he can explain the difficulties with his theory, but rather that he can explain them *away*. Explaining difficulties and explaining them away are two different things. The latter is not a scientific activity. Darwin desperately wanted his sea-beach theory to be true, so contrary evidence was not going to dissuade him. Darwin, therefore, went ahead and published a paper in the *Philosophical Transactions*. Lyell became a convert to Darwin's theory, at least temporarily.

Louis Agassiz, widely regarded at the time as the world's expert on glaciers, proposed that the parallel roads of Glen Roy might be better explained by appeal to glacier lakes. As glaciers melted and formed lakes, the edges of the lakes carved these parallel markings in the rocks, markings that were left behind after the lakes drained and evaporated. Another geologist, T. F. Jamieson, visited the parallel roads in 1861 and accumulated more evidence for the glacier-lake theory, after which Lyell was forced to admit that Darwin was wrong; the parallel roads of Glen Roy had been formed by glacier lakes, not the ocean. Lyell noted that the absence of certain marine organisms in the cold waters of glacier lakes in Switzerland would account for the lack of marine fossils found at Glen Roy and concluded, "I now consider the glacier lake theory as affording by far the most satisfactory solution of this difficult problem."[11]

As the glacier lake theory became a point of geological debate by the mid-1840s, Darwin continued to hold to his sea-beach theory. In an August 1846 letter to Leonard Horner, a geologist and founder of the *Edinburgh Review*, Darwin was in a quandary about how to respond to Horner's request that he write up something about Glen Roy for the Geological Committee. While Darwin did draft a document, he reported to Horner, "but as I have written it, it is too long, ill expressed, seems as if it came from nobody & was going to nobody, & therefore I send it to you in despair, & beg you to turn the subject in your mind." It was easy for Darwin to write up his Glen Roy theory and publish it in the *Philosophical Transactions* in the late 1830s when there was no real alternative theory. But as the glacier lake theory became ascendant, Darwin became much more bashful about putting his theory out in writing. He continued in his letter to Horner, "If Agassiz or Buckland are on the Committee, they will sneer at whole thing & declare the beaches are those of a glacier lake,—than which I am sure I c[d]. convince you, that there never was a more futile theory."

But evidence for the glacier lake theory continued to accumulate, and in 1861 Darwin was forced to eat crow. In a September letter to Jamieson, he wrote:

> I thank you sincerely for your long & very interesting letter. Your arguments seem to me conclusive. I give up the ghost. My paper is one long gigantic blunder. I suppose and hope that you will publish an account of what you have observed. The case seems very interesting. What a wonderful record of the old icy lakes do these shores present! It really is a grand phenomenon. I have been for years anxious to know what was the truth, & now I shall rest contented, though ashamed of myself.

We see here evidence of the familiar Darwinian disingenuousness. Darwin had not really been "for years anxious" to discover the truth about Glen Roy because, during those years, he firmly believed he already had the truth and thought the glacier lake theory was futile. But when his argument could no longer hold up, he capitulated and tried to save face.

On the same day he wrote to Jamieson, Darwin sent Jamieson's letter to Lyell, writing, "I think the enclosed is worth your reading. I am smashed to atoms about Glen Roy. My paper was one long blunder from beginning to end." A year later in October 1862, Darwin was writing to Lyell again: "I return Jamieson's capital letter. I have no comments, except to say that he has removed all my difficulties & that now & for ever more I give up and abominate Glen Roy & all its belongings.—It certainly is a splendid case & wonderful monument of the old Ice Period.—You ought to give a woodcut.—How many have blundered over these horrid shelves."

Actually, not many had blundered over the parallel roads of Glen Roy. The only serious theories ever put forth to explain them were Darwin's sea-beach theory and the glacier lake theory. Darwin was really the only one who blundered over them.

The lack of marine fossils at Glen Roy should have tipped Darwin off early to the fact that his sea-beach theory was problematic. When writing about his excursion into the Andes during the *Beagle* voyage, Darwin noted the existence of marine fossils at such high elevations and exclaimed, "It is an old story, but not the less wonderful, to hear of shells which were once crawling on the bottom of the sea, now standing nearly 14,000 feet above its level."[12] Darwin knew what it meant that Glen Roy was devoid of marine fossils. But as with coral reefs, so with Glen Roy: Darwin was grasping at straws trying to find some geological insight that would cement his status as a real geologist, something he knew he was not. He tried to explain away difficulties rather than meet them head on, suggesting that perhaps he was less interested in the actual origin of the parallel roads and more interested in how his work reflected on his own developing scientific status. This dynamic would also become apparent in Darwin's biological work.

Martin Rudwick provides an enormously detailed analysis of the whole Glen Roy affair, informed by work in the philosophy of science. In noting Darwin's tendency to offer "*ad hoc* explanations of negative evidence,"[13] something Darwin had accused the glacier-lake theorists of doing, Rudwick highlights Darwin's weaknesses as a geologist. But then Rudwick tries to salvage Darwin's geological reputation by writing, "It should be apparent that however critically I have reviewed Darwin's work on Glen Roy, I do not think he was justified in condemning it so extravagantly towards the end of his life."[14] This is a brilliant example of the influence of Darwinian mythology. Even when a scholar highlights Darwin's clear weaknesses as a scientist, there is still a motivation to paint the man and his weaknesses in the most positive light possible.

From Geology to Barnacles

While Darwin received some recognition based on his geological work, especially his observations in South America that supported Lyell's uniformitarian ideas, his desire to really make a mark in science largely faltered. His coral reef theory was found to be too simplistic and his Glen Roy theory completely wrong. As Darwin dabbled in ideas about the origin of species, he was well aware that the controversial nature of what he was thinking would bring harsh criticism, especially since he did not bear the cultural capital bestowed by a degree and professorship in natural history. It appears that Joseph Dalton Hooker, whom Darwin had confided in about his species theory early on, noticed this weakness and suggested that Darwin earn his scientific credibility by comprehensively describing a class of organisms that no one else had yet described. While this would not make for groundbreaking or very exciting work, it would make a contribution to science and demonstrate Darwin's ability to do real natural history research. In essence, Hooker was advising Darwin to do an unofficial thesis in order to earn his scientific stripes.[15]

Thus in 1846, Darwin took up an exhaustive study of barnacles, or *Cirripedia* as he would usually refer to them.

As he pursued his barnacle work to earn scientific credibility, he seems to have decided that geology would no longer be an active area of research for him due to his self-imposed semi-reclusive status. He wrote to Lyell on September 2, 1849: "But I am running on as badly about my Cirripedia as about Geology: it makes me groan to think that probably, I shall never again have the exquisite pleasure of making out some new district.—of evoking geological light out of some troubled, dark region.—So I must make the best of my Cirripedia."

Describing barnacles would not require leaving the confines of Down House. Observing geological formations, as much as Darwin clearly loved doing so, would no longer be possible for one now so averse to travel. Also, we might note, giving up the travel necessary to do geology would also prevent Darwin from developing additional geological theories that might be proven wrong.

Darwin soldiered on, then, collecting thousands of barnacle specimens from correspondents scattered all over the globe, painstakingly examining each one and describing its anatomy and physiology. This work took eight long years and issued in the publication of four volumes on both living and fossil barnacles that established Darwin as a legitimate researcher in natural history. But focusing on barnacles did force Darwin to put his larger species work aside, an act he seems to have found somewhat frustrating. On October 12, 1849, he wrote to Hooker: "By the way, you say in your letter that you care more for my species work than for the Barnacles; now this is too bad of you, for I declare your decided approval of my plain Barnacle work over theoretic species work, had very great influence in deciding me to go on with former & defer my species paper."

Darwin's barnacle work was clearly more Hooker's idea than Darwin's. Seeing that he might have pushed Darwin too hard into the barnacle work, Hooker explained himself in a letter of April 6, 1850, written from India, where Hooker had gone to study the plants of the Himalayas:

> Probably I spoke too strongly about your specific work & Barnacles, but really I was in periculosis[16] when I wrote and much harassed in mind & body.... I remember once dreaming that you were prone to theoretical considerations about species & unaware of certain difficulties in your own way, which I thought a more intimate acquaintance with species *practically* might clear up. Hence I rejoiced at your taking up a difficult genus & in a manner the best calculated to throw light on specific characters and their value etc.

Hooker clearly thought Darwin was too prone to fanciful theoretical speculations and needed training in detailed anatomical and physiological description before getting too far ahead of himself on species.

By October of 1852 Darwin was writing to Fox: "I am at work on the second vol. of the Cirripedia, of which creatures I am wonderfully tired: I hate a Barnacle as no man ever did before, not even a Sailor in a slow-sailing ship. My first vol. is out: the only part worth looking at is on the sexes of Ibla & Scalpellum; I hope by next summer to have done with my tedious work."

It actually took about two more years, for only in September of 1854 could Darwin finally report to Hooker, "I have been frittering away my time for the last several weeks in a wearisome manner, partly idleness, & odds & ends, & sending ten-thousand Barnacles out of the house all over the world.—But I shall now in a day or two begin to look over my old notes on species."

Darwinian mythology often portrays Darwin's barnacle work as indispensable to the development of his species theory. Darwin slaved over barnacles for eight years, the story goes, observing variations that led him to the idea of evolution by natural selection. But the truth seems actually to be quite the opposite. In a May 10, 1848, letter to Hooker, Darwin describes his discovery of a bisexual species of barnacle in which the males are microscopically small and parasitic in the sac of the female. He writes, "I never sh^{d}. have made this out, had not my species theory convinced me, that an hermaphrodite species must pass into a bisexual species by insensibly small stages, & here we have it, for the male organs in the hermaphrodite are beginning to fail, & independent males ready formed." Note here how Darwin employed his already existing species theory as a lens through which to interpret his observations on barnacles.[17] His observations on barnacles did not lead to the development of his species theory, since he had already worked out the latter by 1842,[18] well before beginning the barnacle research.

Darwin clearly viewed his barnacle work as an impediment to his work on species, even if he did make a discovery that he felt supported the latter. The barnacle work had been imposed on him by Hooker simply to help Darwin gain scientific credibility, which it did. Hooker informed Darwin on November 4, 1853, that the Royal Society had voted to give Darwin the Royal Medal for Natural Science based on his barnacle work. Darwin's barnacle volumes were accepted by the scientific community as a significant contribution to scientific knowledge.

Following Darwin's death, Hooker wrote to Darwin's son, Francis, "Your father recognised three stages in his career as a biologist: the mere collector at Cambridge; the collector and observer in the *Beagle*, and for some years afterwards; and the trained naturalist after, and only after the Cirripede work."[19] Huxley also shared his views with Francis. "In my opinion your father never did a wiser thing than when he devoted himself to the years of patient toil which the Cirripede-book cost him," he wrote. "Like the rest of us, he had no proper training in biological science, and it has always struck me as a remarkable instance of his scientific insight, that he saw the necessity of giving himself such training, and of his courage, that he did not shirk the labour of obtaining it."[20]

Through the tedium of zoological description, Darwin had earned his scientific stripes. He could now get back to pursuing his species work having made a legitimate contribution to science. But proposing a new theory to explain the diversity of life would prove far more difficult than describing barnacles. Without relevant formal education, could Darwin solve that mystery of mysteries—the origin of species? As the next several chapters will show, his effort would face some challenges not wholly unlike those his Glen Roy theory met.

3. Darwin the Experimenter

As Darwin was working to further his career as a geologist, he began to bounce what he viewed as heretical ideas around in his head regarding the mutability of species. His early forays into this topic came fairly soon after the *Beagle* voyage, and he wrote up a short sketch of a theory of species transmutation by 1842, which he then expanded into a longer essay by 1844.[1] But how much was Darwin influenced by his *Beagle* experience in entertaining doubts about the permanence of species? The typical answer to this question elicits perhaps the most iconic image of all associated with the mythological Darwin—the finches of the Galapagos.

Virtually every school student learns that Darwin hit upon his idea of natural selection during his *Beagle* voyage upon observing finches with different size beaks in the Galapagos Islands. By noting that finches with different size beaks inhabited different islands, Darwin reasoned that they were all descended from one original South American species whose descendants then diversified as they adapted to the local conditions of life on the different islands. That all this occurred to Darwin from his visit to the Galapagos does make for a great story. Unfortunately, it is pure myth.

Darwin famously admitted that when collecting birds in the Galapagos he did not label them by island. In fact, he did not recognize that his Galapagos birds were all varieties of finches until he returned to England and had his bird specimens examined by the ornithologist John Gould. We see evidence of Gould's influence in Darwin's *Journal of Researches*, published two years after his return. In describing the different land birds he collected in the Galapagos, Darwin wrote:

> The remaining land-birds form a most singular group of finches, related by each other in the structure of their beaks, short tails, form of body, and plumage: there are thirteen species, which Mr. Gould has divided into four sub-groups. All of these species are peculiar to this archipelago.... Seeing this gradation and diversity of structure in one small, intimately related group of birds, one might really fancy that from an original paucity of birds in the archipelago, one species had been taken and modified for different ends.[2]

Thus we find that Darwin appears to have recognized the potential significance of his Galapagos birds only after returning home and conferring with an expert. In fact, Darwin only personally visited three of the Galapagos Islands, and when he asked his shipmates to bring back specimens for him from the other islands they had visited, he asked only for fossil specimens, not living organisms, let alone finches.

Also, Darwin never mentions the Galapagos finches in *The Origin of Species*. He did make a brief mention of them in the unpublished manuscript of his big book on species, remarking on the "marvellous range of difference in their beaks, from that of a gross-beak to a wren."[3] But he left this discussion out of his abstract. He must not have considered it primary evidence for his theory. In the words of Frank J. Sulloway, "Contrary to the legend, Darwin's finches do not appear to have inspired his earliest theoretical views on evolution."[4] So, why are they called today *Darwin's* finches?

In the 1930s, the Ecuadorian government began a program of wildlife conservation in the Galapagos Islands. Because Darwin had visited the Galapagos, and because Darwinian evolution was reaching a point of scientific prominence at that time (the era of the Neo-Darwinian synthesis), the Ecuadorian government promoted the idea of Darwin discovering natural selection in the Galapagos to raise the importance of the islands and justify the conservation efforts.[5] This mythology was then advanced by the publication of *Darwin's*

Finches by British ornithologist David Lack in 1947, and then was taken over by the biological establishment to advance the cause of evolutionary theory. Here again is the pattern: something we take for granted about Darwin turns out to be a later invention to justify twentieth-century ideological commitments—Darwinian mythology obscuring the real Darwin.

Now it does appear that the overall distribution of species around the globe, especially the relationship between continental and island flora and fauna, caught Darwin's attention as significant. But Darwin had already been introduced to the idea of species transmutation through his grandfather Erasmus's *Zoonomia* and the work of French zoologist Jean-Baptiste Lamarck, as well as through his associations with Robert Grant at Edinburgh. What really seems to have sparked Darwin's thinking about natural selection was his reading of Thomas Malthus's *Essay on the Principle of Population* in 1838.

Malthus noted that while human populations grow geometrically, food supplies only increase arithmetically, meaning that human populations would quickly outstrip their food supplies, leading to mass starvation unless the population is checked in some other way (such as by wars or disease). Darwin extended Malthus's insight to the organic world as a whole, reasoning that other species would likewise be locked in a struggle over finite resources in which only those best adapted to the conditions of life would survive and reproduce. If individuals arose in a population that happened by chance to have a variation making them better adapted, they would reproduce more, thus passing the fitter variation to more offspring, a process that if repeated generation after generation would eventually lead to an altered population of organisms.

There is a certain irony in Darwin's intellectual debt to Malthus, however. Malthus was writing specifically in response to people like William Godwin and Nicolas de Condorcet to challenge anarchist and utopian ideas about human society. Godwin and Condorcet believed that the evil actions of people resulted from the corrupting influence of social and political institutions. Removing the influence of these institutions would allow the true moral nature of humanity to shine through and produce a world of peace, harmony, and equality for all. But for Malthus, the peaceful, thriving society envisioned by Godwin and Condorcet would unleash unrestrained population growth. The population would therefore quickly outstrip its food supply, leading to starvation and misery for many, rendering a utopia a practical impossibility. Malthus, to be clear, did wish that these utopian visions could become a reality. "I have read some of the speculations on the perfectibility of man and of society with pleasure," he commented in the essay. "I have been warmed and delighted with the enchanting picture they hold forth. I ardently wish for such happy improvements. But I see great, and to my understanding, unconquerable difficulties in the way to them."[6]

Specifically, due to his conviction that unchecked populations tend to grow geometrically while food supplies grow only arithmetically (an assumption that itself has been critiqued), Malthus could see no way toward the perfectibility of society envisioned by the likes of Godwin and Condorcet.

For Malthus, then, the struggle over finite resources would prevent the kind of unrestrained population growth that would lead to great suffering. But Darwin took Malthus's idea, applied it to biological activities in non-human organisms, and made it a mechanism for biological advancement based on increased levels of reproduction among the fitter. Or as Gillian Beer puts it, "To Malthus fecundity was a danger to be suppressed—particularly by draconian measures among the human poor. To Darwin fecundity was a liberating and creative principle, leading to increased potential for change and development."[7]

Apparently, Darwin was so relieved to have discovered a possible mechanism for evolution that he ignored this contradiction. In the words of Paul Johnson, whose biography of the man is generally favorable, Darwin "swallowed Malthusianism because it fitted his emotional need; he did not apply the tests and deploy the skepticism that a scientist should."[8]

Nevertheless, Darwin believed Malthus had given him the key to providing an evolutionary mechanism, one that paralleled the uniformitarian geology of Charles Lyell that had so enthralled him. Lyell's influence on Darwin is made explicit in the *Origin*:

> I am well aware that this doctrine of natural selection, exemplified in the above imaginary instances, is open to the same objections which were first urged against Sir Charles Lyell's noble views on "the modern changes of the earth, as illustrative of geology;" but we now seldom hear the agencies which we see still at work, spoken of as trifling or insignificant, when used in explaining excavation of the deepest valleys or the formation of long lines of inland cliffs. Natural selection acts only by the preservation and accumulation of small inherited modifications, each profitable to the preserved being; and as modern geology has almost banished such views as the excavation of a great valley by a single diluvial wave, so will natural selection banish the belief of the continued creation of new organic beings, or of any great and sudden modification in their structure.[9]

In the initial reaction to Lyell's geology, people thought that processes like erosion were too insignificant to produce large-scale alterations of the Earth's surface. But over time Lyell's uniformitarian views gained widespread acceptance. Darwin was convinced that people would respond to natural selection in the same way. That is, initially they would say that the perpetuation of slight variations would prove trivial to the production of large-scale evolutionary change, but in time, people would see past this bias, just as they had with Lyell's geological theory.

But to continue the analogy with Lyell, Darwin needed to identify a process currently in operation possessing the power to actually cause organic change. If such a process could be identified, Darwin could then reason (like Lyell) that this same process must have been responsible for organic change in the past. He did not have to search far, for Darwin was well acquainted with the process of artificial selection and the success animal and plant breeders had in creating new varieties of organisms. This led Darwin to perform some of his first experiments related to his species theory—crossbreeding animals to see what changes he could bring about.

Variation under Domestication

On June 15, 1838, Darwin wrote to his cousin William Darwin Fox, "I am delighted to hear, you are such a good man, as not to have forgotten my questions about the crossing of animals. It is my prime hobby & I really think some day, I shall be able to do something on that most intricate subject species & varieties."

Fox was an accomplished breeder of domestic animals, and Darwin seized on artificial selection as a process currently in operation with the power to cause organic change. From different breeds of dogs, pigeons, cattle, and agricultural crop plants, Darwin reasoned that given the kinds of changes skilled breeders could bring about in a short period of time by selecting which organisms to breed in each generation, there was no telling what kinds of variations could be produced by the analogous process of natural selection operating over eons of time. As Darwin says, crossing animals became his prime hobby, his first set of experiments geared toward creating an empirical basis for his species theory.[10]

A series of letters written in the middle and late 1850s attests to the importance of variation under domestication for Darwin's emerging theory. In March of 1856, Darwin wrote to Syms Covington, Darwin's personal assistant aboard the *Beagle* who had later settled in Australia. "I am now employed on a work on the variation of species, and for this purpose am studying all about our domestic animals and am keeping alive all kinds of domestic pigeons, poultry, ducks," Darwin wrote. "Have you ever noticed any odd breeds of poultry, or pigeons, or ducks, imported from China, or Indian, or Pacific islands? If so, you could not make me a more valuable present than a skin of such."

A little more than a year later (July 1857), Darwin finally got up the nerve to confess to his American friend and confidant, Harvard botanist Asa Gray, that he had thrown over the idea of the permanence of species: "But as an honest man I must tell you that I have come to the heterodox conclusion that there are no such things as independently created species—that species are only strongly marked varieties."

Darwin went on to explain his reasoning:

> I must say one more word in justification (for I feel sure that your tendency will be to despise me & my crotchets) that all my notions about *how* species change are derived from long-continued study of the works of (& converse with) agriculturalists; & I believe I see my way pretty clearly on the means used by nature to change her species & *adapt* them to the wondrous & exquisitely beautiful contingencies to which every living being is exposed.

Less than two months later, in September, Darwin again reiterated to Gray, "I am convinced that intentional and occasional selection has been the main agent in making our domestic races." He then continues: "Now suppose there was a being, who did not judge by mere external appearance, but could study the whole internal organization—who never was capricious,—who should go on selecting for one end during millions of generations, who will say what he might not effect!" This then leads Darwin to conclude, "I think it can be shown that there is such an unerring power at work, or *Natural Selection* (the title of my Book), which selects exclusively for the good of each organic being." Darwin makes clear that his belief in the power of natural selection to account for the evolutionary history of life rests on the analogy with domestic selective breeding.

Not surprisingly then, we see this line of argument playing a prominent role in the *Origin*. "We cannot suppose that all the breeds were suddenly produced as perfect and as useful as we now see them; indeed, in many cases, we know that this has not been their history," he comments there regarding domestic varieties. "The key is man's power of accumulative selection: nature gives successive variations; man adds them up in certain directions useful to him. In this sense he may be said to have made for himself useful breeds."[11]

Several pages later, he draws the crucial analogy. "No one supposes that all individuals of the same species are cast in the same actual mould," he writes. "These individual differences are of the highest importance for us, for they are often inherited, as must be familiar to every one; and they thus afford materials for natural selection to act on and accumulate, in the same manner as man accumulates in any given direction individual differences in his domesticated productions."[12] He then brings the point home:

> Slow though the process of selection may be, if feeble man can do much by artificial selection, I can see no limit to the amount of change, to the beauty and complexity of the coadaptations between all organic beings, one with another and with their physical conditions of life, which may have been effected in the long course of time through nature's power of selection, that is by the survival of the fittest.[13]

Both in his letters and in the *Origin*, Darwin seized on the idea of the "accumulative selection" employed by animal and plant breeders as the best way to demonstrate his conception of natural selection. Darwin was extremely impressed by what breeders could accomplish through this process. In his September 1857 letter to Gray he wrote, "It is wonderful what the principle of Selection by man, that is the picking out of individuals with any desired quality, and breeding from them, and again picking out, can do. Even Breeders have been astonished at their own results. They can act on differences inappreciable to an uneducated eye."

But in all this Darwin ignored the fault lying at the base of his analogy between natural and artificial breeding. Artificial selection is purposive. Animal breeders have a goal in mind of what kinds of characteristics they want to produce in their domestic animals. If you want to create a dog breed specially designed to be good at herding sheep, for example, you will identify characteristics consistent with this distant goal and then select only individuals from each litter that display these characteristics more than the others, and allow them and only them to breed.

A moment's thought will reveal why breeders are so successful. By selecting based on a future goal, they can select with this goal in mind generation after generation and accumulate small variations heading in the same direction, thus eventually creating variations as distinct as a St. Bernard and a Chihuahua.

Darwin seems not to have recognized the flaw in his logic. Natural selection cannot select for the attainment of a future goal. Natural selection is just a phrase to refer to differential reproduction, the way certain organisms with small variations may be more fit in their present environment and will therefore happen to breed more prolifically. There is no intentional selection going on (the term "intentional selection" being itself redundant). And even if in the interest of colorful storytelling we depict nature as a sort of natural-selection genie picking and choosing among characteristics, this genie cannot pick and choose for a future goal. It does so only for immediate survival and reproductive advantage. It cannot ignore these immediate concerns and work toward a distant goal over many generations, only at the end of which some new and fitter variety emerges. Natural selection, unlike artificial selection, is all about *what have you done for me lately,* and never mind the morrow. Artificial selection is thus a very imperfect analogy for natural selection.

Darwin seems to have been aware of these imperfections and attempted to address the problem. In an October 31, 1859, letter to Charles Lyell, he wrote, "I daresay selection by man would generally work quicker than natural selection; but the important distinction between them is that man can scarcely select except external & visible characters, & secondly he selects for his own good whereas under nature characters of all kinds are selected exclusively for each creature's own good."

Here Darwin makes one concession, namely that natural selection works more slowly than artificial; but then he argues that another difference breaks in natural selection's favor, namely that it always selects for the animal's good, which isn't the case with domestic breeding.

That point is good as far as it goes, but Darwin continues to skirt around natural selection's fundamental lack even as he enthuses about the activities and powers that artificial selection alone possesses. Writing later in *The Variation of Animals and Plants under Domestication*, he notes the following about artificial selection: "In the great majority of cases a new character, or some superiority in an old character, is at first faintly pronounced, and is not strongly inherited; and then the full difficulty of selection is experienced. Indomitable patience, the finest powers of discrimination, and sound judgment must be exercised during many years. A clearly predetermined object must be kept steadily in view."

This is an excellent description of artificial selection. But if a "predetermined object must be kept steadily in view" in order to effect significant change, then either natural selection has this same power of predetermination or Darwin's analogy utterly fails. And, of course, his conception of natural selection lacks any such power.

The co-developer of the theory of evolution by natural selection, Alfred Russel Wallace, emphasized another difficulty with the analogy to artificial selection. In his famous paper written from the Southeast Asian Island of Ternate which he sent to Darwin in the summer of 1858, Wallace flatly states, "No inferences as to variations in a state of nature can be deduced from the observation of those occurring among domestic animals.... Domestic animals are abnormal, irregular, artificial; they are subject to variations which never occur and never can occur in a state of nature: their very existence depends altogether on human care."

In other words, precisely because domesticated animals are shielded from the rigorous winnowing of natural selection, they are free to vary in directions nature would never allow. "Our quickly fattening pigs, short-legged sheep, pouter pigeons, and poodle dogs could never have come into existence in a state of nature, because the very first step towards such inferior forms would have led to the rapid extinction of the race," he notes; "still less could they now exist in competition with their wild allies."[14]

Darwin read Wallace's paper, but this point seems to have been lost on him. Almost a year later (April 6, 1859) he wrote to Wallace, "You are right, that I came to conclusion that Selection was the principle of change from the study of domesticated productions; & then reading Malthus I saw at once how to apply this principle." Darwin had to know when writing this that Wallace disagreed with his artificial selection/natural selection analogy. But he seems to have ignored this difference in their theories, though it appears he tries to address it in the *Origin* without naming Wallace: "I may here refer to a statement often made by naturalists—namely, that our domestic varieties when run wild, gradually but invariably revert in character to their aboriginal stocks. Hence it has been argued that no deductions can be drawn from domestic races to species in a state of nature. I have in vain endeavoured to discover on what decisive facts the above statement has so often and so boldly been made."[15]

Darwin ignores Wallace's point about domestic productions being unviable in the wild and their enjoying protections from the harsh vicissitudes of nature, the very forces understood to do the selective work in the case of natural selection. That Wallace saw the problem clearly and from the first may have had something to do with why he later modified his take on the creative power of natural selection, arriving at the view that while natural selection could manage some feats, it lacked the power, for instance, to have originated the human species.

Upon the publication of the *Origin*, some reviewers noted the weaknesses in the analogy as a point of criticism of Darwin's theory. W. R. Church, writing in the *Guardian*, wondered how natural selection could have a motive for the kind of careful and repeated selection employed by animal breeders. The analogy between natural selection and artificial selection seemed to Church to imply some intentionality in natural selection, which Darwin clearly did not intend.[16] T. V. Wollaston, writing in the *Annals and Magazine of Natural History*, quoted the famous philosopher of science William Whewell: "We cannot in any of the paleontological sciences ascend to a beginning which is of the same nature as the existing cause of events, and which depends upon causes that are still in operation."[17] In other words, we find no presently acting natural cause that can account for the origin of the many new biological forms attested to in the fossil record. One might disagree with this, but it is worth noting that Darwin had a very high opinion of Whewell as a philosopher of science.

So why did Darwin downplay Wallace's point? Guessing motives is always a dicey enterprise, but we do know that Darwin wanted to propose a mechanism for evolution that was purely naturalistic and would parallel Lyell's uniformitarian geology, with its emphasis on gradualism and on the presently acting causes being the key to the past. So Darwin had to find a material cause now in action that could produce organic change, and then hypothesize that this same process worked in the past to generate life's great diversity of forms. Artificial selection was the only presently acting cause known to produce appreciable positive organic change, so Darwin had no choice but to seize upon it and ignore the glaring problem in using it as a proxy for natural selection.

Artificial selection possessed one other weakness. As even Darwin's defender Thomas Henry Huxley would later point out, artificial selection, though it may have the power to create different breeds of animals and plants, had never created a new species, much less an entirely new order, class, or body plan. Darwin's theory of natural selection, therefore, would remain nothing more than a proposition until domestic breeders performed such a feat.

Darwin had to know that his analogy was flawed on multiple levels. But he made it the basis of his work anyway, likely because it was his only option for maintaining the parallelism with Lyell's uniformitarian geology to which, as we have seen, Darwin had a near-religious commitment. And yet it is perhaps telling that in the late 1850s Darwin abandoned work on his big book, titled *Natural Selection*, to instead write up a mere abstract of his theory, and that this abstract, *The Origin of Species*, focuses less on demonstrating an adequate cause for evolution and much more on documenting that evolution has occurred. The *Origin* is primarily occupied with showing that the idea of independent creation of each species makes little sense in the face of data regarding the geographical distribution of plants and animals around the world. This involved Darwin in a number of experiments related to the dispersal of plants and animals from continents to islands, experiments that, as we will see, betray the rather amateurish nature of some of Darwin's scientific work.

The *Origin's* Foil

Aside from proposing a naturalistic explanation for the mechanism driving evolution, it is clear that one of Darwin's main goals in his species work was to put the final nail in the coffin of creationist approaches to the diversity of life. Natural selection was actually subordinated to this latter goal. Darwin wrote to Gray on May 11, 1863, "Personally, of course, I care much about Natural Selection; but that seems to me utterly unimportant compared to question of Creation or Modification." As a result, a book widely hailed as proposing a true mechanism for evolution actually reads more like an anti-creationist polemic.

In contrast to the view that species represent ideal types in the mind of God that were created in the form we see them today and placed in the locations where we encounter them today, Darwin argued that the geographical distribution of species in the world represented evidence for a long history of evolutionary development from common ancestors. There are many places in the *Origin* where Darwin makes explicit that the evidence he is describing makes little sense on the assumption that species were each specially created.

For example, when discussing the lack of certain species of animals and plants on oceanic islands Darwin writes, "He who admits the doctrine of the creation of each separate species, will have to admit that a sufficient number of the best adapted plants and animals were not created for oceanic islands."[18] Here Darwin seems to assume that a creator would have no reason to leave oceanic islands devoid of these "best adapted plants and animals," so their absence stands as evidence against creationism. A few pages later Darwin argues:

> As the amount of modification which animals of all kinds undergo partly depends on the lapse of time, and as islands which are separated from each other or from the mainland by shallow channels, are more likely to have been continuously united within a recent period than the islands separated by deeper channels, we can understand how it is that a relation exists between the depth of the sea separating two mammalian faunas, and the degree of their affinity,—a relation which is quite inexplicable on the theory of independent acts of creation.[19]

That is, because the mammalian fauna on islands close to continents is more like the continental fauna than that found on oceanic islands much farther away from continents, it is reasonable to believe there is a relationship between continental and island fauna rather than to believe that a creator decided to make the fauna of oceanic islands more different from continental fauna.

Darwin doubles down on this line of argument when discussing the way in which closely allied species can often be found in separate but nearby locations, suggesting a common ancestor that inhabited both places that then diverged into two new species. To illustrate, he again invokes the island/continent relationship. "We see this in the striking relation of nearly all plants and animals of the Galapagos archipelago, of Juan Fernandez, and of the other American islands, to the plants and animals of the neighboring American mainland; and of those of the Cape de Verde archipelago, and of the other African islands to the African mainland," he writes. "It must be admitted that these facts receive no explanation on the theory of creation."[20]

Time after time Darwin discusses some specific observation about the distribution of living organisms and then insists that a theory of independent creation of each species is powerless to explain it. Yet surely it is hazardous to assume one knows what a creator of the natural world would and would not do.

There is also the fact that many of Darwin's best examples of geographical distribution pointing to evolutionary change involve rather less than dramatic modifications. In light of this, perhaps natural selection can diversify a species into a family of species and no further. The Darwin skeptic could thus contend, why not the special creation of types that then diverged into families of species via natural processes? Or perhaps the diversification fueled by natural selection reaches another rung or two up the taxonomic ladder, to orders or classes. Or perhaps universal common descent is the case, but it proceeded from intelligent input rather than by a purely blind mechanism.

One searches the *Origin* in vain for a thoughtful engagement with these other options. Darwin's theory of descent with modification may indeed be a better explanation than independent creation of each species, but Darwin does not merely declare his explanation better than this one alternative; he implies it is the only possible explanation. Thus could one be forgiven for seeing in Darwin's argumentation the classic either/or fallacy, wherein the person knocks down one option and declares a second option the clear winner, never mind that there are other live options available.

In Darwin's defense, he does invoke a more sweeping defeater for any theory of biological origins invoking a creator. We find this in a passage where he is discussing the phenomenon of typology—the structural similarity between many organisms such as the four-limbed pattern found in mammals, birds, and reptiles: "On the ordinary view of the independent creation of each being, we can only say that it is so;—that it has pleased the Creator to construct all the animals and plants in each great class on a uniform plan; but this is not a scientific explanation."[21]

Darwin's problem with creationist explanations is not that they are demonstrably false or impossible; it is that they are not, in his view, scientific. Here we find one of Darwin's wider goals for the *Origin*: to stamp out creationist explanations and put natural history on a firmly naturalistic (by his lights, scientific) foundation. But it never seems to have occurred to him that his "God wouldn't do it this way" argument was itself theologically driven, and therefore, on his own accounting, itself not a particularly scientific mode of argument.[22]

Of course, Darwin knew he would be on firmer ground if he could produce empirical evidence to support his view and overcome various difficulties confronting it. One such difficulty: If all organisms had descended from one or a few common ancestors, how had life spread all over the planet? Certain animals like birds and fish can move over long distances, but what about stationary organisms like plants? How could plants travel over long oceanic distances to colonize islands? Trying to answer this question sent Darwin into a series of experiments related to seed dispersal.

Experimenting with Seeds

On May 11, 1855, Darwin reported to Joseph Dalton Hooker, "I doubt whether I shall come up for the next Philos. Club for that is the day, when about 40 salted seeds 'come due', & you wd. be surprised at the time which my little experiment takes, as I do everything with my own hands." Darwin assumed seeds of continental plants must have somehow crossed the ocean to take root on islands. But could seeds possibly stand extended time immersed in salt water? Would they germinate after such harsh exposure? To find out, Darwin began soaking seeds in salt water for extended periods and then planting them to see if they would grow. But of course, even if seeds would germinate after prolonged immersion in salt water, would they float long enough to reach an island? Later in the same letter Darwin continues, "I begin to think the floating question more serious than the germinating one; & am making all the enquiries which I can on the subject, & hope to get some little light on it."

Darwin then wondered if fish could swallow seeds, swim to an island area, and void the seeds. If those seeds could then wash ashore, would they germinate? To find out, Darwin went to London to the Zoological Society to feed seeds to fish in the ponds. He reported to Hooker on May 15: "Everything has been going wrong with me lately; the fish at the Zoolog. Soc. ate up lots of soaked seeds, & in imagination they had in my mind been swallowed, fish & all, by a heron, had been carried a hundred miles, been voided on the bank of some other lake & germinated splendidly,—when lo & behold, the fish ejected vehemently, & with disgust equal to my own, *all* the seeds from their mouths."

Darwin's imaginative daydream was spoiled by spitting fish! Similarly, Darwin had asked his nephew, Edmund Langton, to perform these kinds of experiments, only to have Langton write to Darwin's son Francis on February 21, 1856: "Will you tell your papa that I have tried the experiments with all the seeds but the minnows only took a very little Dutch clover and spit it out again, and the Prussian carp took one anthoxanthum seed and spit it out again."[23]

If the fish would not eat the seeds, they could not be a vector for dispersal. Undeterred by this setback, Darwin continued in the letter to Hooker: "But I am not going to give up the floating yet: in first place I must try fresh seeds, though of course it seems far more probable that they will sink; & secondly as a last resource I must believe in the pod or even whole plant or branch being washed into sea; with floods & ships & earthquakes; this must continually be happening, & if kept wet, I fancy the pods, etc., w^{d}. not open & shed their seeds."

The method by which seeds could be dispersed across the ocean continued to vex Darwin. Nevertheless, he wrote up for the *Gardeners' Chronicle* some of his early results regarding seed germination following saltwater immersion and sent a copy of the paper to Asa Gray, prompting Gray to respond on June 30, "Many thanks for the paper containing your experiments on seeds exposed to sea-water. Why has nobody thought of trying the experiment before! instead of taking it for granted that salt water kills seeds."

Two days later Darwin reported some of these preliminary results to his old Cambridge botany professor, John Stevens Henslow: "Do you see Gardeners' Chronicle, & did you notice some little experiment of mine on salting seeds: Celery & Onion seed have come up after 85 days immersed in salt water, which seems to me surprising, & I think throws some light on wide dispersion of certain plants."

Darwin seemed to be feeling confident about the scientific importance of his seed experiments, though he was not without friendly detractors. Darwin related to the botanist, M. J. Berkeley, on June 12, 1855, that Hooker had expressed interest in his seed experiments, but "they seem to have had very little influence, or no influence, in making him think that plants thus get distributed, which I am rather surprised at." Hooker, as a trained botanist, may have noted methodological problems with Darwin's seed experiments.

By November 1855, Hooker's doubts were the least of his worries. Darwin's hopes hit a snag, and he reported the final results of his seed experiments, again in the *Gardeners' Chronicle*.

The results came in two parts. First was the matter of germination rates. These results, although falling short of dashing his hopes, were somewhat discouraging. Though some immersed seeds germinated after up to 137 days of immersion, many did not. Darwin reports that only six of about one hundred celery seeds came up. Only a single canary seed came up after 120 days' immersion while some oats half-germinated after the same period of immersion. "A few, and but very few, seed of Lettuce, Carrot, Cress, and Radish came up after 85 days' immersion."

Yet the fact that some seeds might germinate following immersion in salt water does not mean they would float long enough to cross great ocean distances. On this point Darwin continues:

> With respect to an important point in my former communication of May 26th, permit me to cry *peccavi*;[24] having often heard of plants and bushes having been seen floating some little distance from land, I assumed—and in doing this I committed a scientific sin—that plants with ripe seed of fruit would float at least for some weeks. I always meant to try this, and I have now done so with sorrowful results; for having put in salt-water between 30 and 40 herbaceous plants and branches with ripe seed of various orders, I have found that all (with the exception of the fruit of the evergreens) sink within a month, and most of them within 14 days. So that, as far as I can see, my experiments are of little or no use (excepting perhaps as negative evidence) in regard to the distribution of plants by the drifting of their seeds across the sea.

Here again we find the plucky if thoroughly amateurish experimentalist at work. Immersing some common seeds in containers of saltwater in one's basement hardly counts as a faithful laboratory imitation of what happens to seeds when they encounter a harsh ocean environment.

In his defense, Darwin did seem to take from the experience at least some measure of instruction. "I think we may learn a lesson of caution," he wrote in the *Gardiners' Chronicle*, "not to infer with too much certainty which seeds will endure longest when naturally buried in damp earth, from knowing what kinds will keep best in an artificial state."[25]

Another amateur naturalist, Hewett Cottrell Watson, who, like Darwin, never held a paying job, tried to rescue Darwin with some creative reasoning. In a November 10, 1856, letter, he asks, "Would not plants resist putrefaction much longer in agitated water, than in still water?" If you take a glass of muddy water from a turbid stream, Watson reasoned, the particles of earth making the water muddy will quickly sink to the bottom. But those particles will stay afloat much longer in turbid water like that of the ocean. Likewise, seeds might stay afloat much longer in turbid than still water. Of course, seeds are bigger and heavier than grains of dirt, so it is unclear if Watson's solution to Darwin's problem is really that helpful. But it does point out the inappropriateness of Darwin trying to experiment with seeds in containers in his house as an analogy to what happens to seeds in the open ocean.

Still, Darwin tried to reach out to anybody who could help validate his dispersal ideas, but with little luck. For example, sometime in 1856, he wrote to Victor de Robillard, a resident of the Indian ocean island of Mauritius. Darwin had visited Mauritius during the *Beagle* voyage, and he wanted to know if Robillard, a member of the Natural History Society of Mauritius, could shed any light on his concerns about the dispersal of seeds and animals to oceanic islands. (Mauritius is about 1,000 miles east of Madagascar.) Robillard wrote two letters to Darwin with his thoughts and observations. On September 20 Robillard reported that he had never seen trees thrown up on the shore by the sea. It might at times appear that way, but during hurricanes, trees sometimes are washed down into the sea and then wash back onto shore, but are recognizable as local trees. Robillard further reports being unaware of any cases of flocks of birds migrating to the island and taking up residence. Non-native birds living on the island were all introduced by humans. As an oceanic island resident and observer of nature, Robillard could not endorse any of Darwin's dispersal theories.

In a second letter written on February 26, 1857, Robillard goes even further. First he writes:

> You say in some cases, the same molluscs are found inhabiting different islands, although separated by the sea. In the islands that surround us, it is very rare to see the same shells on different islands—Mauritius has many more land shells than Bourbon,[26] and they are not the same species, with the exception of an achatina in common and a small cyclostome of the woods—none of the land shells of the Seychelles exist on Mauritius nor do those of Madagascar.

Once again, Robillard countered Darwin's expectations of evidence showing that mollusks had dispersed from island to island. Further, he tells Darwin that he does not think eggs could be transported by the sea from island to island because they would encounter too many enemies. Moreover, he writes, "As for freshwater molluscs, there are two or three species of Mauritius that are found on Bourbon; I think they are indigenous to the two islands without having been transported from one to the other." Finally, Robillard concludes, "I believe now it is very easy to transport species from one island to another, either the molluscs themselves or their eggs, it only takes the will of man."

Since Darwin wrote to Robillard for his opinion, he must have respected Robillard as a reliable observer of nature. But Robillard's experience as an oceanic island resident contradicted virtually every theory of dispersal that Darwin could conceive of.

Earlier, in 1855 (May 7), Darwin had reported his frustrations with his experiments to his cousin Fox: "I am rather low today about all my experiments,—everything has been going wrong—the fan-tails have picked the feathers out of the Pouters in their Journey home—the fish at the Zoological Gardens after eating seeds would spit them all out again—Seeds will sink in salt water—all nature is perverse & will not do as I wish it, & just at present I wish I had the old Barnacles to work at & nothing new."

Darwin's frustration at nature not doing what he wished is telling. Darwin was clearly less interested in really figuring out how nature works than being able to prove a new theory that would bring him scientific respect. By not cooperating, nature dared stand in the way of Darwin's personal concerns. But the dispersal of seeds across the ocean was not his only problem.

Other Experiments and Observations

Eventually Darwin put his seed experiments aside, and in the years after the publication of the *Origin*, he turned to other botanical concerns, especially the mechanisms by which flowers are fertilized by insects. He first studied and then published a volume on orchids.

(See Chapter 7.) But he also became fascinated by dimorphic plants, those that occurred with two different flower forms—some having long styles but others short styles.[27] Then he discovered that Lythrum, a genus of flowering plants known popularly as purple loosestrife, was trimorphic, occurring with three different flower forms—a long-styled form, a medium-styled form, and a short-styled form. Given Darwin's self-imposed semi-reclusiveness, he would not go out into the field to collect specimens of Lythrum by himself (though once he had received samples from others, he planted some in his garden for experimentation). So he enlisted members of his family to do the field work for him.

On August 2, 1862, Darwin wrote to his son William, then 22 years old and working in banking in Southampton, for help in collecting Lythrum. He told him to "employ the Boys; but caution them to gather only one twig from each plant." The boys he refers to are his sons George and Francis, who were on a visit to their older brother. George would have been seventeen and Francis thirteen at the time. Darwin had exacting standards for this collecting work ("gather only one twig from each plant") because purple loosestrife is an invasive weed that grows in dense webs, making it very difficult to identify individual plants. But to understand the ratio in which the three flower forms exist, Darwin needed to make sure each flower specimen came from a different plant. Yet despite the difficulty of this fieldwork, Darwin was willing to entrust it to untrained teenagers. William replied to his father on August 5, "I have got your fine long Lythrum letter, and have packed off the boys at once to watch and gather 99 pieces cautioning particularly about taking different plants."

Apparently unconcerned with entrusting his fieldwork to untrained teenagers, Darwin not only employed his sons in this project but also his nineteen-year-old niece, Margaret Susan Wedgwood. She wrote to her uncle on August 4:

> Of 256 specimens of Lythrum gathered this morning from different plants, we find
>
> 94 with long pistil

> 95 with middle length pistil
> 69 with shortest pistil.
>
> These plants were all in one large field or near it but tomorrow we will go if we can manage it in a different direction for more—We find it rather difficult in gathering to know what are distinct plants and what only offsets.

As his niece admits, identifying distinct plants is rather difficult, raising questions about the accuracy of the data. Two days later she wrote again to her uncle:

> We made a mad rush this morning after the Hottonia (an aquatic herb) before we started, but I am sorry we could only find one specimen of long pistil and we had no time to hunt for more and they were rather withered as we could not pack them at once—We are much obliged to you for sending us such a full account of the Lythrums but I am afraid it must have been a great deal of trouble—We went out Lythrum-hunting again but could only find 8 plants of which 1 was long style 2 mid-style & 5 short style.

This reliance on amateur plant-hunters rather than doing his own fieldwork or employing trained botanists underscores the amateur nature of Darwin's experimental work. Could he really trust that the flower specimens he received all reflected unique plants?

In addition to Lythrum, Darwin became interested in how hive bees fertilize clover. He asked his son George to observe hive-bee behavior while he was out searching for Lythrum. George reported back to his father on August 5: "On Tuesday I went to watch the Lythrums—& had a very wet scrummage. I caught 3 hive-bees sucking & saw any number of others & also caught 5 flies sucking & saw lots of others; saw butterfly suck several flowers but could not catch it."

Darwin believed that hive bees came in two forms: one with a short proboscis and one with a longer proboscis. The short proboscis bees would suck nectar through a hole in the base of the flower, while the bee with the longer proboscis would suck from the top of the flower. Darwin was trying to document co-evolutionary relationships between plants and pollinators. By simply observing bees sucking, George seems not to have made a distinction between those that sucked nectar from the top of the flower and those that sucked at the bottom. But what would one expect from an untrained seventeen-year-old?

Darwin therefore turned to his naturalist neighbor, John Lubbock, writing on September 2:

> I write now in great haste to beg you to look (though I know how busy you are, but I cannot think of any other naturalist who w[d]. be careful) at any field of common red clover (if such a field is near you) & watch the Hive Bees: probably (if not too late) you will see some sucking at the mouth of the little flowers & some few sucking at the base of the flowers, at holes bitten through the corollas—All that you will see is that the Bees put their Heads deep into the head and rout about.—Now if you see this, do for Heavens sake catch me some of each & put in spirits & *keep them separate*.—I am almost certain that they belong to two castes, with long & short probosces. This is so curious a point that it seems worth making out.—I cannot hear of a clover field near here.

A curious point indeed, if true. The very next day, Darwin wrote to Asa Gray: "All my semibotanical work, as you know, has been connected with insects, & now I am almost sure (but I find it a disgusting truth that with me first observations are generally all a blunder) that flowers have led me to a curious little discovery with respect to the best-known insect in the world, the Hive Bee."

Actually, this *was* another Darwinian blunder. Darwin learned that hive bees do not come in two different forms, confessing to Gray in a postscript: "Since writing the above by Jove I have found I have as usual at first blundered about the proboscis; but if you had seen the Bees, the blunder was almost excusable—What an ass I was to scribble all the above."

The same day he embarrassingly wrote to Lubbock, whom he had sent on a wild goose chase: "I beg a million pardons. Abuse me to any degree but forgive me—it is all an illusion (but almost excusable) about the Bees. I do so hope that you have not wasted any time for my stupid blunder.—I hate myself I hate clover & I hate Bees."

The results of Darwin's experimental work were not impressive. Crossing domestic animals really didn't shed much light on the action of natural selection. Seed dispersal experiments were poorly conceived and produced mostly negative results. Plant collecting was left up to mostly untrained teenagers. And hive bees failed to fit into Darwin's theoretical scheme. In a moment of frank self-assessment, Darwin told Hooker on April 24, 1855, "If you knew some of the experiments (if they may be so called) which I am trying, you would have a good right to sneer for they are so *absurd* even in *my* opinion that I dare not tell you." We can only imagine what other kinds of experiments Darwin was engaged in. Darwin biographer Paul Johnson remarks: "The truth is, he (Darwin) did not always use his ample financial resources to the best effect. He might build new greenhouses and recruit an extra gardener or two, but he held back on employing trained scientific assistants."[28]

Darwin certainly could have benefited from scientifically trained assistants, and he certainly could have afforded to employ them. But they might have told Darwin things he didn't want to hear—uncomfortable truths about the amateur nature of his work.

Writing to Hooker on November 12, 1862, Darwin revealed something very important about his approach to scientific work: "I am now working on cultivated plants & rather like my work, but I am horribly afraid I make the rashest remarks on value of differences; I trust to a sort of instinct & God knows can seldom give any reason for my remarks."

Darwin's instincts, alas, often proved unreliable. Following the publication of the *Origin*, he was particularly stung by criticisms that he had not followed inductive method. But such criticisms should not have come as a surprise for someone so guided by instinct. Darwin did not accumulate data and then reason from the data to general principles. He rather developed general principles by instinct and then tried to find data to support them, frequently becoming frustrated when perverse nature defied his will.

The portrait that emerges when this oft-ignored side of Darwin is attended to is not that of a professional scientist but of an amateur trying to cultivate a scientific persona in order to justify his position in elite Victorian scientific society. And he was well aware of this. In an April 25, 1855, letter where he introduces himself to Asa Gray, he states, "As I am no Botanist, it will seem so absurd to you my asking botanical questions." In an 1877 monograph containing all his observations about dimorphic and trimorphic plants, he repeats, "The subject of the present volume, namely the differently formed flowers normally produced by certain kinds of plants, either on the same stock or on distinct stocks, ought to have been treated by a professional botanist, to which distinction I can lay no claim."[29]

Reviewers of this monograph were able to spot some of the marks of Darwin's amateurish missteps, one writing that "the experiments conducted by Mr. Darwin, of which he summarizes the result in the present volume, are in themselves by no means satisfactory. Most of the observations of the writer were made, it would seem, on plants in his own garden; whereas all experiments made, and all observations tabulated, would be more satisfactory if made on plants in a state of nature."[30]

Presumably, this reviewer did not know that the plants that were collected in the wild were collected by scientifically untrained teenagers. One can only imagine what he would have thought of Darwin's results had he been privy to this fact.

Darwin's scientific endeavors were useful to him in at least one way; they helped him avoid a career as a parish priest in the Church of England, the only career he was academically trained for but a career for which he clearly had no commitment. Darwin's attempt to make a mark in the world of British science would eventually lead to the publication of his abstract, *The Origin of Species*. But as the next two chapters will show, Darwin's thoughts as he wrote his abstract, the response of other scientists to his abstract, and Darwin's response to his critics further fills in this emerging portrait of an amateur naturalist.

4. Writing *The Origin of Species*

What was going through Charles Darwin's mind as he conceived, developed, and wrote the species theory that culminated in the 1859 publication of *The Origin of Species*? This question is easily answered by a Darwinian correspondence brimming with Darwin's thoughts, concerns, and anxieties concerning his work. Through the correspondence we encounter a man harboring enormous reservations about his species theory and the level of scientific credibility he possessed to even propose such a radical new idea.

Darwin's long delay in publishing has garnered the attention of Darwinian biographers, with many ascribing the delay to fears Darwin harbored about how his ideas would be received. More recently, John van Wyhe has argued against this common wisdom, ascribing the delay instead to Darwin's understandable busyness with other work. According to van Wyhe, Darwin had no hesitations about his species work, and intended to publish only after other projects had been completed.[1]

But van Wyhe fails to engage with many of the letters germane to the question of Darwin's mindset, and in what follows, it will be clear that the common wisdom surrounding Darwin's delay is on firm evidential ground—Darwin was almost pathologically ambivalent about publishing his theory. Van Wyhe's dissent, however, demonstrates well the power of Darwinian mythology, which influences scholars to cast every aspect of Darwin's life and work in the most positive light possible.

Darwin had completed a sketch of his species theory by 1842, which he then expanded into a longer essay by 1844. But he was very cautious about whom he shared his ideas with. Emma was one of the first with whom he dared share what he viewed as the bombshell idea that species were not fixed and immutable. He wrote to her on July 5, 1844, "I have just finished my sketch of my species theory. If, as I believe that my theory is true & if it be accepted even by one competent judge, it will be a considerable step in science." Darwin then instructed Emma that in the event of his untimely death she should enlist someone to expand and improve upon his sketch and then have it published, suggesting Charles Lyell as a good choice for editor.

Darwin desperately wanted the world to know of his theory, but he was also reticent to publish it in the form of this short sketch, knowing that in this form it would fail to convince skeptical readers and would likely bring on harsh criticism. At least if his sketch was published posthumously, he would not have to face the criticism that surely would come, and the world could learn what he had been thinking. But there was no way that Darwin was going to publish this short sketch while he was alive. Publication would have to wait until he had accumulated considerably more evidence and produced a case strong enough to challenge the skeptics. He mostly, then, kept his thoughts to himself and plugged away with his geological work and biological experiments until such time as he felt confident that he could produce a fully convincing scientific argument for natural selection. But this time never arrived. Darwin's insecurities about his species theory dogged him right up to and beyond the publication of the *Origin*. In fact, if it had been left entirely up to him, it is quite possible that nothing even resembling the *Origin* would have ever seen the light of day.

Darwin's Insecurities

Hooker appears to be the first of Darwin's scientific friends to whom he was comfortable revealing his ideas. Darwin described his work to Hooker on January 11, 1844:

> Besides a general interest about the Southern lands, I have been now ever since my return engaged in a very presumptuous work & which I know no one individual who w^{d}. not say a very foolish one.—I was so struck with distribution of Galapagos organisms &c &c & with the character of the American fossil mammifers, &c &c that I determined to collect blindly every sort of fact, which c^{d}. bear any way on what are species.—I have read heaps of agricultural & horticultural books, & have never ceased collecting facts—At last gleams of light have come, & and I am almost convinced (quite contrary to the opinion I started with) that species are not (it is like confessing a murder) immutable.... You will now groan, & think to yourself "on what a man have I been wasting my time in writing to."—I sh^{d}, five years ago, have thought so.

We see exhibited here many of the rhetorical features so characteristic of the Darwinian correspondence. He predicts that his critics will see his ideas as presumptuous and foolish, he admits his own surprise that he has come to these ideas himself, and he anticipates Hooker's negative reaction. Darwin was a master at rhetorically disarming his critics by sympathizing with their anticipated negative reactions to his work. But having now "confessed a murder" to Hooker, Darwin would have to gradually let others in on the secret. Later that same year (on October 12), Darwin shared with his naturalist friend Leonard Jenyns:

> I have continued steadily reading & collecting facts on variation of domestic animals & plants & on the question of what are species; I have a grand body of facts & I think I can draw some sound conclusions. The general conclusion at which I have slowly been driven from a directly opposite conviction is that species are mutable & that allied species are co-descendants of common stocks. I know how much I open myself, to reproach, for such a conclusion, but I have at least honestly & deliberately come to it.

Once again Darwin assures Jenyns that he (Darwin) has been forced to this heretical idea almost against his will by facts and facts alone. And he anticipates Jenyn's negative reaction.

If Darwin had facts at hand overwhelming enough to drive him to a conclusion directly opposite to what he had always held, why was he so reticent to share those facts with the scientific community in the form of a publication? As we know from elsewhere in his correspondence, he was not really driven against his inclinations. Quite the opposite. Darwin, as we saw in the previous chapter, admitted to coming to his ideas via instinct, after which he attempted to scrounge up evidence to backfill the conclusion with experimental efforts that were at once valiant but also amateurish.

That being said, his reticence was assuredly no put-on. Darwin very much wanted to make his mark with his theory of evolution, but at the same time, he feared the slings and arrows that attend challenging powerful orthodoxies. These competing considerations left him in a constant state of ambivalence about whether, when, and in what form to publish his views. His letters to Hooker and Jenyns appear to have been trial balloons to see what kind of a reaction he would get.

The response from Jenyns appears to have been less than encouraging, for a little more than a month later (November 25) Darwin was again writing to him:

> With respect to my far-distant work on species, I must have expressed myself with singular inaccuracy, if I led you to suppose that I meant to say that my conclusions were inevitable. They have become so, after years of weighing puzzles, to myself *alone*; but in my wildest day-dream, I never expect more than to be able to show that there are two sides to the question of the immutability of species, ie whether species are *directly* created, or by intermediate laws, (as with life & death of individuals).

In response to apparent criticism from Jenyns, Darwin retreats to a more modest goal of simply showing that there can be two sides to the question of the immutability of species, recognizing that his belief in the mutability of species will really only be convincing to him. Later in this same letter he writes, "Pray do not think, that I am so blind as not to see that there are numerous immense difficulties on my notions, but they appear to me less than on the common view." He then ends the letter with, "Excuse this very long & egotistical & ill written letter, which by your remarks you have led me into." Clearly, Darwin was responding to critical remarks Jenyns had made in response to the October 12 letter, leading Darwin to backpedal a good bit.

After these early forays into sharing his views with trusted scientific friends, Darwin seems to have concluded that he was a long way from being able to publish his theory and be taken seriously by the scientific community. As we saw earlier, Hooker knew that Darwin had not earned the level of scientific gravitas necessary to propose such a grand new theory about the origin of species, a theory that would fly in the face of much scientific (and religious) orthodoxy; and he encouraged Darwin to improve his credentials by closely describing some class of animals. Darwin responded to Hooker on September 10, 1845, "How painfully (to me) true is your remark that no one has hardly a right to examine the question of species who has not minutely described many." For this reason, Darwin put his species work aside and launched into an eight-year project to describe the world's barnacles. This, as we saw, would serve as his unofficial doctoral thesis and provide him with the scientific credibility necessary to shock the world with the theory of natural selection.

Writing the Big Book on Species

As Darwin's work on barnacles came to a close, he turned his attention once again to his species work, but not without considerable trepidation. On March 26, 1854, he wrote to Hooker, "How awfully flat I shall feel, if I when I get my notes together on species &c &c, the whole thing explodes like an empty puff ball." Two years later, on March 8, 1856, Darwin laid out his plan in a letter to George Thwaites, a botanist and entomologist who had worked for some years in Ceylon:

> The course of my work makes me more & more sceptical on the eternal immutability of species; yet the difficulties on the other theory of common descent seems to me frightfully great. In my work, which I shall not publish for 2 or 3 or perhaps more years; it is

> my intention to give, as far as I can & that will be very imperfectly, all the arguments & facts on *both* sides of the case, stating which side seems to me to preponderate.

Once again, it appears that Darwin had essentially given up publishing a strong defense of his theory of common descent and natural selection (due to its clear difficulties) to instead simply provide an assessment of the strengths and weaknesses of the two positions—the immutability and the mutability of species. And it is clear that he was committing himself to no certain timeline for the production of such a work (two or three or perhaps more years). As we have seen, Darwin was in no hurry to put his ideas into print. But once he had shared his views with a few close associates, they began to wonder why he was delaying publication. It fell to Charles Lyell to force the issue.

A month after Darwin had written to Thwaites, Lyell visited Darwin at Down House. It was probably during this visit that Darwin first shared his theory in any detail with Lyell. Given Lyell's stature within the British scientific establishment, and Darwin's near religious zeal for Lyell's uniformitarian geology, it must have taken real courage for him to finally open up to Lyell. A negative reaction from Lyell would likely have crushed Darwin's spirits about his species work, perhaps for good. Fortunately for Darwin, it appears Lyell was intrigued. On May 1, 1856, Lyell wrote to Darwin, "I wish you would publish some small fragment of your data *pigeons* if you please & so out with the theory & let it take date—& be cited—& understood." Lyell's exhortation to publish put Darwin in a considerable bind, as is demonstrated in his response to Lyell two days later:

> With respect to your suggestion of a sketch of my view; I hardly know what to think, but will reflect on it, but it goes against my prejudices. To give a fair sketch would be absolutely impossible, for every proposition requires such an array of facts. If I were to do anything it could only refer to the main agency of change, selection,—& perhaps point out a very few of the main difficulties. But I do not know what to think: I rather hate the idea of writing for priority, yet I certainly sh^{d}. be vexed if any one were to publish my doctrines before me.

We can certainly sympathize with Darwin here. Being driven by a desire to make a mark in science, he hated the thought that a delay in publication might lead to someone else publishing similar ideas before him (a fear that Lyell clearly shared). Yet, he was afraid to publish just a short sketch of such a radical theory, knowing that he would receive harsh criticism for not supplying all the facts and evidence for it. And there was one additional problem. He ends this letter to Lyell with, "If I did publish a short sketch, where on earth should I publish it?"

As Darwin wrestled with what to do, he reached out to Hooker for advice on May 9, "Lastly, & of course especially, about myself; I very much want advice & *truthful* consolation if you can give it," he wrote. "I had good talk with Lyell about my species work, & he urges me strongly to publish something. I am fixed against any periodical or Journal, as I positively will *not* expose myself to an Editor or Council allowing a publication for which they might be abused."

Darwin decided instead to publish his theory as an independent volume. But many problems remained, as he noted to Hooker in the same letter:

> If I publish anything it must be a *very thin* & little volume, giving a sketch of my views & difficulties; but it is really dreadfully unphilosophical to give a resumé, without exact references, of an unpublished work. But Lyell seemed to think I might do this, at the suggestion of friends, & on the ground which I might state that I had been at work for 18 years, & yet could not publish for several years, & especially as I could point out difficulties which seemed to me to require especial investigation. Now what think you? I sh[d]. be really grateful for advice. I thought of giving up a couple of months & writing such a sketch, & trying to keep my judgment open whether or no to publish it when completed. It will be simply impossible for me to give exact references; anything important I sh[d]. state on authority of the author generally; & instead of giving all the facts on which I ground any opinion, I could give by memory only one or two. In Preface I would state that the work could not be considered strictly scientific, but a mere sketch or outline of future work in which full references &c sh[d]. be given.

Darwin seems to indicate here that he had an unpublished work in progress and could alert the readers that the sketch in hand would be followed up by this longer work, one containing all the evidence and references. But then he ends the letter on a pessimistic note: "I believe I sh^{d}. sneer at anyone else doing this, & my only comfort is, that I *truly* never dreamed of it, till Lyell suggested it.... I am in a peck of troubles & do pray forgive me for troubling you."[2] If Darwin did go ahead and publish a short sketch without evidence, he wanted to be sure Hooker knew it was not his idea—that he would never have decided to do such a thing on his own volition. But Darwin clearly did not want to disappoint Lyell, nor take the risk of losing priority.

Hooker appears to have suggested Darwin write a preliminary essay simply introducing his ideas to the larger public and then following up later with an extensive monograph. But two days after the May 9 letter, Darwin reiterated to Hooker his fear of placing an editor or council in the position of publishing his essay and then Darwin having to humbly apologize for leading them into a scrape. "I begin *most heartily* to wish that Lyell had never put this idea of an Essay into my head," wrote Darwin. Nevertheless, Darwin reported on June 8 to his cousin William Darwin Fox that he was going ahead with the preliminary essay but complained that "my work will be horridly imperfect & with many mistakes, so that I groan & tremble when I think of it."

The twin elements of lowering expectations and running himself down continued as Darwin began to share his ideas with a larger circle of scientific correspondents. He wrote to S. P. Woodward, a professor at the Royal Agricultural College, on July 18, 1856: "I am growing as bad as the worst about species & hardly have a vestige of belief in the permanence of species left in me, & this confession will make you think very lightly of me, but I cannot help it, such has become my honest conviction though the difficulties & arguments against such heresy are certainly most weighty."

On August 5 he reported to Hooker, "I thank you most sincerely for all your assistance; & whether or no my Book may be wretched you have done your best to make it less wretched. Sometimes I am in good spirits & sometimes very low about it. My own mind is decided on the question of origin of species but good Heavens how little that is worth."

And on September 29, he confessed to James Dwight Dana, Professor of Geology at Yale University: "You will be rather indignant at hearing that I am becoming, indeed I sh[d]. say have become, skeptical on the permanent immutability of species: I groan when I make such a confession, for I shall have little sympathy from those, whose sympathy I alone value.— But anyhow I feel sure that you will give me credit for not having come to so heterodox a conclusion without much deliberation."

He concluded this letter with, "Agassiz, if he ever honours me by reading my work, will throw a boulder at me & many others will pelt me."

As the circle of people with whom Darwin shared his heresy widened, he continued to "work the refs," attempting to pre-empt critical responses by beating his critics to the punch.

As he began to write his preliminary essay, he realized he could not condense his work down to such a small format and began instead to write a much longer manuscript. He described his difficulties to Hooker on December 10: "It is a most tiresome drawback to my satisfaction in writing, that though I leave out a good deal & try to condense, every chapter runs to such an inordinate length: my present chapter on causes of fertility & sterility & on natural crossing has actually run out to 100 pages M.S., and yet I do not think I have put in anything superfluous."

By the next summer (June 18, 1857), Darwin reported to Asa Gray, "I am quite conscious that my speculations run quite beyond the bounds of true science." And then a month later, he discovered he had made a significant blunder.

Darwin had been pouring over zoological and botanical catalogues, trying to show that varieties were most numerous in genera that contained a large number of species and that were geographically widespread with many individually abundant species. His calculations seemed to support his hypothesis that varieties would be most numerous in large and geographically widespread genera. But John Lubbock,

Darwin's naturalist neighbor, discovered a flaw in Darwin's methodology. Darwin had apparently been defining the size of genera in an arbitrary way rather than determining at the outset a fixed number of species that would set off a large genus from a small one and then using this as a standard against which to categorize the various genera. According to Lubbock, Darwin should have decided first on the number of species that would constitute a large versus a small genus, then scanned the catalogues using this fixed standard to count the number of varieties occurring in each. By scanning the catalogues and counting varieties first, and then arbitrarily assigning the associated genera to large or small categories, Darwin was assuring that his hypothesis about varieties being more numerous in large genera was certain to be confirmed. This seems like a pretty basic error, one that James Costa termed a "disgraceful blunder,"[3] and Darwin was nonplussed when it was brought to his attention, leading him to effusively thank Lubbock for saving him. He wrote to Lubbock on July 14:

> You have done me the greatest possible service in helping me to clarify my Brains. If I am as muzzy on all subjects as I am on proportions & chance,—what a Book I shall produce!.... I am quite shocked to find how easily I am muddled, for I had before thought over the subject much, & concluded my way was fair. It is dreadfully erroneous. What a disgraceful blunder you have saved me from. I heartily thank you.... It is enough to make me tear up all my M.S. and give up in despair.

That same day he described his blunder to Hooker, saying it would cost him two or three weeks' worth of work, and calling himself "the most miserable, bemuddled, stupid Dog in all England, & am ready to cry at vexation at my blindness & presumption." As we saw in previous chapters, Darwin's lack of scientific training often led him into questionable scientific conclusions, like his erroneous theory about the parallel roads of Glen Roy.

By late November of 1857, it became clear that Darwin had bit off more than he could chew in trying to produce some kind of publication to honor Lyell's exhortations to publish. On November 29 he agreed with Asa Gray regarding concerns Gray had apparently raised about the work: "What you hint at generally is very very true, that my work will be grievously hypothetical & large parts by no means worthy of being called inductive; my commonest error being probably induction from too few facts."

Two days later he sent a letter to the President of the Linnean Society, George Bentham. "Thank you heartily for what you say about my Book; but you will be greatly disappointed; it will be grievously too hypothetical," wrote Darwin. "It will very likely be of no other service than collocating some facts.... But, alas, how frequent, how almost universal it is in an author to persuade himself of the truth of his own dogmas."

By the following spring (May 18, 1858), Darwin had completely given up on writing just an essay or short sketch, and appears to have been fully involved in writing a big book on species. "I have for some years been preparing a work for publication which I commenced 20 years ago, and for which I sometimes find facts in your handwriting!" he wrote to his old *Beagle* assistant Syms Covington. "This work will be my biggest; it treats on the origin of varieties of our domestic animals and plants, and on the origin of species in a state of nature. I have to discuss every branch of natural history, and the work is beyond my strength and tries me sorely."

But as Darwin slaved over a work he was unsure he would ever be able to bring to satisfactory completion, let alone publish, the whole trajectory of his life would be fundamentally upended by a letter and manuscript that arrived at Down House in June of 1858.

A Letter from Ternate

While Darwin was agonizing over whether, when, and in what form to publish his species theory, he received perhaps the shock of his life upon opening his mail sometime around June 18, 1858. Among his letters that day was a package sent to him from Southeast Asia by Alfred Russel Wallace containing a manuscript of a paper bearing the title "On the Tendency of Varieties to Depart Indefinitely from the Original Type." In this short paper, Wallace had laid out a theory about the origin of varieties and species closely mirroring Darwin's, confronting Darwin with the real possibility, predicted by Lyell, that his reticence to publish would result in him losing priority and any scientific fame that might go along with it. A year earlier, on February 22, 1857, Darwin had written to his cousin Fox: "I am got most deeply interested in my subject; though I wish I could set less value on the bauble fame, either present or posthumous, than I do, but not, I think, to any extreme degree; yet, if I know myself, I would work just as hard, though with less gusto, if I knew that my Book wd. be published for ever anonymously."

Darwin was quite transparent here about his desire for scientific fame. He desperately wanted recognition for his species work while simultaneously being afraid to publish it and provoke controversy, leaving him in a state of confusion as to how to respond to Wallace's manuscript. How could someone else have independently hit on so similar a theory as his? All his seeming originality appeared to be going up in smoke.

Wallace (born in 1823) was, like Darwin, an amateur naturalist who traveled the world collecting specimens of all kinds of organisms. Unlike Darwin, however, who represented the upper class of Victorian society and never needed to hold a paying job, Wallace was from the working class and struggled with financial security through much of his long life (he lived to 90). He had learned land surveying from his older brother and had worked as a surveyor and engineer during his early adulthood. But he soon decided he wanted to explore nature and so set off with a traveling companion, Henry Bates, to South America to explore the tropics. Also unlike Darwin, whose travels in South America were dictated by the movements of the *Beagle* and who used his social connections to secure lodgings from British expatriates where he could continue to enjoy some of the comforts of civilization, Wallace and Bates left civilization behind and sailed up the Amazon River deep into the tropical rainforest, living among indigenous peoples and enduring bouts of malaria. Their trip was financed not by a wealthy father (as Darwin's was), but by selling their specimens to British museums. Unfortunately, on Wallace's return to England (Bates stayed behind for further collecting), the ship caught fire and all of Wallace's specimens were lost; Wallace and the ship's crew had to be rescued by a passing ship.

After recovering from this ordeal back in London, Wallace set off again, this time to the Malay Archipelago in Southeast Asia. Once again, he lived for nearly eight years in primitive huts among native peoples as he studied nature and collected specimens. It was while he was on the island of Ternate, and recovering from another bout of malaria, that Wallace hit on the idea of natural selection as the driving force of evolutionary change. He was aware that Darwin was working on varieties and species and had already had some correspondence with him, so he decided to write up his paper on natural selection and send it to Darwin, asking Darwin to share it with Lyell. Wallace had no idea how closely his theory resembled Darwin's (since Darwin had not yet published anything), and it does not appear that Wallace was looking to have his paper published. He simply sought Darwin's and Lyell's thoughts regarding his theory.

Back at Down House in June of 1858, Darwin agonized over how to respond to Wallace. While he saw all his priority and originality melting away, he also valued honor and integrity, and would not think of burying Wallace's paper and then rushing his own work into publication to secure priority. So he did as Wallace requested; he sent Wallace's manuscript to Lyell, writing on June 18:

> Some year or so ago, you recommended me to read a paper by Wallace in the Annals, which had interested you & as I was writing to him, I knew this would please him much, so I told him. He has to day sent me the enclosed & asked me to forward it to you. It seems to me well worth reading. Your words have come true with a vengeance that I sh^{d}. be forestalled. You said this when I explained to you here very briefly my views of "Natural Selection" depending on the Struggle for existence.—I never saw a more striking coincidence, if Wallace had my M. S. sketch written out in 1842 he could not have made a better short abstract! Even his terms now stand as Heads for my Chapters.

> Please return me the M. S. which he does not say he wishes me to publish; but I shall of course at once write & offer to send to any Journal. So all my originality, whatever it may amount to, will be smashed.

One wonders here if Darwin may have been secretly relieved by the arrival of Wallace's manuscript. Publishing Wallace's paper would relieve Darwin of the pressure to publish his own theory, and all the criticisms he so feared would fall on Wallace's shoulders, not his. It seems from this letter that Darwin seriously considered giving up his priority to Wallace. But Lyell had other plans.

Seeing Wallace's paper, Lyell sprang into action and worked out a plan with Hooker to have both Wallace's paper and a short abstract written by Darwin read before the Linnean Society. That way, both would receive recognition without either one necessarily being able to claim priority. Lyell hoped then that Darwin would quickly go ahead with publishing a longer work while Wallace was still immersed in the Southeast Asian jungle, and Darwin would then receive most of the recognition.

Lyell's plan left Darwin rather ambivalent. He wrote to Lyell on June 25:

> There is nothing in Wallace's sketch which is not written out much fuller in my sketch copied in 1844, & read by Hooker some dozen years ago. About a year ago I sent a short sketch of which I have copy of my views (owing to correspondence on several points) to Asa Gray, so that I could most truly say & prove that I take nothing from Wallace. I sh^{d}. be *extremely* glad **now** to publish a sketch of my general views in about a dozen pages or so. But I cannot persuade myself that I can do so honourably. Wallace says nothing about publication, & I enclose his letter.—But as I had not intended to publish any sketch, can I do so honourably because Wallace has sent me an outline of his doctrine?—I would far rather burn my whole book than that he or any man sh^{d}. think that I had behaved in a paltry spirit.

While Darwin craved recognition, he also wanted to protect his honor. He knew that his own views had originated in the late 1830s and 1840s and were completely independent of Wallace's work. But since he had been so reticent to publish even a short sketch, wouldn't doing so now appear as if he were trying to usurp Wallace's priority? Or even worse, might it not look as if Darwin were plagiarizing Wallace's work? Lyell and Hooker's plan to protect Darwin's priority only served to exacerbate Darwin's many anxieties.

Darwin was so dogged by fears that publishing now might make him appear dishonorable that he wrote to Hooker four days later, "I send sketch of 1844 **solely** that you may see by your own handwriting that you did read it." Apparently, Hooker had annotated his copy of the 1844 sketch and Darwin wanted to prove to Hooker that Hooker had seen Darwin's theory long before Darwin ever became aware of Wallace's work! Darwin was positively haunted by the prospect that people might think he stole Wallace's ideas. But Hooker was not the one who needed convincing. He already knew that Darwin had stolen nothing from Wallace—that it was mere coincidence that they had come up with similar theories independently. It was Darwin's own conscience that needed the convincing. Later in this same letter Darwin confessed, "It is miserable in me to care at all about priority." Perhaps. But Darwin most certainly *did* care about priority.

On June 30, Lyell and Hooker wrote to the Linnean Society, presenting Darwin and Wallace's papers:

> The accompanying papers, which we have the honour of communicating to the Linnean Society, and which all relate to the same subject, viz. the Laws which affect the Production of Varieties, Races, and Species, contain the results of the investigations of two indefatigable naturalists, Mr. Charles Darwin and Mr. Alfred Wallace.
>
> These gentlemen having, independently and unknown to one another, conceived the same very ingenious theory to account for the appearance and perpetuation of varieties of specific forms on our planet, may both fairly claim the merit of being original thinkers in this important line of inquiry, but neither of them having published his views, though Mr. Darwin has for many years past been repeatedly urged by us to do so, and both authors having now unreservedly placed their papers in our hands, we think it would

> best promote the interests of science that a selection from them should be laid before the Linnean Society.

The letter goes on to describe how Hooker had read Darwin's 1844 sketch proving that Darwin's work was independent and earlier than Wallace's, tactfully and tacitly supporting Darwin's priority while acknowledging Wallace's originality. The papers were read before the Linnean Society in the summer of 1858, but to little fanfare. Still, Darwin's theory was now finally out in the public realm, and he had little choice but to follow up with a more detailed account.

Darwin, however, continued to fret that he might be viewed as having stolen priority away from Wallace, or worse that he might have actually stolen Wallace's ideas. Darwin wrote to Hooker on July 5, "Lastly you said you would write to Wallace; I certainly sh[d]. much like this, as it would quite exonerate me." Darwin hoped Hooker would make it clear to Wallace that Hooker had read Darwin's sketch in 1844, proving Darwin had come to the idea of natural selection independently of Wallace, and likely long before him. On July 13 Darwin again wrote to Hooker: "I always thought it very possible that I might be forestalled, but I fancied that I had grand enough soul not to care; but I found myself mistaken & punished; I had, however, quite resigned myself & had written half a letter to Wallace to give all priority to him & sh[d]. certainly not have changed had it not been for Lyell's and yours quite extraordinary kindness. I assure you I feel it, & shall not forget it."

Darwin cared deeply about priority because his work was motivated so much by a desire to establish himself among the Victorian scientific elite, not simply by a desire to solve the question of the origin of species. A letter written by Wallace to Hooker on October 6 demonstrates that Wallace was not as tied up in knots about this whole affair as Darwin was: "It would have caused me much pain & regret had Mr. Darwin's excess of generosity led him to make public my paper unaccompanied by his own much earlier & I doubt not much more complete views on the same subject, & I must again thank you for the course you have adopted, which while strictly just to both parties, is so favourable to myself."

Wallace did not expect the manuscript he sent to Darwin to be read before the Linnean society and published in their proceedings. He was just sharing ideas with Darwin and Lyell and valued their feedback. Priority and fame appear to have been the furthest things from his mind as he continued to immerse himself in the flora and fauna of the tropical jungle. Wallace seems to have been much more interested in science for science's sake than was Darwin.

Writing the *Origin*

With his ideas now finally in the public realm, Darwin set about writing what he would come to call his abstract—the abstract of the big book on species he had been working on until Wallace's letter arrived to change his life. On December 24, 1858, Darwin reported to Hooker that he had written 330 folio pages of his abstract, predicting that another 200 pages would be necessary.

He worried about how people would react and the responsibility he would face to defend his views. He continues in his letter to Hooker, "The subject really seems to me to be too large for discussion at any Society, & I believe Religion would be brought in by men, whom I know." Darwin was greatly concerned that people would view his work as anti-religious, and he seems here to be testing out an excuse for why he should not be expected to discuss his work at the Royal Society or other scholarly venues. Of course, big topics like the origin of species are exactly the kind of topics that scientific societies exist to discuss and debate. But even before completing his abstract, Darwin was already developing rationales for why he would hide from his critics. The mere anticipation of seeing his ideas circulate throughout the scientific establishment placed Darwin under incredible stress, leading to a major flare-up of his physical symptoms; the very work of writing the abstract became an onerous burden.

On January 23, 1859, he exclaimed to Hooker, "My God how glad I shall be when the abstract is finished & I can rest." On March 24, he wrote to Fox: "I hope in month or six weeks to have proof-sheets. I am weary of my work. It is a very odd thing that I have no sensation that I overwork my brain; but facts compel me to conclude that my Brain was never formed for much thinking.... We have set up a Billiard Table, & I find it does me a deal of good, & drives the horrid species out of my head."

Since Darwin was simply writing an abstract of a longer work already in substantial existence, it is hard to fathom why he would find the work of abstracting it so much more taxing than writing the big book itself. Perhaps it is because he knew he could delay publication of the big book for as long as he wanted, removing from him much of the pressure to produce. But owing to Wallace's letter and the subsequent reading of his sketch before the Linnean Society, he no longer had that luxury. The abstract had to be published and in a timely manner. And being forced into publishing played havoc with Darwin's physical and emotional health.

As he neared completion of the abstract, Darwin's next problem concerned who might publish it. Since it was Lyell who had goaded Darwin into publishing in the first place, it was logical for Lyell to recommend Darwin's work to the publisher who had printed his *Principles of Geology*, John Murray. Even though Lyell had not yet seen Darwin's manuscript, Darwin believed that Lyell might be warming up to his views and would therefore be open to approaching Murray on his behalf. In a letter written to Wallace on January 25, Darwin relates:

> You ask about Lyell's frame of mind. I think he is somewhat staggered, but does not give in, & speaks with horror often to me, of what a thing it would be & what a job it would be for the next Edition of Principles, if he were "*per*verted".—But he is most candid & honest & I think will end by being *per*verted.—Dr. Hooker has become almost as heterodox as you or I.—and I look at Hooker as **by far** the most capable judge in Europe.

It appears that Lyell described his interest in Darwin's theory as a form of perversion rather than conversion! But he nevertheless wanted to see it published.

On March 28, 1859, Darwin wrote to Lyell, "If I keep decently well I hope to be able to go to press with my volume early in May....

I fancy that you have spoken to Murray. Is it so? And is he willing to publish my Abstract? If you will tell me whether anything & what has passed, I will then write to him: does he know at all the subject of Book?"

Once again, Darwin's insecurities got the best of him. He continued in his letter to Lyell:

> Would you advise me to tell Murray that my Book is not more unorthodox, than the subject makes inevitable. That I do not discuss origin of man.—That I do not bring in any discussions about Genesis &c, & only facts, & such conclusions from them, as seem to me fair. Or had I better say *nothing* to Murray, & assume that he cannot object to this much unorthodoxy, which in fact is not more than any Geological Treatise, which runs slap counter to Genesis.

Darwin tied himself up in knots of indecision about how best to approach Murray, concerned with whether Murray would be put off with the unorthodox nature of his book. But these fears were unfounded. Darwin soon heard from Lyell that Murray was very interested in his work on the strength of Lyell's recommendation and his familiarity with Darwin's previous publications.

Murray did have one concern, however. Darwin wrote to Lyell (March 30), "I am sorry about Murray objecting to the term abstract as I look at it as only possible apology for *not* giving References & facts in full."[4] Murray's concern makes good sense; why would he want to publish a work on such a controversial topic that its author presents as a mere abstract? These concerns aside, the next day Darwin wrote to Murray, "I have heard with pleasure from Sir C. Lyell that you are inclined to publish my work on the Origin of Species, but that before deciding & offering any terms you require to see my M.S." Darwin then proceeded to describe the work in more detail, claiming that it represented more than 20 years of work, while reiterating to Murray, "but as here given, is only a popular abstract of a larger work on the same subject, without references to authorities & without long catalogues of facts on which my conclusions are based." Why Murray did not request to see the larger work is impossible to know. But fortunately for Darwin, Murray wrote on April 1:

> I hasten to thank you for your obliging letter of yesterday & for the interesting details regarding your work on species contained in it.—On the strength of this information & my knowledge of your former publications, I can have no hesitation in swerving from my usual routine & in stating at once even without seeing the MS. that I shall be most happy to publish it for you on the same terms as those on which I publish for Sir Charles Lyell.

And the publishing terms were handsome indeed. Darwin was given a 67 percent royalty on the manuscript of a mere abstract that Murray hadn't even seen! We must assume Lyell's influence was working behind the scenes here much to Darwin's benefit. Still, while thanking Murray for such generous terms, Darwin wrote the next day informing Murray that if once Murray saw the manuscript, he deemed it unlikely to generate significant sales, Darwin would free him from his obligation to publish. At every step in the process of writing and publishing the *Origin*, Darwin continually sought possible exit strategies that would result in his ideas remaining unpublished.

For his part, Murray may have been too hasty regarding his decision to publish Darwin's abstract without seeing the manuscript, for once he received the manuscript he sent it to Whitwell Elwin, editor of the *Quarterly Review* and a close associate of Murray, with whom Murray often shared manuscripts he was considering for publication. Elwin's opinion was rather critical. He wrote to Murray on May 3: "I have been intending for some days to write to you upon the subject of Mr. Darwin's work on the Origin of Species. After you had the kindness to allow me to read the Ms. I made a point of seeing Sir C. Lyell, who I understood had, in some degree, advised the publication. I had myself formed a strong opinion the other way, & I stated to him fully my conviction, & the grounds of it."

Elwin's chief complaint revolved around the issue that had so tormented Darwin. Could he publish such a revolutionary theory without providing all the evidence for it? Elwin continued:

> It seemed to me to put forth the theory without the evidence would do grievous injustice to his views, & to his twenty years of

> observations & experiment. At every page I was tantalized by the absence of the proofs. All kinds of objections, & possibilities rose up in the mind, & it was fretting to think that the author had a whole array of facts, & inferences from the facts, absolutely *essential* to the decision on the question which were not before the reader. It is to ask the jury for a verdict without putting the witness into the box.

Elwin clearly believed that Darwin must have had at hand all the facts and evidence accumulated over twenty years of work. So why withhold all the evidence from the jury by publishing a mere abstract? Elwin's confusion was well founded. And given that Darwin never did publish all the facts and evidence the conclusions of the *Origin* were said to be founded on, we certainly have a right to be suspicious about the existence of those facts.

Elwin continued his review by comparing the *Origin* to Darwin's *Journal of Researches*, calling the latter "one of the most charming books in the language." The *Origin*, on the other hand, was quite the opposite, in his view:

> The dissertation on species is, on the contrary, in a much harder & drier style. I impute this to the absence of the details. It is these which give relief & interest to the scientific outline—so that the very omission which takes from the philosophical value of the work destroys in a great degree its popular value also. Whatever class of public he wishes to win he weakens the effect by an imperfect, & comparatively meagre exposition of his theory.

We get a clear view of the influence of Darwinian mythology by comparing Elwin's reaction to the *Origin* with the reaction of noted science historian Robert J. Richards: "What the book lost in detail, it gained in economy and force of expression. Examples stacked high in the "Species Book" manuscript were distilled into telling illustrations. Experiments of rigor and variety were recorded. The most severe objections were anticipated. And the argument stood out."[5]

Elwin certainly did not think that Darwin's argument "stood out" without the evidence to support it.

Elwin informed Murray that Lyell agreed with his criticisms. Lyell's motivation in pushing Darwin to publish something—even something as imperfect as the *Origin*—lay, according to Elwin, in his belief that left to himself, Darwin's anxiety to produce something perfect would result in him never publishing anything at all, thus depriving the world of the fruits of his labors. For his part, Elwin stated that his sole desire in raising criticisms of Darwin's abstract was to "do justice to the extraordinary merit of his investigations, & procure him that fame which belongs to him."

Between March and November of 1859, as Murray put Darwin's abstract to press, an exhausted and ill Darwin went to another water cure establishment at Ilkley Wells for treatment. It was there that he corrected the page proofs of his abstract and fretted about the reaction his work would elicit when it finally hit the streets. On November 2, a long-awaited package and letter arrived at Ilkley from Murray: "By this day's post I send you a specimen copy of your book bound—I hope it may receive your approval. Please reply by return & not a moment shall be lost in getting ready the early copies—your instructions seem quite clear & shall be carefully followed."

The next day Darwin responded, "I have received your kind note & the copy: I am *infinitely* pleased & proud at the appearance of my child." Murray then set about preparing a number of presentation copies for Darwin to send out to his many scientific correspondents. With each copy, Darwin included a letter designed to disarm these readers' criticisms before they even opened the book to page one. To fully appreciate the force of Darwin's rhetorical efforts, we will need to consider these presentation letters in detail.

Only an Abstract

On November 11, 1859, Darwin sent out ten letters to scientific correspondents to alert them to the arrival of a presentation copy of *The Origin of Species* being sent to them by John Murray. Each letter is a rhetorical masterpiece.

To Louis Agassiz, Swiss geologist who became Professor of Comparative Zoology at Harvard University, and who held firm creationist views:

> I have ventured to send you, a copy of my Book (as yet only an abstract) on the origin of species. As the conclusions at which I have arrived on several points differ so widely from yours, I have thought (should you at any time read my volume) that you might think that I had sent it to you out of a spirit of defiance or bravado; but I assure you that I act under a wholly different frame of mind. I hope that you at least will give me credit, however erroneous you may think my conclusion, for having earnestly endeavoured to arrive at the truth.

To Alphonse de Candolle, Swiss botanist:

> I have thought that you would permit me to send you a copy of my work (as yet only an abstract) on the Origin of Species.... Should you be induced to read my volume, I venture to remark that it will be intelligible only by reading the whole straight through, as it is very much condensed. It would be a high gratification to me, if any portion interested you.—But I am perfectly well aware, that you will entirely disagree with the conclusion, at which I have arrived.

To James Dwight Dana, American geologist and Professor of Natural History at Yale University:

> I have sent you a copy of my Book (as yet only an abstract) on the Origin of Species. I know too well that the conclusion, at which I have arrived, will horrify you, but you will, I believe & hope, give me credit for at least an honest search after the truth.... It took me many long years before I wholly gave up the common view of the separate creation of each species.

To Hugh Falconer, Scottish geologist and botanist who became superintendent of the Royal Botanical Gardens in Calcutta, India:

> I have told Murray to send you a copy of my book on the 'Origin of Species,' which as yet is only an abstract. If you read it, you must

> read it straight through, otherwise from the extremely condensed state it will be unintelligible. Lord, how savage you will be, if you read it, and how you will long to crucify me alive.

To Asa Gray, American botanist and Professor of Botany at Harvard University:

> I have directed a copy of my Book (as yet only an abstract) on the Origin of Species to be sent to you. I know how you are pressed for time, but if you can read it, I shall be infinitely gratified. From its condensed state it is *indispensable* to read it *all* straight through.... Let me add that I fully admit that there are very many difficulties not satisfactorily explained by my theory of descent with modification, but I cannot possibly believe that a false theory would explain so many classes of facts, as I think it certainly does explain.—On these grounds I drop my anchor & believe that the difficulties will slowly disappear.

To John Stevens Henslow, botanist and Professor of Botany and Geology at Cambridge University, a close mentor to Darwin during his Cambridge days:

> I have told Murray to send a copy of my Book on species to you, my dear master in natural history. I fear, however, that you will not approve of your pupil in this case. The book in its present state does not show the amount of labour which I have bestowed on the subject.

To Richard Owen, comparative anatomist and Superintendent of the Natural History Department of the British Museum:

> I have asked Mr. Murray to send you a copy (as yet only an abstract) on the origin of species. I fear that it will be abominable in your eyes, but I assure you that it is the result of far more labour than is apparent on its face.—If you honour me by reading it at all, I beg you to read it straight through, otherwise from being much condensed it will be unintelligible.

To John Phillips, geologist and member of the Geological Survey of Great Britain:

> I have directed Murray to send you a copy of my book on the Origin of Species, which as yet is only an abstract.—I fear that you will be inclined to fulminate awful anathemas against it. I assure you that it is the result of far more labour than is apparent in its present highly condensed state. If you have time to read it, let me beg you to read it all straight through; otherwise it will be unintelligible. Try not to condemn it utterly, till you have finished it & reflected on the recapitulation. Not that I am so foolish as to expect to convert anyone, who has long viewed the subject from an opposite point of view. I remember too well how many long years my own conversion took.

To François Jules Pictet de la Rive, Swiss zoologist and Professor of Zoology and Comparative Anatomy at the University of Geneva:

> I have taken the liberty to send you, as a mark of my respect, a copy of my work (as yet only an abstract) on the Origin of Species.... If you should be induced to read my volume, I venture to state, that it is so much condensed, that it will not be intelligible, unless it be read straight through.

To Adam Sedgwick, Professor of Geology at Cambridge University. One of Darwin's teachers at Cambridge:

> I have told Murray to send you a copy of my book *On the Origin of Species*, which is as yet only an abstract. As the conclusion at which I have arrived after an amount of work, which is not apparent in this condensed sketch, is so diametrically opposed to that which you have often advocated with much force, you might think that I send my volume to you out of a spirit of bravado and with a want of respect, but I assure you that I am actuated by quite opposite feelings.

With one exception, Darwin alerts every correspondent that his work is as yet only an abstract, and therefore should not be evaluated as a complete and thorough treatment of the subject. It does not, Darwin assures them, fairly represent the full scale of his two decades of work. He also implores his correspondents to read his work straight through, feeling it will be unintelligible if read over time in smaller chunks. Exactly what Darwin was getting at here is unclear. The first version of the *Origin* was over five hundred pages. Few people would have the time or the stamina to read such a long work straight through. Perhaps Darwin only meant to urge his readers not to jump around in the book and skip portions. Or perhaps he feared that all the deficiencies of facts and evidence would be more apparent if one read the book in smaller chunks. Reading it straight through in one or two sittings might emphasize the rhetorical aspects of the work and make it seem more convincing.

Darwin further warns his readers that they will vehemently disagree with him. This is a brilliant rhetorical move. Who would harshly criticize someone who has gone to such lengths to humbly anticipate your negative reaction? At any rate, these presentation letters betray a very insecure person trying to prevent criticism before it starts. Finally, in two places, Darwin notes disingenuously how his own heterodox view on species was the result of long years of study, ostensibly based on all the facts and evidence he failed to provide his readers. It is well established that Darwin had given up the idea of species fixity soon after returning from the *Beagle* voyage. His conversion did not require long years of study.

Returning to the letter to Henslow, Darwin further commented, "If you have time to read it carefully & would take the trouble to point out what parts seem weakest to you & what best, it w[d]. be a most material aid to the writing of my bigger book, which I hope to commence in a few months."

Commence? This is curious, because just two days later Darwin told Leonard Jenyns that the greater part of his big book was already written out. More curious still, Darwin wrote to Wallace on the same day he wrote to Jenyns: "I am writing this at Ilkley Wells, where I have been with my family for the last six weeks & shall stay for some few weeks longer. As yet I have profited very little. God knows when I shall have the strength for my bigger book."

All these presentation letters were written while Darwin was undergoing hydropathy treatment at Ilkley Wells. Why does he tell Henslow he hopes to commence his big book on species in a few months, the same book he tells Jenyns is already mostly written out (which it was), and then complain to Wallace that he has no idea when he will have the strength to work on his big book? It is not clear that Darwin, in the wake of the reaction he would receive to the *Origin*, really wanted to publish his big book, even though he had led his correspondents to expect it. We are therefore left with the great irony that arguably the most famous scientific treatise in the Western scientific canon was considered by its author to be nothing more than a mere abstract, lacking many of the facts, evidence, and authorities on which its conclusions are based. To be sure, *The Origin of Species* outlined a new evolutionary theory, but it proved nothing about whether that theory was at all consistent with what actually happens in nature.

The puzzle of the origin of species was never going to be solved by a mere abstract. How, then, was Darwin to proceed? A comprehensive engagement with the Darwinian correspondence reveals a man wracked by terrible insecurities about whether, when, and in what form to publish his views on natural selection. He thought that his species theory gave him the best shot at winning scientific fame, but he realized that the fame he craved would not come without controversy. And given his own insecurities about the correctness of his theory, the latter was not something he felt he could stomach. His constant hesitation almost cost him his priority when Wallace's letter arrived from Ternate. But his well-connected scientist friends Lyell and Hooker stepped in to rescue him. Still, Darwin felt pushed into publishing despite his great reservations, a situation that wreaked havoc with both his physical and emotional health. Had Wallace not sent his manuscript to Darwin in the summer of 1858, Lyell's fear that Darwin would never publish his theory might well have come true.

But ready or not, Darwin's abstract was now in the public domain, and Darwin had little choice but to endure the criticisms that would surely come from tantalizing his readers with a bold controversial theory about the origin of species with only a promissory note offered for the bulk of the evidence. And those criticisms certainly came. In the next chapter we will consider what the scientific establishment had to say about Darwin's mere abstract and how Darwin responded.

5. Reacting to *The Origin of Species*

Even before Darwin's abstract hit bookstore shelves, Darwin was steeling himself against the criticisms that would surely come. He began a process of score-keeping, deciding whose opinions he would give credence to and whose he would simply ignore as unworthy of his attention. Not surprisingly, the opinions he valued most were the seemingly positive reactions of his closest associates: Joseph Dalton Hooker, Thomas Henry Huxley, and Charles Lyell. These would come to function as Darwin's personal trinity of support. On February 12, 1859, Darwin reported to his cousin Fox, "I have had the great satisfaction of converting Hooker & I believe Huxley & I think Lyell is much staggered." He then followed up on April 6 with a more detailed assessment in a letter to Alfred Russel Wallace:

> I forget whether I told you that Hooker, who is our best British Botanist & perhaps best in World, is a *full* convert, & is now going immediately to publish his confession of Faith; & I expect daily to see the proof-sheets.—Huxley is changed & believes in mutation of species: whether a *convert* to us, I do not quite know.—We shall live to see all the *younger* men converts. My neighbor & excellent naturalist J. Lubbock is enthusiastic convert.

Hooker's support and Huxley and Lyell's apparent interest in Darwin's theory (even if the latter two were not yet full converts) boosted Darwin's confidence. Six months later (on October 15), Darwin told Huxley, "I am very far from expecting to convert you to many of my heresies; but if on the whole, you & two or three others think I am on the right road, I shall not care what the mob of naturalists think."

Darwin had decided, even before the onset of public reaction, to accept what appeared to be the positive verdict of his friends and ignore the anticipated criticisms of his more general readers. He reinforces this point in an October 23 letter to Hooker:

> I remember thinking above a year ago; that if ever I lived to see Lyell, yourself & Huxley come round, partly by my Book & partly by their own reflexions, I sh^{d}. feel that the subject was safe; & all the world might rail, but that ultimately the theory of Natural Selection (though no doubt imperfect in its present condition, & embracing many errors) would prevail. Nothing will ever convince me that three such men, with so much diversified knowledge, & so well accustomed to search for truth, could err greatly.

We hear here the voice of someone lacking confidence in his views and fearing the inevitable criticisms that would come. Darwin had convinced himself that as long as Hooker, Huxley, and Lyell felt he was on the right track, he would take confidence in this fact regardless of what anyone else thought, because of the status of these three in the scientific community. Unfortunately for Darwin, many of his critics shared just as exalted a position in the British scientific establishment as Darwin's personal trinity of support.

On November 22, Darwin told his neighbor John Lubbock, "I care not for Reviews, but for the opinion of men like you & Hooker & Huxley & Lyell &c." This is a curious statement since the book was still two days away from official publication, so few reviews had yet appeared. But Darwin obviously expected the reviews to be negative when they did appear, so he decided beforehand to essentially ignore them. The very next day, Darwin revealed to Lyell his fears that he might have devoted his life to a "phantasy," but that he now could take comfort in the fact that it is "morally impossible that investigators of truth like you & Hooker can be wholly wrong; & therefore I feel that I may rest in peace." What Darwin means by "morally impossible" is unclear. Of course, it was possible for Hooker and Lyell to be wrong; anyone can be wrong about anything. But Darwin was so torn by insecurity that he had to convince himself that Hooker and Lyell could not be wrong, thus allowing Darwin to hang his hat on their support when the inevitable wave of criticisms struck.

The Origin of Species officially appeared on November 24, 1859. The next day, Darwin once again called on his personal trinity in a letter to Huxley:

> Like a good Catholic, who has received extreme unction, I can now sing "nunc dimittis."[1] I should have been more than contented with one quarter of what you have said. Exactly fifteen months ago, when I put pen to paper for this volume, I had awful misgivings, & thought perhaps I had deluded myself like so many have done; & then I fixed in my mind three judges, on whose decision I determined mentally to abide. The judges were Lyell, Hooker & yourself. It was this that made me so excessively anxious for your verdict. I am now contented, & can sing my nunc dimittis.

With Huxley's positive response secured, Darwin could rest in peace for a short while at least, but before long his restful peace would be disturbed by a wave of substantive criticisms. Yet not all the early reviews were negative. Even as Darwin found himself at the center of controversy, he could find some comfort in occasional positive reports he would receive from unlikely sources. For instance, on January 14, 1860, Darwin reported to Lyell:

> What a grand, immense benefit you conferred on me by getting Murray to publish my Book.—I never till today realised that it was getting widely distributed; for in a letter from a lady today to Emma, she says she heard a man enquiring for it at *Railway Station*!!! at Waterloo Bridge; & the Bookseller said that he had none till new Edit. was out.—The Bookseller said he had not read it but had heard it was a very remarkable book!!!

The triple exclamation points demonstrate how important these positive reports were for Darwin's self-confidence. A more important such report came from Henry Fawcett, Professor of Political Economy at Cambridge, who wrote to Darwin on July 16, 1861: "I was spending an evening last week with my friend Mr. John Stuart Mill and I am sure you will be pleased to hear from such an authority that he considers that your reasoning throughout is in the most exact accordance with the strict principles of Logic."

This was music to Darwin's ears. He wrote back to Fawcett four days later, "You could not possibly have told me anything which would have given me more satisfaction than what you say about Mr. Mill's opinion." Hearing that a philosopher of Mill's reputation approved of his reasoning, Darwin quickly dashed off letters to Lyell and Gray repeating verbatim Fawcett's report about Mill.

Darwin's admirers, not surprisingly, also included Robert Grant, who had shared his view of species transmutation with Darwin when Darwin was a medical student at Edinburgh. Grant penned a wonderfully flowery encomium to Darwin on May 16, 1861:

> Intellectual triumphs like yours, which have been hailed with the assent and applause of all competent unbiassed minds at home and abroad, while they charm away the clouds of mysticism which overhang some parts of our science and of philosophy, and obscure the greatest truths of nature, alone add permanent glories to the annals of our country in the great struggle for intellectual preeminence and ascendency among the nations of the earth. With one fell sweep of the wand of truth, you have now scattered to the winds the pestilential vapours accumulated by "species-mongers" over every step of this ever-varying, ever-charming part of nature's works.

It is noteworthy that Grant does not praise Darwin for developing an empirically confirmed theory, but simply one that accords with Grant's philosophical bias toward material causation. Nonetheless, Grant's reaction must have brought a smile to Darwin's face. One can almost hear Darwin utter to himself, "I did all that?!"

Such effusive praise was undoubtedly comfort to Darwin as he steeled himself for the criticisms he anticipated from "the mob of naturalists." What he had not steeled himself for is criticism much closer to home. Darwin would ultimately be disappointed by his personal trinity.

Though Lyell was the person most responsible for Darwin finally publishing his theory, he resisted jumping on the bandwagon. On

April 10, 1860, Darwin wrote to Lyell, "By the way it is a great blow to me that you cannot admit to potency of natural selection; the more I think of it, the less I doubt its power for great & small changes." But Lyell never did get fully on board, and three years later, on March 12, 1863, Darwin complained to Lyell:

> As you say you have gone as far as you believe on species-question, I have not a word to say; but I must feel convinced that **at times**, judging from conversation, expression, letters &c, you have as completely given up belief in immutability of specific forms, as I have done.—I must still think a clear expression from you, *if you could have given it*, would have been potent with the public, & all the more so, as you formerly held opposite opinion.

Even if Lyell was vacillating on the power of natural selection, Darwin seems to have thought that Lyell at least had given up belief in the immutability of species. Yet Lyell was apparently reticent to fully defend Darwin in public, much to Darwin's chagrin. Darwin depended greatly on Lyell's scientific status as a bulwark against a critical public, rendering Lyell's ambivalence a bitter pill for Darwin.

Darwin's frustration with Lyell spilled over two months later in letters to Hooker and Gray. Apparently, Asa Gray had called Lyell a judge on the species question, prompting Darwin to complain to Hooker on May 9, "I enclose A. Gray's letter, as you might like to read all. I quite disagree with what he says about Lyell acting as a Judge on Species; I complain that he has *not* acted as a judge; I sometimes wish he had pronounced dead against us rather than possessed such inability to decide."

And on May 11, he complained directly to Gray, "You speak of Lyell as a Judge; now what I complain of is that he declines to be Judge. It put me into despair, when I see such men as Lyell & you incapable (as you think) of deciding: I have sometimes almost wished that Lyell had pronounced against me."[2]

One can certainly sympathize with Lyell here. His uniformitarian geology dealt only with the inanimate features of the earth. While Darwin may have drawn an analogy between Lyell's geology and the living world, Lyell understood the difficulties inherent in accounting for living organisms by way of material processes similar to those which shaped non-living matter. The final paragraph of Lyell's 1863 work, *The Antiquity of Man*, says it well: "It may be said that, so far from having a materialistic tendency, the supposed introduction into the earth at successive geological periods of life—sensation—instinct—the intelligence of the higher mammalia bordering on reason—and lastly the improvable reason of Man himself, presents us with a picture of the ever-increasing dominion of mind over matter."[3]

Lyell's view on this point agrees better with that of Alfred Russel Wallace than it does with Darwin's. Despite having developed a theory of natural selection himself, Wallace came to believe that there were clear limits on what natural selection could accomplish, and that a full accounting for natural phenomena would require proposing the action of an intelligent mind.

This theme is sounded repeatedly in Wallace's last book, *The World of Life*. For example, after discussing what he calls the "mechanical, physical, and chemical adjustments of the earth as a planet, which were absolutely essential to the development of life upon its surface," Wallace calls these adjustments, "an exceedingly powerful argument for an overruling MIND, which so ordered the forces at work in the material universe as to render the almost infinitely improbable sequence of events to which I have called attention an actual reality."[4] Later, Wallace proposes that beyond all the phenomena of nature and immediate causes there is the action of mind and purpose, the ultimate purpose being "the development of mankind for an enduring spiritual existence."[5] Wallace, surprisingly, was not conventionally religious. Nevertheless, the evidence against nature being the product of blind processes was just too strong in his view.

Darwin, in contrast, wanted to stamp out any hint of immaterial forces in the evolutionary process. Similarly, Darwin bristled at Lyell's suggestion that Darwin's theory was a mere modification of Lamarck's, which Darwin viewed as insufficiently scientific. Though Darwin put great stock in the opinions of Hooker, Huxley, and Lyell, the latter two—Lyell in particular—would ultimately fail to provide a full-throated endorsement. They simply did not see enough evidence to establish a theory of species transmutation driven primarily by natural selection. When the criticisms came pouring in, then, Darwin was unable to fully stand on the foundation of his personal trinity, leaving him to have to engage his critics himself, something he was loath to do.

Pre-publication Responses to the *Origin*

Several people were given access to the page proofs of the *Origin* prior to its publication. Not surprisingly, Lyell was one of them. On October 3, 1859, he wrote to Darwin, "I have just finished your volume & right glad I am that I did my best with Hooker to persuade you to publish it without waiting for a time which probably could never have arrived tho' you lived to the age of 100, when you had prepared all your facts on which you ground so many grand generalizations."

Clearly, Lyell thought Darwin would never have published without Lyell's prompting, but he also seems to imply that the resulting publication was short on facts and evidence. This is confirmed when he continues, "I mean that when as I fully expect a new edition is soon called for you may here & there insert an actual case to relieve the vast number of abstract propositions." It is not clear what Lyell expected from a mere abstract, but he certainly hoped for more, just as Whitwell Elwin had.

Lyell also advised Darwin to remove the section on the evolution of the eye, fearing it would give critical readers an advantage by "putting forth so abruptly & crudely such a startling objection." Lyell thought it better to say nothing about the eye in this first edition, and then include it in a later edition when Darwin could provide a more convincing case for it. The consistent theme of Lyell's pre-publication review of the *Origin* was the book's lack of persuasive evidence.

Hooker also was given a pre-publication copy and wrote to Darwin on November 21: "I am a sinner not to have written you ere this, if only to thank you for your glorious book—What a mass of close reasoning on curious facts & fresh phenomena—it is capitally written & will be very successful. I say this on the strength of 2 or 3 plunges into as many chapters, for I have not attempted to read it."

But once Hooker got down to actually reading the book in detail, his opinion changed. He still liked the *Origin*, but confessed to Darwin on December 12:

> I have not yet got ½ through the book, not from want of will, but of time—for it is the very hardest book to read to full profit that I ever tried—it is so cram full of matter & reasoning—I am all the more glad that you have published in this form—for the 3 vols—unprefaced by this would have choked any Naturalist of the 19th Century & certainly have softened my brain in the operation of assimilating their contents.

Given how difficult Darwin's abstract was for Hooker to read, the big book on species would have been in his opinion completely incomprehensible. Recall that in the presentation copies of the *Origin*, Darwin had exhorted his readers to read the *Origin* straight through. Hooker clearly found this a difficult task.

Not everyone did, however. On November 21, Darwin had received some good news from Hewett Cottrell Watson, an amateur botanist who, like Darwin, lived on an inheritance. Watson reported to Darwin, "Once commenced to read the 'Origin' I could not rest till I had galloped through the whole. I shall now begin to re-read it more deliberately." Unlike Hooker, Watson obeyed Darwin's exhortation on how to read his abstract and called Darwin "the greatest Revolutionist in natural history of this century, if not of all centuries." We don't know if Watson changed his opinion upon re-reading the *Origin* more deliberately, but it should not escape our notice that this effusive praise came from another amateur scientist; the professionals like Lyell and Hooker were less sanguine.

One of the most telling early reactions to the *Origin* came from Darwin's older brother, Erasmus. The day before the official publication, he praised Darwin for writing the most interesting book he had ever read. Erasmus was taken with Darwin's treatment of the geographical distribution of species, especially the relationship between continental and island flora and fauna. But he continued, "In fact the a priori reasoning is so entirely satisfactory to me that if the facts won't fit in, why so much the worse for the facts is my feeling."

Of course, if the facts won't fit in, the theory cannot be said to have proven anything about what actually happens in nature. The rhetorical features of the *Origin* might sound persuasive, and they clearly did to Erasmus, but his comment is not necessarily complimentary when applied to a scientific work.

Darwin's half-first cousin, Francis Galton, appears to have reacted quite similarly. Darwin wrote to him on December 13, 1859, "Oddly enough your words are nearly the same as those used by my Brother." From this we might infer that Galton, like Erasmus Darwin, came very close to concluding that, as far as the *Origin* is concerned, facts matter less than a priori reasoning. Regardless of how much they may have enjoyed reading the *Origin*, such an assessment is a serious indictment of a scientific treatise.

Huxley also weighed in on November 23: "Nothing I think can be better than the tone of the book—it impresses those who know nothing about the subject." Huxley, notice, is praising a rhetorical feature of the *Origin*. As for the book's substance, Huxley was more ambivalent. "The only objections that have occurred to me are 1st that you have loaded yourself with an unnecessary difficulty in adopting 'Natura non facit saltum'[6] so unreservedly," he wrote. "I believe she does make *small* jumps—and 2nd, it is not clear to me why if external physical conditions are of so little moment as you suppose variation should occur at all."

Huxley also admitted that he had not yet fully understood chapters three, four, and five, and would reserve comment until he had engaged with them more thoroughly. These chapters form the heart of Darwin's argument for natural selection as the main driver of evolution, and it is not clear that Huxley ever got fully on board with this key pillar of Darwin's theory. In fact, Huxley came to believe that until breeders were able to create a new species via artificial selection, speciation by natural selection would stand as just an unproven hypothesis.[7]

The most negative of the early reactions to the *Origin*, however, came from Darwin's old Cambridge geology professor, Adam Sedgwick. He wrote to Darwin on November 24, the publication date of the *Origin*:

> I have read your book with more pain than pleasure. Parts of it I admired greatly; parts I laughed at till my sides were almost sore; other parts I read with absolute sorrow; because I think them utterly false and grievously mischievous—You have *deserted*—after a start in that tram-road of all physical truth—the true method of induction—& started up a machinery as wild I think as Bishop Wilkin's locomotive that was to sail with us to the Moon.[8] Many of your wide conclusions are based upon assumptions which can neither be proved nor disproved. Why then express them in the language & arrangements of philosophical induction?

Darwin had earlier expressed concern that his work (and he was referring then to the big book, not the abstract) would constitute induction from too few facts. Sedgwick easily recognized that this was a major weakness of Darwin's abstract. Sedgwick also bristled at "the tone of triumphant confidence in which you appeal to the rising generation... and prophecy of things not yet in the womb of time, nor ever likely to be found anywhere but in the fertile womb of man's imagination."

The *Origin* is full of many hypothetical scenarios not grounded in evidence, and it may be that one or more of these were what Sedgwick found laughable.[9]

This certainly was the case for Irish botanist William Harvey. In his August 24, 1860, letter containing his response to the *Origin*, he noted that the "speculation on the bear & the whale, of which I dare say you have heard enough, simply made me laugh." The reference is to Darwin's argument that when species engage in behaviors not normal to their kind, these new habits may in time lead to large-scale evolutionary change. In the first edition of the *Origin*, Darwin had written:

> In North America the black bear was seen by Hearne swimming for hours with widely open mouth, thus catching, like a whale, insects in the water. Even in so extreme a case as this,... I can see no difficulty in a race of bears being rendered, by natural selection, more and more aquatic in their structure and habits, with larger and larger mouths, till a creature was produced as monstrous as a whale.[10]

Harvey (and maybe Sedgwick) obviously read this as Darwin proposing that bears, by swimming with their mouths open, evolved into whales, thus prompting Harvey's laughter. Darwin responded to Harvey on September 20, 1860:

> You object to all my illustrations: they are all necessarily conjectural, & may be all false; but they were the best I could give. The Bear case has been well laughed at & disingenuously distorted by some into my saying that a bear could be converted into a whale; as it offended persons I struck it out in 2^{d}. Edition; but I still maintain that there is no especial difficulty in a Bear's mouth being enlarged to any degree useful to its changing habits,—no more difficulty than man has found in increasing the crop of the pigeon, by continued selection, until it is literally as big as whole rest of the body.

But Darwin's charge of distortion by those who viewed him as suggesting that a bear could evolve into a whale is disingenuous, for this is exactly what Darwin had suggested in the first edition of the *Origin.* Moreover, Darwin once again falls back inappropriately on the analogy with artificial selection. Pigeon breeders can increase the size of the pigeon's crop by selecting for the same characteristic generation after generation, producing, as Wallace noted, an artificial form that can never occur in nature. The large-mouthed bear envisioned by Darwin simply does not exist in nature. And of course, for bears to evolve into whales would require an enormous number of other anatomical and physiological changes beyond just an enlarged mouth. No wonder some of his scientist friends found the bear-to-whale example risible.

Even though Darwin defended his bear/whale example in his response to Harvey, he did shorten this example in the second and subsequent editions of the *Origin* to, "In North America the black bear was seen by Hearne swimming for hours with widely open mouth, thus catching, almost like a whale, insects in the water."[11]

But that some had found unintended humor in the first edition of the *Origin* was the least of Darwin's problems. Once the *Origin* was in full circulation, many other men of science weighed in with a variety of pointed criticisms.

Post-publication Responses to the *Origin*

In a December 10, 1859, letter to Lyell, Darwin stated that he had heard through some roundabout way that John Herschel, son of the famous astronomer William Herschel and a noted mathematician and astronomer himself, called natural selection the "law of higgledy-piggelty." "What this exactly means," Darwin wrote, "I do not know, but it is evidently very contemptuous.—If true this is a great blow & discouragement."

Other responses were more substantive. Henry Holland, a physician to Queen Victoria to whom Darwin had turned for advice about his own medical problems, wrote to Darwin on December 10, 1859. His first complaint involved Darwin's ambiguity on what the concept of natural selection means. Some passages, Holland thought, portrayed natural selection as necessity, others as accident, while others portrayed it as intellectual volition. Necessity, however, seemed to be the principle meaning. Holland viewed this as problematic:

> Your understanding of *natural selection*, does virtually exclude *reason* from any part of the result. That the various parts of the Eye, *including the Humours*, could reach their highest state of completeness & mutual adaptation, by any means short of *prevision* in their formation, I cannot comprehend. No scheme of causalities, granting indefinite time for their multiplication, seems to me capable of reaching this result.... I confess I never look at a Spider's web, & at the astute artist armed with its strange instincts, sitting amidst its work, without a certain feeling of awe at the many mysteries it involves.

Recall that in his pre-publication review of the *Origin*, Lyell had warned Darwin about discussing the eye until he had more facts to show how natural selection could evolve something so intricate. But Darwin kept the eye example in and, not surprisingly, this was one example that his critics jumped on. Holland was not alone.

Asa Gray, Professor of Botany at Harvard University, though a supporter of Darwin, was one of those who found eye evolution via natural selection suspect. On January 23, 1860, he told Darwin, "Well, what seems to me the weakest point in the book is the attempt to account for the formation of organs,—the making of eyes, &c by natural selection. Some of this reads quite Lamarckian."

Darwin responded on February 8, "About weak points I agree. The eye to this day gives me a cold shudder, but when I think of the fine known gradations, my reason tells me I ought to conquer the cold shudder." By April 3, Darwin could say in another letter to Gray, "It is curious that I remember well time when the thought of the eye made me cold all over, but I have got over this stage of the complaint, & now small trifling particulars of structure often make me very uncomfortable. The sight of a feather in a peacock's tail, whenever I gaze at it, makes me sick!"

Though Darwin had come to accept that natural selection could produce intricate complexity, even if his readers hadn't, the idea that extremely small variations (trifling particulars) would be preserved and perpetuated by natural selection to form magnificent structures continued to haunt him. How could natural selection produce something so non-adaptive as a peacock's tail? Darwin would eventually give up trying to explain such maladaptive ornaments on the basis of natural selection, and proposed another process, sexual selection, to explain them instead (sexual selection has come under increasingly critical scrutiny today, as we will see in Chapter 8).

Naturalist and clergyman Leonard Jenyns, though he accepted aspects of Darwin's theory, could not follow Darwin all the way. Jenyns was concerned with the lack of transitional forms between higher taxonomic categories among both living and fossil organisms. He wrote on January 4, 1860: "It seems to me that if 'all organic beings that have ever lived on earth, had descended from some one primordial form,' as you seem to think possible,—we should find (either among the fossil or living species) the same connecting links, & 'fine gradations' between the highest groups, that we *do* find among the lower, & which renders classification & definition so difficult."

Jenyns conceded the likelihood of common ancestry among closely related species but could not conceive of how different phyla and kingdoms of life could have descended from some primordial ancestor in the absence of any connecting links between them, even in the fossil record.

Jenyns also struggled with the implication of Darwin's theory for human origins, not a surprise given Jenyns's role as a clergyman:

> One great difficulty to my mind in the way of your theory is the fact of the existence of Man. I was beginning to think you had entirely passed over the question, till almost in the last page I find you saying that 'light will be thrown on the origin of man & his history.' By this I suppose is meant that he is to be considered a modified & no doubt *greatly* improved orang! I doubt this will find acceptance with the generality of readers.

Of particular concern to Jenyns was the implication that human reason and moral sensibility could be explained by appeal to descent from "irrational progenitors." Jenyns was hardly alone here. Even Wallace, despite his advocacy for natural selection, ultimately concluded that the human mind was beyond such material explanation.

In a January 7 response to Jenyns, Darwin expressed surprise but pleasure at how far Jenyns had gone with him. But regarding the lack of transitional forms linking higher taxonomic categories in the fossil record, Darwin simply appealed to the imperfection of the fossil record. To Jenyns's problem with the inclusion of humans in Darwin's evolutionary scheme, Darwin made it clear that in his view, his theory had to explain all of life or none of it. "Of course, it is open to everyone to believe that man appeared by separate miracle, though I do not myself see the necessity or probability."

On the issue of the fossil record, the Swiss zoologist, François Jules Pictet de la Rive, appears to have agreed with Jenyns. In a short, somewhat cryptic, note of February 19, he wrote, "Your book makes science young, clear, elevated, but no facts to prove that principle that slight modification multiplied by any factor of time no matter how long could reach the character of families &c or cd. produce profound modifics. in organization."

On April 1 Darwin responded to de la Rive with great humility:

> There have been many reviews in England, opposed to me, but yours is the single one which seems to me *perfectly* fair & just & candid. I literally agree to every word you say. I admit there are

> no *direct* proofs of the greater modifications which I believe in.—I most fully admit that I by no means explain away all the vast difficulties. The only difference between us is that I attach much more weight to the explanation of facts, & somewhat less weight to the difficulties than you do.—I am conscious that I always jump at any theory which groups & explains facts; & attach too little weight to unexplained difficulties. Your mind is more cautious & I fear that the world would say more philosophical.

This may be the most transparent admission in all the Darwinian correspondence of Darwin's shortcomings as a scientist. Ignoring contrary evidence is what had led earlier to the embarrassment of his Glen Roy paper. Yet despite this seeming awareness of this shortcoming, Darwin continued to jump at, and cling to, theories that he felt grouped and explained facts, even in the face of contrary evidence.

Twice, Darwin laid out in detail the way he felt his argument should be viewed; once in a March 6, 1860, letter to the naturalist S. P. Woodward, and again nearly verbatim on March 12 to geologist Joseph Prestwich:

> I find that I have not put clearly how, as it seems to me, the general argument ought fairly to be viewed; namely, natural selection as a mere hypothesis (rendered in some slight degree probable by the analogy of domestication and the struggle for existence.) which hypothesis has to be judged of by whether it explains a number of facts in Geographical Distribution, Geological Succession, Classification, Homology, Embryology &c. If it does explain such facts then the hypothesis seems to me to rise in rank to a theory.

And on April 23, 1861, he would write to Hooker about Hooker's reaction to a review of the *Origin* by geologist and army officer Frederick Hutton: "I quite agree with what you say on Lieut. Hutton's Review (who he is, I know not): it struck me as very original: he is one of the very few who see that the change of species cannot be directly proved & that the doctrine must sink or swim according as it groups & explains phenomena. It is really curious how few judge it in this way, which is clearly the right way."

But is it really so very curious? Lacking direct empirical evidence to show that Darwin's theory accords with what actually happens in nature, his reviewers realized that though Darwin's theory appeared to explain a number of facts, another theory could equally explain those same facts. The problem of underdetermination continued to plague the *Origin*.

Three years later, on February 5, 1863, Yale University geologist J. D. Dana shared with Darwin reasons why he could not accept Darwin's views: "I have thought that I ought to state to you the ground for my assertion on page 602,[12] that Geology has not afforded facts that sustain the view that the system of life has been evolved through a method of development from species to Species."

Dana laid out three reasons for this view. First was the lack of transitional fossils showing the fine gradations of change required by Darwin's theory. Second, Dana pointed to a fossil record showing that many species appear suddenly, fully formed. He cites the shark as an example of a type of fish appearing suddenly in the fossil record, without any of the lower forms supposedly leading up to it. And third, although exterminations of species often cut the threads of genera, families, and sometimes even orders and classes, the threads often begin again in new species. Importantly, many of Dana's geological objections to Darwin's theory still resonate today.[13]

On February 14, 1860, George Henry Thwaites, superintendent of the botanical gardens in Ceylon, wondered how natural selection could produce the exquisite beauty and symmetry observed in every organized structure given that simpler organisms dominate the planet: "It is not easy to understand how, with a similar capability of modification in all, some cells should remain in their originally simple condition whilst others should within the same period, have become modified by mere natural selection into the most highly organized & complicated structures."

That is, Thwaites seems to be asking why bacteria still exist and dominate the planet if more complicated organisms are better adapted to the conditions of life. Thwaites also pointed to what he called the degradation that takes place in certain circumstances, like an organ that is "complicated in structure in some species, but found rudimentary only in allied ones." Darwin had addressed this problem in the *Origin*, arguing that vestigial organs result from disuse. For example, the eyes of underground mammals degenerated due to lack of use in a dark environment. But in making the argument about use and disuse of organs, Darwin, ironically, sounded more Lamarckian than he did Darwinian. He was also attributing one of the clearest evidences of evolutionary linkage to devolution rather than evolution, surely no small concession given the chorus of demands for more concrete evidence from Darwin that evolution by natural selection could build complex new organs and body plans.

The longest and most comprehensive engagement with Darwin's theory in the form of a letter (rather than a published review) came from the Irish botanist William Harvey. We should note that prior to publishing the *Origin*, Darwin had enough respect for Harvey's scientific acumen that he wrote to him with a question about the sexes in algae. Harvey was an expert in algae and responded to Darwin's question in January of 1857.

On August 24, 1860, Harvey sent Darwin a ten-page letter outlining his response to the *Origin*, most of which was quite critical. Of course, the fact that Harvey took the time to write such a long letter shows that he found the *Origin* worthy of his time and attention. He informs Darwin that he finished reading the book during a summer vacation and came to this initial impression: "I cannot as yet (probably never shall) receive the theory of Natural Selection as a satisfying explanation of the Origin of species—but I am willing to admit that it explains several facts which are not otherwise easily to be accounted for."

He follows by saying that as long as Darwin dealt in generalities, Harvey could follow his arguments with general agreement. But unhappily, "my assent is most ready in cases where your data are *fewest*! and I find that particular instances, intended to illustrate how Natural Selection has acted or might be supposed to act in certain cases, almost always incline me to withdraw my assent to the previous argument."

Harvey's point is telling. The *Origin of Species* does make a compelling argument in the abstract, which is probably why Darwin implored his readers to read the work straight through. That organisms born with variations rendering them better adapted to their conditions of life will out-reproduce their more poorly adapted kin, and that this process repeated over eons of time will lead to the creation of new species, does brim with a certain almost irresistible logic, a logic, as we have seen, which impressed Darwin's brother and cousin. But once one gets down to the level of details, problems begin to multiply.

Harvey felt that Darwin had made a reasonably good argument about how the facts of classification favor the idea of "mutation" (i.e., transformation of species). The cases in which it is difficult to draw a clear line of distinction between genera, orders, and classes constituted difficult data for believers in special acts of creation. If God had specially created every species, clear lines of distinction should be the order of the day. But even if the idea of mutation is admitted to explain these data, Harvey emphasizes, "it does not necessarily follow that the mutation has been effected through 'natural selection' *alone*." More to the point, if animals had descended from at most four or five progenitors, then Darwin was admitting that special creative acts had occurred. To Harvey's mind, then, "there is no more difficulty in believing in 50, or 500 or 5000 absolute acts of creation, than in believing in one solitary creative act;... What has *once* occurred, may occur more than once."

Concerning the origin of life, Harvey calls the production of the first living organism "a stupendous miracle." He then elaborates:

> Certain atoms of carbon, oxygen, hydrogen & azote, changing into cellulose & protoplasm, became a living body, endowed with growth; capable, by feeding, of changing mineral atoms into more cellulose & protoplasm; having *an instinct* to turn to the light & perhaps the germs of indefinitely progressive instincts; and above all, possessing a procreative power, enabling it to transmit from generation to generation of similar organisms, throughout all time, similar powers & capacities.

No modern critic of theories about the chemical evolution of life could say it any better. Though Darwin did not specifically address the origin of life in *The Origin of Species*, Harvey realized that the event, however it occurred, was assumed. If all organisms descended from one or a few common ancestors, those had to have arisen somehow. And if natural laws cannot account for this, then a creative act of some kind had to have occurred, and therefore could occur again.

Darwin, perhaps surprisingly, seems to have agreed with Harvey on this point. Although eight years later, in a February 1, 1871, private letter to Hooker, Darwin would conjecture in the vaguest terms about the possibility of the first life somehow emerging from a "warm little pond" via purely blind natural forces, in an 1863 article he faced the origin-of-life problem squarely, stating it beautifully:

> He who believes that organic beings have been produced during each geological period from dead matter must believe that the first being thus arose. There must have been a time when inorganic elements alone existed on our planet: let any assumptions be made, such as that the reeking atmosphere was charged with carbonic acid, nitrogenized compounds, phosphorus, &c. Now is there a fact, or a shadow of a fact, supporting the belief that these elements, without the presence of any organic compounds, and acted on only by known forces, could produce a living creature? At present it is to us a result absolutely inconceivable.[14]

But Harvey went even further:

> This first organism in fact possessed distinct *personality*; hence (my reason assures me) the Power that called it into being & endowed it with secondary powers must be a **Personality**, & not merely "a law or laws acting around us." And as *every* organism in Nature has its *personality*, so, whether every one were separately created, or the higher derived through the lower, we require a *personal*, creative or moulding Power alike in all cases. Secondary (or physical) laws suffice for all the phenomena of the inorganic world, but life is made up of contingencies which physical laws, unmodified by personal Agency, will not always meet.

If we admit that such a power acted once, "we cannot presume to limit the further working of that Power." Harvey was acutely aware of the enormous gulf that stands between inorganic and organic matter. Darwin was trying to account for living organisms by appeal to the same kinds of laws that regulate inorganic matter. Harvey remained skeptical. On his view, living organisms are fundamentally different from inanimate matter and therefore require a fundamentally different explanation.

In one final criticism, Harvey understood Darwin to be advocating a theory of continual progress toward more complex organisms. It was thus important to determine whether the most dominant organisms were also the most improved organisms. In Harvey's opinion, "Viewing organic nature in its widest aspect I think it is unquestionable that the truly dominant races are not those of high, but those of low organization. The simpler any animal's structure is, the less is it dependent on outward conditions; hence, the better is it fitted to conquer in the struggle for life, & to perpetuate its kind to a remote posterity."

In simpler terms, bacteria rule the world; and in Harvey's view, this placed the final nail in the coffin of natural selection being the primary driving force of evolution, assuming evolution had even occurred, a point which Harvey was not willing to concede.

Darwin penned a three-page response to Harvey on September 20, 1860. He accused Harvey of not understanding the meaning of natural selection. In Darwin's view, Harvey thought Darwin had proposed natural selection as the "sole agency of modification." But Darwin emphasized how he had repeatedly stated that selection could do nothing without variation. "I consider Natural Selection as of such high importance, because it accumulates successive variations in any profitable direction, & thus adapts each new being to its complex conditions of life."

But there is no evidence in Harvey's letter that he discounted the importance of variations. Indeed, he mentions them repeatedly. And in an October 8, 1860, response, Harvey emphasized that, contrary to Darwin's insistence, Harvey well understood the role of variation in Darwinian theory but believed Darwin had gone too far in viewing variation as virtually unlimited. Harvey wrote: "I am strongly impressed with the notion (perhaps wholly wrong) that there is no law of organic or inorganic nature *unlimited* in its operation. And so, however widely a species may vary, I suspect an oscillation in every case. In the case of your divaricating pigeons for instance, I should anticipate, after endless variations from type, either a return to type or extinction; but not the passage into a new type."

Natural selection, in Harvey's reading of the *Origin*, was presented as dependent on favorable variations, and so accumulates "any *profitable* item of differentiation;—but, in strict language, to *originate* nothing." So we see that Harvey actually was well versed in Darwin's theory.

Interestingly, Harvey wrote to the *Gardeners' Chronicle* in February 1860, noting the appearance of a new species of Begonia reported by William Hooker, Director of the Royal Botanical Gardens at Kew.[15] This Begonia appears to have suddenly developed bisexual flowers without any intermediate stages standing between unisexual and bisexual flowers. Harvey viewed this as a direct challenge to Darwin's gradualist view of evolution.

Hooker responded in the February 25 edition of the *Gardeners' Chronicle*, defending Darwin's theory in a short article titled, "The Monstrous Begonia frigida at Kew, in Relation to Mr. Darwin's Theory of Natural Selection."[16] In Hooker's view, what appeared to be a rather sudden appearance of this new Begonia species could be explained on the basis of Darwinian gradualism. But Harvey may well get the last laugh. What was observed at Kew was likely an example of polyploidy, the sudden doubling of the chromosome compliment in plants that can lead to the appearance of a new species in one generation. Polyploidy, while observed in animals, is especially common in plants, and does indeed stand as a kind of saltational evolution inconsistent with Darwin's emphasis on gradualism.[17] Harvey's criticisms of Darwin's theory were well informed.

Though Darwin knew he would never make a convert of Harvey, he couldn't resist the urge to make sure Harvey knew that the *Origin* had received positive feedback from the likes of Lyell, Hooker, Gray,

Huxley, Watson, and others. At the end of the day, Darwin's best response to Harvey's substantive and penetrating critique was essentially to pull rank by appealing to the authority of his friends, rather than providing substantive counterarguments of his own.

Of course, in name-dropping his supporters, Darwin failed to mention that even some of them held critical views toward the *Origin.* These ranks included Gray. In a series of letters over a two-year period, Darwin and Gray debated the issue of design in nature. In a letter dated February 18, 1862, Gray referred to Darwin's "very shocking principles and prejudice against *design in nature.*" He is referring back to an extended debate between them in 1860 and 1861. Gray could never accept selection as a purely contingent and undirected process. Darwin could never accept design in the origin of new biological forms, though at times he did allow for the possibility of design in the laws of nature. He wrote to Gray on May 22, 1860:

> With respect to the theological view of the question; this is always painful to me.—I am bewildered.—I had no intention to write atheistically. But I own that I cannot see, as plainly as others do, & as I sh^{d}. wish to do, evidence of design & beneficence on all sides of us. There seems to me too much misery in the world.... On the other hand I cannot anyhow be contented to view this wonderful universe & especially the nature of man, & to conclude that everything is the result of brute force. I am inclined to look at everything as resulting from designed laws, with the details, whether good or bad, left to the working out of what we may call chance. Not that this notion *at all* satisfies me.

A little more than a month later (July 3), Darwin again wrote to Gray: "One word more on 'designed laws' & 'undesigned results.' I see a bird which I want for food, take my gun & kill it, I do this *designedly.*—An innocent and good man stands under tree & is killed by a flash of lightning. Do you believe (& I really sh^{d}. like to hear) that God *designedly* killed this man? Many or most persons do believe this; I can't & don't." In a later letter of September 17, 1861, Darwin told Gray that he had asked Lyell whether Lyell thought Darwin's nose was designed.

Darwin could not seem to separate the idea of design in the development of new organisms with the idea of divine intervention in every circumstance of life. It seems Gray was able to make this distinction.

Darwin never stopped wrestling with the relationship between design and accident. He wrote to John Herschel on May 23, 1861, "I am in a complete jumble on the point. One cannot look at this Universe with all living productions & man without believing that all has been intelligently designed; yet when I look to each individual organism, I can see no evidence of this." On August 1 of the same year, Darwin shared similar thoughts with Lyell. Lyell apparently agreed with Gray regarding the intelligent direction of variations. But Darwin would have none of it: "The view that each variation has been providentially arranged seems to me to make natural selection entirely superfluous, & indeed takes whole case of appearance of new species out of the range of science. But what makes me most object to Asa Gray's view, is the study of the extreme variability of domestic animals."

Darwin held that variations in both domestic and wild animals were due to unknown causes and entirely accidental. They became purposeful only when selected for. Yet Darwin still concluded, "I do not wish to say that God did not foresee everything which would ensue; but here comes very nearly the same sort of wretched embroglio as between free-will & preordained necessity." We don't know how Lyell responded, but we do know that neither Gray nor Lyell ever got fully on board with Darwin's insistence on a fully contingent evolutionary process (an insistence that left even Darwin himself unsatisfied).

As we've seen, in his mere abstract, *The Origin of Species*, Darwin often relied on rhetorical arguments rather than hard evidence to make his point. The German paleontologist H. G. Bronn critiqued one of these rhetorical arguments in an October 13, 1860, letter to Darwin: "You say further that we explain many electrical phenomena on the basis of a theory of electricity without knowing what electricity really is,—and that we are able with as much justification to formulate a theory about the origin of life (without being able to prove that origin?). But, the two cases are far from being analogous." According to Bronn, all matter possesses certain properties, and electricity is a property of certain kinds of elements. But we cannot say the same for life. "Life is not a property that is inherent in matter. *Life presupposes life*, and *life generates life*: but where there is no life, then no life can arise. Matter is therefore independent of life and life is not necessarily bound to any kind of matter." Just as with the faulty analogy between artificial and natural selection, Darwin's grasping at straws led him into what Bronn thought was another poor analogy.

Bronn wrote to Darwin again on March 11, 1862, reporting that he had read many reviews of the *Origin* in German, Dutch, English, and American journals. Some were favorable but many were unfavorable. Bronn's opinion, however, remained the same. Darwin had provided the only natural route to a solution of the enigma of creation, "Yet, your theory contradicts the *current* state of our knowledge of the formation of *organic matter* from inorganic, of the *vitality* of organic matter and its organisation into organic form **without** *previous influence*." (Emphasis in original.) Under the current state of knowledge, Bronn could not accept Darwin's theory, though he allowed that future knowledge might change the situation. However, the problem of abiogenesis (the origin of life from non-life) has grown only more acute in the intervening decades, as molecular and cell biology has taught us just how stupendously complex a single cell really is. Along with Bronn, we still have never observed life emerging from non-life, and the obstacles to conceiving how this could happen, let alone proving it, are immense (more in Chapter 8).

In 1861 Darwin took another stab at a rhetorical defense of his theory. On March 8, he wrote to the naturalist Alexander Goodman More, who had apparently indicated to Darwin his objection to Darwin's theory. In defense, Darwin wrote:

> You ask why I sh^{d}. not draw a line & allow natural selection to do a little work & no more. I can give no direct answer to this. But I think you do not fully see how, as it seems to me, the subject may fairly be approached. Take the case of Light,—existence of Ether, and the existence of its undulations are both absolutely hypothetical or conjectural; but because this hypothesis explains and groups

> together a multitude of phenomena, it is now universally admitted as a true theory.

Darwin is arguing, in other words, that just as the hypothesized ether so neatly explains certain facts about light and therefore should be accepted despite a lack of confirming evidence, so too should Darwin's theory of descent with modification via natural selection be accepted even in the absence of decisive confirming evidence, since it too groups together and explains many phenomena.

Darwin was so taken with this analogy to the undulation theory of light that he repeated it several more times that year. The first was in a March 14 letter to Cuthbert Collingwood, Lecturer in Botany at the Royal Infirmary Medical School in Liverpool: "The manner in which I wish to approach the whole subject, & in which it seems to me it may fairly be approached, I can best illustrate by the case of Light.—The Ether is hypothetical, as are its undulations; but as the undulatory hypothesis groups together & explains a multitude of phenomena, it is universally now admitted as the true theory."

Darwin then goes on to confess that he cannot prove in any case that natural selection changed one species into another, but he accepts it as true because it groups together and explains a host of facts in a variety of fields of natural history just as the undulatory theory of light does.

On April 20, he was at it again in a letter to Frederick Hutton, a British naval officer:

> I am actually weary of telling people that I do not pretend to adduce direct evidence of one species changing into another, but that I believe that this view in the main is correct, because so many phenomena can be thus grouped together and explained. But it is generally of no use, I cannot make persons see this. I generally throw in their teeth the universally admitted theory of the undulation of Light—neither the undulation, nor the very existence of the Ether being proved,—yet admitted because the view explains so much.

On April 30, he used the argument one more time in a letter to T. W. St. C. Davidson, an artist and paleontologist: "No one urges as a fatal objection to the Theory of Light that the undulations in the ether cannot be proved—or the very existence of the ether, yet because the undulatory theory explains much it is now universally admitted."

And finally, he reported to Gray on June 10, 1862, that Alphonse de Candolle wanted proof of natural selection, to which Darwin responded, "He will have to wait a long time for that. Opticians do not wait for direct proof of undulation of ether."

The irony, of course, is that hypothetical ether has turned out not to exist. So even if this theory concerning light did in fact group together and seem to explain various phenomena, its ability to do so was most definitively not decisive confirmation of its truth. Likewise, while Darwin's theory of evolution by natural selection could be understood to group together and explain disparate phenomena, this hardly cinches the case for it. Darwin needed something more; he needed hard evidence—evidence that he had already led many to believe would make its debut in his big book on natural selection, the magnum opus for which the *Origin* was merely the abstract.

The Ambiguity of Natural Selection

One consistent theme characterizing criticisms of the *Origin* revolved around the meaning of the term "natural selection." Asa Gray objected to the term on the grounds that Darwin treated it like an active agent intentionally selecting which organisms to breed. Darwin responded that he used the term much like a geologist might use "denudation" to describe the result of several combined actions. In a letter dated November 29, 1857, in reference to his big book that he planned to title *Natural Selection*, Darwin told Gray that he had to use the term, for otherwise he would be forced to constantly repeat the following expression every time he wanted to refer to the concept:

> the tendency to the preservation (owing to the severe struggle for life to which all organic beings at some time or generation are exposed) of any the slightest variation in any part, which is of the slightest use or favourable to the life of the individual which has thus varied; together with the tendency to its inheritance.

This *would* be a mouthful, and having to repeat it over and over would have immeasurably lengthened Darwin's already lengthy book! The two-word phrase "natural selection" was, according to Darwin, a practical accommodation.

Gray was not the only one to object to the term, however. Darwin's publisher, John Murray, objected to including "natural selection" in the subtitle to *The Origin of Species.* Darwin, however, pushed to retain it but with the explanatory gloss "the preservation of favoured races." Darwin told Lyell on March 30, 1859, "Why I like the term is that it is constantly used in all works on Breeding, & I am surprised that it is not familiar to Murray." Once again Darwin appeals to the analogy to artificial selection, ignoring how breeders intentionally select which animals to breed, a power Darwin clearly did not ascribe to natural selection.

Once the *Origin* was in circulation, Darwin had to admit that the term "natural selection" produced considerable misunderstanding among his readers. Writing to Lyell on June 6, 1860, he confessed, "Several Reviews, & several letters have shown me too clearly how little I am understood. I suppose 'natural selection' was bad term; but to change it now, I think, would make confusion worse confounded." Darwin admitted that he could not think of a better term. Some suggested "natural preservation" instead, but, as Darwin continued to Lyell, "'Natural preservation' would not imply a preservation of particular varieties & would seem a truism; & would not bring man's & nature's selection under one point of view."

Once again, the failed analogy to artificial selection reared its head. In an October 1, 1862, letter to Hugh Falconer, a paleontologist and botanist stationed in India, Darwin stated that in trying to account for how animals became so exquisitely adapted to their conditions of life, he concluded that "natural selection solves the problem, as artificial selection solves the adaptation of domestic races for man's use." This is the key point. Breeders select for characteristics useful to breeders, not for the benefit of the organism (such as the inadaptive short legs of the Dachshund). The natural selection/artificial selection analogy was so foundational to Darwin's thinking—and so clearly problematic—that it threatened to unravel his entire theory.

Lyell could see the problem. Along with Gray, he also believed Darwin was turning selection into an active agent despite Darwin's protestations to the contrary. In defense, Darwin wrote to Lyell on June 14, 1860:

> I have expressly stated that I believe physical conditions have more direct effect on Plants than on animals.—But the more I study the more I am led to think that natural selection regulates in a state of nature most trifling differences.—As squared stones, or bricks, or timber are the indispensable materials for a building & influence its character; so is variability not only indispensable, but influential; Yet, in same manner, as the architect is the *all*-important person in a Building, so is Selection with organic bodies.

Lyell was unimpressed with Darwin's architect analogy, writing to Darwin the next day, "Your comparison of Selection to the Architect—variations to the stones, is what I deduced from some passages but cannot accept." Lyell noted that an architect plans beforehand what he is to produce out of the raw materials. If Darwin insisted on the analogy of natural selection to an architect, then, in Lyell's view, Darwin was arguing for "the deification of Natural Selection."

On June 17, Darwin rejected Lyell's deification charge and again reiterated the comparison of natural selection to an architect. But he concluded in some frustration, "But we shall never agree, so do not trouble yourself to answer." Lyell may not have answered, but Hooker did. In his view, variation was more important than selection. "N. S. [natural selection] is as powerless as physical causes to make a variation;—the law that 'like shall *not* produce like' is at the bottom of all, & is as inscrutable as life itself," he wrote to Darwin on November 26, 1862. "This it is that Lyell & I feel you have failed to convey with force enough to us & the public: & this is at bottom of half the infidelity of the scientific world to your doctrine."

Hooker, in concert with Lyell, then flatly accused Darwin of greatly inflating the powers of natural selection. "There is some truth

I now see in the objection to you," Hooker wrote, "that you make N.S. the 'Deus ex machina.'"

We should not forget that despite the status of the term "natural selection" in modern biological discourse, it was a problematic term for Darwin's early readers and one that even Darwin himself regretted coining.

The Huxley-Wilberforce Debate

One of the better-known aspects of the Darwinian narrative concerns a debate over Darwin's theory between Thomas Henry Huxley and Bishop Samuel Wilberforce at the British Association Meeting at Oxford on June 30, 1860. Wilberforce is supposed to have asked Huxley if it was through his grandfather on his mother's side or his father's side that he was descended from an ape. Huxley is said to have replied that he would rather have an ape for a grandfather than a pompous member of the church establishment who injects ridicule into a serious scientific discussion, at which point women fainted. The received version of this event presents Huxley as the serious scientist and man of reason who won the debate over the unreasoning bishop who was unable to accept evidence when it flew in the face of church doctrine. The reality is more nuanced, however.

Darwin did not attend the British Association meeting due (of course) to health problems. But Hooker did and reported to Darwin on July 2 that a furious debate had ensued between Huxley and the anatomist Richard Owen the day before Hooker arrived, a debate that rendered Darwin's book the topic of conversation at the meeting. He then continued:

> Well Sam Oxon got up & spouted for half an hour with inimitable spirit uglyness & emptyness & unfairness, I saw he was coached up by Owen & knew nothing & he said not a syllable but what was in the Reviews—he ridiculed you badly & Huxley savagely—Huxley answered admirably & turned the tables, but he could not throw his voice over so large an assembly, nor command the audience; & he did not allude to *Sam's* weak points nor put the matter in a

> form or way that carried the audience. The battle waxed hot. Lady Brewster fainted, the excitement increased as others spoke—my blood boiled, I felt myself a dastard; now I saw my advantage—I swore to myself I would smite that Amalekite Sam hip & thigh if my heart jumped out of my mouth & I handed my name up to the President (Henslow) as ready to throw down the gauntlet.

Hooker then tells Darwin that he verbally smashed Wilberforce, prompting rounds of applause. Unfortunately, the letter breaks off at this point. But on Hooker's accounting, it appears it was he, not Huxley, who turned the tables on Wilberforce. Perhaps the version that places Huxley in the spotlight is merely the received wisdom consistent with Huxley's later reputation as Darwin's bulldog. On the other hand, Hooker was famously averse to public speaking, the principal reason he could never take up a teaching position, so perhaps Hooker embellished his own role at the meeting.

Darwin wrote back to Hooker the same day:

> How I sh^{d}. have liked to have wandered about Oxford with you, if I had been well enough; & how still more I sh^{d}. have liked to have heard you triumphing over the Bishop.—I am astounded at your success & audacity. It is something unintelligible to me how anyone can argue in public like orators do. I had no idea you had this power. I have read lately so many hostile reviews, that I was beginning to think that I was wholly in wrong & that Owen was right when he said whole subject would be forgotten in ten years; but now that I hear that you & Huxley will fight publicly (which I'm sure I never could do) I fully believe that our cause in the long run will prevail. I am glad I was not in Oxford, for I sh^{d}. have been overwhelmed, with my stomach in its present state.

The next day Darwin wrote to Gray in a similar vein, informing him about the goings on at the British Association meeting and confidently asserting, "Owen will not prove right, when he said that the whole *subject* would be forgotten in 10 years."

What exactly happened at the British Association meeting may be lost to history. The reports that have survived simply don't match up. A third take on the meeting, appearing in the *Athenaeum*, paints a staider portrait:

> The BISHOP OF OXFORD stated that the Darwinian theory, when tried by the principles of inductive science, broke down. The facts brought forward did not merit the theory. The permanence of specific forms was a fact confirmed by all observation.... He was glad to know that the greatest names in all of science were opposed to this theory, which he believed to be opposed to the interests of science and humanity.[18]

As for "Darwin's bulldog," as he later came to be called:

> Prof. HUXLEY defended Mr. Darwin's theory from the charge of its being merely an hypothesis. He said, it was an explanation of phenomena in Natural History, as the undulating theory was of the phenomena of light. No one objected to that theory because an undulation of light had never been arrested and measured.... Without asserting that every part of the theory had been confirmed, he maintained that it was the best explanation of the origin of species which had yet been offered.[19]

From these notes it does not sound like Huxley launched the kind of full-throated ridicule of Wilberforce that the received wisdom says he did, though, as will be shown presently, evidence exists to suggest that the *Athenaeum* may have intentionally left this part out.

In 2017, Richard England brought to light an overlooked report on the British Association meeting published in the *Oxford Chronicle* that appears to be based on the same source as the *Athenaeum* report but with important differences. The *Oxford Chronicle* does in fact cite the famous exchange between Huxley and Wilberforce, a point that seems to be corroborated by other contemporary sources that recall the exchange. Thus, England concludes that the *Athenaeum* left the Huxley-Wilberforce exchange out in order to "prune controversial and indecorous material."[20] At the same time, England notes that the *Oxford Chronicle* was a liberal publication often critical of Wilberforce.[21]

But what about Hooker? Both versions support the idea that Hooker made a statement meant to ridicule Bishop Wilberforce. According to the notes, Hooker charged Wilberforce with not understanding Darwin's theory. Darwin never envisioned the transmutation of existing species into new ones. He merely envisioned the successive development of species by variation and natural selection. Hooker further rejected the idea that he accepted Darwin's view as though it was a creed, for creeds have no place in science. Hooker had simply begun his work in natural history under the assumption that species were original creations, but now understood this to be just a hypothesis, "which in the abstract was neither more nor less entitled to acceptance than Mr. Darwin's."[22]

Whether it was Huxley or Hooker or both who ridiculed Wilberforce, the received narrative portrays Wilberforce as a bit of a buffoon, lacking the seriousness and knowledge necessary to criticize Darwin's theory. John Bowlby terms him "an able man who knew nothing of science"[23] while William Irvine says of Huxley, "It was well known that he had devoured alive the worthy Bishop of Oxford almost before the eyes of his congregation, leaving nothing but a shovel hat and a pair of gaiters visible on the platform."[24]

The reality appears quite different. Hooker's charge that Wilberforce misunderstood Darwin's theory runs counter to the nearly 14,000-word review of the *Origin* Wilberforce published in the *Quarterly Review*, a review that documents how deeply Wilberforce understood Darwin's work. Given Wilberforce's status as a church official, we might expect his criticisms to have been based on theological objections. But Wilberforce appears to have anticipated this expectation and addressed it directly:

> Our readers will not have failed to notice that we have objected to the views with which we have been dealing solely on scientific grounds. We have done so from our fixed conviction that it is thus that the truth or falsehood of such arguments should be tried. We have no sympathy with those who object to any facts or alleged facts in nature, or to any inference logically deduced from them, because they believe them to contradict what appears to them is taught by

> Revelation. We think that all such objections savour of a timidity which is really inconsistent with a firm and well-instructed faith.[25]

In contrast to the stereotypes that paint Wilberforce as a staunch defender of the absolute immutable nature of life forms, he makes clear that he is not averse to the doctrine of evolution by natural selection should the evidence weigh clearly in its favor. He even acknowledges not only that organisms vary, but also that natural selection has led to great diversity within specific types. Moreover, the struggle for life clearly exists, "and that it tends continually to lead the strong to exterminate the weak, we readily admit; and in this law we see a merciful provision against the deterioration, in a world apt to deteriorate, of the works of the Creator's hands."[26] So natural selection for Wilberforce acts to maintain the fitness of species in their environment, thus preventing their deterioration.

But Wilberforce notes that what Darwin needs to show is that there is active in nature a power capable of accumulating favorable variations through successive generations toward the production of entirely new species. And on this point, according to Wilberforce, Darwin fails.

Commenting on the emphasis that Darwin places on pigeon breeding, Wilberforce argues, "With all the change wrought in appearance, with all the apparent variation in manners, there is not the faintest beginning of any such change in what that great comparative anatomist, Professor Owen, calls 'the characteristics of the skeleton or other parts of the frame upon which specific differences are founded.'"[27] Likewise, humans have been breeding dogs for thousands of years, creating an enormous variety of breeds. But whether pigeons or dogs, artificial selection has never come close to creating a new species. Wilberforce then suggests that, given this, it is foolish to make an analogy between artificial selection and natural selection.

His scientific critique continues. "We think it difficult to find a theory fuller of assumptions; and of assumptions not grounded upon alleged facts in nature, but which are absolutely opposed to all the facts we have been able to observe."[28] In addition, the variations produced in domestic animals by breeders are selected because of their utility to people, not for the good of the animal. So artificial selection is simply irrelevant to what happens in nature. If natural selection is continually producing innumerable variations, where, Wilberforce asks, is the evidence for this in the geological record?

Wilberforce notes Darwin's own concessions regarding the lack of geological evidence for his theory. Wilberforce writes, "This 'Imperfection of the Geological Record,' and the 'Geological Succession,' are the subjects of two laboured and ingenious chapters, in which he tries, as we think utterly in vain, to break down the unanswerable refutation which is given to his theory by the testimony of the rocks."[29] Wilberforce is unconvinced by Darwin's argument that the geological refutation of his theory is only apparent, resulting from limited sampling of, and the inherent imperfection of, the geological record. Darwin recognized the seeming sudden appearance of complex animals during the Cambrian era—a feature of the geological record known today as the Cambrian explosion—and openly admitted that if a long line of diversification in Precambrian deposits failed to show up in the fossil record, his theory would be in ruins.[30] Wilberforce took this concession and ran with it. "Now it is proved to demonstration by Sir Roderick Murchison, and admitted by all geologists, that we possess these earlier formations, stretching over vast extents, perfectly unaltered, and exhibiting no signs of life."[31]

Did the ensuing decades make a fool of Wilberforce? In fact, the findings of modern paleontology substantially agree with Wilberforce here. The wealth of Precambrian transitional fossils that Darwin hoped would be discovered and so rescue his theory have remained persistently absent, despite assiduous efforts to locate them, and despite the fossil record having shown itself quite capable of preserving other Precambrian fossils.[32]

Wilberforce further objected to Darwin's handling of time: "The other solvent which Mr. Darwin most freely and, we think, unphilosophically employs to get rid of difficulties, is his use of time. This he shortens or prolongs at will by the mere wave of his magician's rod."[33] Wilberforce accuses Darwin of positing enormous stretches of time in places where his theory requires them, but then gathering up into a point the duration in which certain forms of life prevailed, thus obscuring the fact that, as the fossil record shows, many forms of life endured for many millions of years without undergoing substantial change.

Similarly, Wilberforce also objected to Darwin's employment of facts: "Together with this large licence of assumption we notice in this book several instances of receiving as facts whatever seems to bear out the theory upon the slightest evidence, and rejecting summarily others, merely because they are fatal to it. We grieve to charge upon Mr. Darwin this freedom in handling facts, but truth extorts it from us."[34]

The stereotype portraying Wilberforce as the pompous bishop rejecting Darwin on theological grounds is easily dispelled by the scientifically informed, scientifically focused, and comprehensive nature of his lengthy review. Hooker may have accused Wilberforce of not understanding Darwin's theory, but Wilberforce's review suggests he understood it only too well.

As we saw earlier with William Harvey, Darwin's favorite line of response to his critics was to accuse them of not understanding his theory. Darwin wrote to his publisher, John Murray, on August 3, 1860, "The Bishop makes me say several things which I do not say, but these very clever men think they can write a review with a very slight knowledge of the Book reviewed or subject in question." Darwin accused Wilberforce of being aided by Richard Owen in the writing of this review, ostensibly because Darwin assumed Wilberforce incapable of writing such an in-depth review himself.[35] But Owen's extensive review of the *Origin* in the *Edinburgh Review* bears little resemblance to the issues Wilberforce raised.

Ironically, in questioning the scientific acumen of Wilberforce because of his role as a man of the cloth, Darwin was treading on treacherous ground. For Darwin's only formal education was a general bachelor of arts from Cambridge with only a smattering of math and science. Wilberforce, however, had obtained a first-class degree in mathematics from Oxford, hardly the sort of education one expects from a man supposedly allergic to hard-nosed scientific thinking.

A similar review appeared in America in 1861 in the pages of the *Methodist Quarterly Review*. Penned by W. C. Wilson of Dickinson

College in Pennsylvania, this review might be expected, given the journal, to emphasize religious arguments against Darwin's theory. But as with Wilberforce's review, the arguments are substantially scientific in nature. As Wilson put it, "We have discussed this as a scientific question only, to be decided upon its merits without reference to its theological bearings."[36]

First, he did not accept that analogy so important to Darwin, between Lyell's uniformitarian geology and Darwin's theory:

> We cannot see the parallelism between the changes of inorganic matter and the production of living beings with all their existing diversity. Science has determined pretty clearly all the properties of inorganic matter and the nature of all the physical forces. The law of these forces has been reduced to strict mathematical expression, and their effects have all been calculated.... The transmutation of inorganic matter into living form has not yet been accounted for by any of the natural agencies which produce physical phenomena.[37]

Just as H. G. Bronn had written to Darwin, in our uniform and repeated experience life always emerges from life. Darwin thus had to presuppose, at least in his public stance in the pages of the *Origin*, the initial creation of one or a few forms from which all others diversified. And for Wilson, "We certainly cannot see any insuperable difficulty in admitting a supernatural agency for the production of each new form introduced, after admitting it for the first one, or as Mr. Darwin prefers, the first four or more; especially until some secondary cause has been proved sufficient to account for their origin, and thus dispense with the further necessity for a primary one."[38]

Moreover, Wilson rejected the notion of the struggle for existence as Darwin portrayed it on the grounds that many political economists had shown that Malthus's theory about population dynamics was false when applied to human societies. So how much the more would it be "false and wicked when applied to the organization of the animal kingdom."[39]

Not only did Wilson reject Darwin's analogy with Lyell's geology, he also, like Wilberforce, objected to Darwin's analogy to artificial selection. The variations produced in animals under domestication are controlled by the intelligence of the breeder. How, then, can an unintelligent process produce anything similar? Wilson writes, "Haphazard and accidental as his natural selection seems to others, to him it appears endowed with the highest attributes of wisdom and omnipotence."[40] But this would seem to be only in Darwin's imagination, for "has Mr. Darwin furnished one instance of a new species produced by natural selection?"[41] Darwin of course does produce speculative scenarios, like, as Wilson cites, the famous bear-to-whale example. But, says Wilson, "We should like to know how much credulity is necessary to enable one to adopt such stories as proofs of a scientific theory."[42]

Finally, Wilson also considers the problem of the geological record contradicting the expectations set up by Darwin's theory. He, like Wilberforce, notes the phenomenon of the Cambrian explosion and comments on Darwin's genius for special pleading in explaining away facts which oppose his theory. Thus, in Wilson's view, Darwin "entirely failed to re-establish on a scientific basis the often rejected theory of the transmutation of species."[43]

While Wilberforce and Wilson may both have been influenced by their religious sympathies in opposing Darwin's theory, they could nevertheless mount up significant scientific arguments against it that paralleled many of the objections registered by Darwin's correspondents who were not as wedded to a particular religious worldview.

In January of 1862, Huxley gave a series of lectures at the Philosophical Institute of Edinburgh titled "The Relation of Man to the Lower Animals." These lectures caught the attention of the Scottish press, and several newspapers printed summaries and reviews of the lectures. Though these reviews were in response to Huxley's lectures, the reviewers did not hesitate to take the opportunity to opine about Darwin's work, given Huxley's close association with Darwin. Nowhere is this more apparent than in the January 17 edition of the *Week*, which announced, "In the second of the two lectures which he recently delivered before the Philosophical Institution here, Professor Huxley declined to acknowledge that these lectures were to be taken as advocating Mr. Darwin's theory of the Origin of Species. They were, he said, a mere statement of facts which any man could verify for himself. Was this expected to be taken seriously?"[44]

The author accuses Huxley of squeamishness; he was clearly advocating Darwin's theory but not willing to state it outright for fear of reprisal.

The author does, however, agree that Darwin's theory has to be considered at least possible; one cannot discount a priori the possibility that new species were derived from former ones. "The question is one of fact," he writes. "Is there any evidence of such a thing ever or anywhere taking place, as a new species being physically derived from an old one? After the most heedful examination of all facts adduced, science has answered and answers, No."[45]

The problem with Darwin's book, according to this writer, is that it failed to provide evidence to support its main point—transmutation of species by natural selection. By dwelling instead on the similarities one can observe between various species, "it simply added some new illustration of what was perfectly well known before, but nothing that was in the least fitted to alter the balance of argument or evidence on the question."[46] The writer admits that there was "much entertaining detail about pigeons and other impressible creatures," but all this was known two thousand years ago by the Greeks and Romans.

This author, however, fully recognized the rhetorical force of Darwin's work.

No wizard, the author states, is needed to make Darwin's theory seem likely, for "Mr. Darwin succeeds, so pleasantly and so ingeniously, that many an unwary reader imagines that he is proving his theory. All he is proving is, that if you admit the fundamental principle of his theory, it might possibly work in practice."[47]

I can think of no more accurate characterization of *The Origin of Species*. The elegance of Darwin's writing married to exhaustively detailed descriptions of the most minute characteristics of living organisms produced a rhetorical tour de force. Surely someone who observed nature in such exquisite detail knew what he was talking about. But according to the author of the review, Darwin's "agreeable but overrated book has therefore left the real question where it found it."[48]

The complaint was by now a common one, voiced by opponents and supporters alike. While he made arguments, he provided little evidence and essentially proved nothing.

But *The Origin of Species* was, to be fair, only an abstract—and abstracts should not be expected to supply all the facts and evidence on which a theory is founded. As we have seen, Darwin did have a longer work well on its way to completion, which he said would provide the crucial evidence missing from the abstract. And his readers looked forward to seeing this longer work with great anticipation. Surely Darwin would want to make every effort to complete this work and bring it to publication so as to satisfy his supporters and silence his critics.

But Darwin did no such thing. In the years immediately following 1859, the big book on species lay dormant while Darwin instead turned his attention to botany. He wrote up the results of many years' worth of study of the fertilization mechanisms in orchids. Why he would make such an unexpected turn, thus depriving his readers of the research forming the foundation of the *Origin*, will occupy us in the next chapter.

6. Darwin's Unfinished Book under the Microscope

GIVEN THE STATUS OF *THE ORIGIN OF SPECIES* AS A MERE ABSTRACT of a larger work some three-quarters complete, one would naturally expect Darwin to have followed up the *Origin* by publishing this larger work, a work promising to contain all the facts, evidence, and references Darwin was unable to include in the abstract. Indeed, he wrote to his cousin Fox on Christmas day 1859, just a month after the publication of the *Origin*, that he intended now to plunge into "my bigger book, which I shall publish as 3 separate volumes, with distinct title, but with a general title in addition." Of course, Darwin had already created this expectation in the *Origin* itself. In the introduction, Darwin characterized his larger species book as "nearly finished" but also noted that "it will take me many more years to complete it."[1] In the body of the work, Darwin repeatedly whetted his readers' appetites by noting the places where he was unable to provide all the facts on which his various propositions were based, implying (or outright stating) that those facts would be forthcoming in the larger work.

For example, in the beginning of the chapter on variation under nature, Darwin wrote, "To treat this subject properly, a long catalogue of dry facts ought to be given; but these I shall reserve for a future work."[2] Likewise, in a place where Darwin pronounces the following theoretical principle, *"A Part developed in any Species in an extraordinary degree or manner, in comparison with the same Part in allied Species, tends to be highly variable,*" he adds, "It is hopeless to attempt to convince any one of the truth of the above proposition without giving the long array of facts which I have collected, and which cannot possibly be here introduced."[3]

In discussing the struggle for existence, he says, "In my future work this subject will be treated, as it deserves, at greater length."[4] And again, when describing the phenomenon of analogous variations, Darwin states, "I have collected a long list of such cases; but here, as before, I lie under the great disadvantage of not being able to give them."[5]

Likewise, in a discussion of intercrossing, he writes, "I must here treat the subject with extreme brevity, though I have the materials prepared for an ample discussion."[6] Repeatedly, Darwin tantalizes his readers by referencing the long catalogues of facts which he had collected on numerous topics, facts which he could not include in the *Origin* due to its being a mere abstract. This rhetorical ploy had the effect of building tremendous anticipation for the appearance of the big book on species.

A month after the *Origin*'s publication (on December 24, 1859), Darwin wrote to the Swiss zoologist François Jules Pictet de la Rive: "I am now going at once to commence getting ready for press my larger Book, as quickly as my weak health permits." About a month later (January 29, 1860), Darwin wrote to the publisher Charles Griffin, who was preparing an entry on Darwin for his forthcoming *Dictionary of Contemporary Biography*. Griffin had sent Darwin a draft of this entry and wanted Darwin to sign off on the text, to which Darwin, after making emendations and additions, gave his assent. The finished entry included the following passage: "He has recently (November, 1859) published a work entitled, 'The Origin of Species by Means of Natural Selection; or, The Preservation of Favoured Races in the Struggle for Life.' This volume, as stated in the introduction, gives only in a condensed form the result of more than twenty years' study; and will hereafter be followed by a more detailed treatise on the same subject." Note that the part about "this volume" being only a "condensed form" that was to be "followed by a more detailed treatise" was not in Griffin's original draft but was added by Darwin.

So we see that Darwin gave every indication of intending to follow up the *Origin* with his big book on species, and his readers took him at his word, as reviews of the *Origin* and letters written to Darwin will reveal.

Anticipating the Big Book

Early reviewers of the *Origin* afforded Darwin the benefit of the doubt. Days before official publication, John Leifchild reviewed the *Origin* in the pages of the *Athenaeum*: "After all, this book is but an abstract:—it is the pilot balloon to a greater machine.... The larger work is nearly finished, but it will demand two or three more years for completion. Health, labour, and observations are wanting for awhile, but in due season we hope to see the work 'with references and authorities for several statements.'"[7]

An anonymous reviewer in the *Spectator* had much the same view, describing the book as "an abstract, necessarily imperfect, of an elaborate work that will require two or three more years for its completion," and adding, "Meanwhile it must be remembered in justice to him that his case is not yet fully set forth, and that no final decision can be pronounced upon it so long as he has had but a partial hearing."[8]

So also in the *Examiner*: "Mr Darwin's work, although extending to 500 pages, is but an abstract of a greater which he is preparing, and which two or three years hence will be completed."[9] Moreover, W. C. Wilson's review in the *Methodist Quarterly Review*, examined in the previous chapter, while generally critical, still informed his readers that the *Origin* "is, however, as he informs us, but an abstract of what he has done, to be followed soon by a much fuller work containing 'in detail all the facts, with references,' on which his conclusions have been founded."[10]

And even Darwin's sworn enemy, Richard Owen, in writing about the *Origin*, graciously conceded that "a rich mine of such researches is alluded to and promised by Mr. Darwin, in a more voluminous collection of his researches."[11]

Thus we see that the scientific community awaited with great anticipation Darwin's big book on speciation by natural selection.

And these reviewers were not alone. Darwin's correspondents also impressed upon him the growing anticipation for, and the importance of publishing, the big book on species. January 30, 1860, saw the botanist Charles Bunbury registering his lack of agreement with Darwin's theory, but also noting, "I cannot feel satisfied till I see your 'Piéces Justificatives'—the body of evidence which you are to bring forward in your big book." Alfred Russel Wallace was so confident in Darwin's soon publishing the big book that in a November 30, 1861, letter from Sumatra, he advised on how to present it:

> I trust your great work goes on & is soon to appear. I hope however you will have it copiously illustrated. I am sure it will be for the publisher's interest to do so as it will I have no doubt double the circulation. There are so many things that are weak when merely mentioned or described by numbers which become clear & strong when an appeal is made to the eye. The *varieties of pigeons* the *stripes of horses*, the variation in *ants*, the formation of *honeycombs* & a hundred other things will be better for good illustrations—They will also make the book newer & more distinct from its forerunner in the eyes of the public to whom it will otherwise appear as perhaps a mere enlargement—If this point is not decided, pray take it seriously into consideration.

As we will soon see, Darwin may have followed Wallace's advice, not in his big book on species, but rather in his richly illustrated monograph on orchids.

By February 1862, more than two years after the publication of the *Origin*, anticipation of the big book had not waned. The paleontologist Searles Wood wrote to Darwin:

> I presume that you are still employed collecting & arranging data for your work of which the essay published is you tell us but an outline. I hope that I may live to see it & that you may have health & strength to complete the work you have begun.

In April of that same year, the Boston essayist and poet Thomas Appleton informed Darwin, "We are here all impatiently waiting for the continuation of your wonderful book." Even Darwin's old *Beagle* shipmate, Philip King, contacted him from Australia on September 16, "If you ever publish your promised large work on your favorite Subject I shall look out for it eagerly." And the Swiss botanist Alphonse de Candolle inquired on June 13, 1862, "Will we soon have the great work that you announce as providing detailed evidence of facts mentioned in your book on the origin of species? I await it with great impatience."

De Candolle and the rest of Darwin's correspondents waited and waited, but they would be disappointed in the end. For Darwin would never publish the great majority of his big book. He instead took up the study of fertilization mechanisms in orchids and published a monograph on this botanical subject in 1862, and after this chased other projects.

Why did Darwin switch from his work on species to the finer points of botany? Before tackling this question, we should consider Darwin's notes from his personal journal.[12] For the year 1860 we find the following entries:

> Jan. 9- Began looking over M.S. for Work on Variation (with many interruptions)
>
> March 24- Began Introduction to Vol. on Variation
>
> June 10- Finished 2nd ch. on pigeons
>
> Aug. 11- Began Ch. III

In the immediate aftermath of the publication of the *Origin*, Darwin was beginning work on what he seems to have by this time viewed as the first of the three volumes that would make up his big book, a volume he titled *Variation under Domestication*. But if we follow his journal forward, we find that his attention quickly strayed from the big book. For the year 1861, we find the following entries:

> March 20- Finished Ch. III on Variation under Domestication & began Ch. IV
>
> July 1- During stay at Torquay did paper on Orchids
>
> All rest of year Orchid Book

So, sometime between March and July 1861, Darwin seems to have set aside working on the big book to focus on orchids instead. What happened? This question finds an answer in Darwin's incomplete manuscript of the big book on species. Examining this manuscript will make it clear why Darwin abandoned its publication despite having created tremendous anticipation for it.

Darwin's Big Book on Species

Darwin's unpublished manuscript, to be titled *Natural Selection*, ran to nearly 300,000 words in its unfinished form. It adheres closely to the structure of *The Origin of Species*, as we can see from *Natural Selection*'s chapter headings:

Chapter I:	Variation under Domestication
Chapter II:	Variation under Domestication (continued)
Chapter III:	On Possibility of All Organisms Crossing
Chapter IV:	Variation under Nature
Chapter V:	Struggle for Existence
Chapter VI:	Natural Selection
Chapter VII:	Laws of Variation: Varieties and Species Compared
Chapter VIII:	Difficulties in Transitions
Chapter IX:	Hybridism and Mongrelism
Chapter X:	Instinct
Chapter XI:	Geographical Distribution

Chapters appearing in the *Origin* that are not reflected in this unpublished manuscript include "Miscellaneous Objections to the Theory of Natural Selection," "On the Imperfection of the Geological Record," "On the Geological Succession of Organic Beings," "Mutual Affinities of Organic Beings," and "Recapitulation and Conclusion." Had Darwin included these subjects in the big book, we can project that the final manuscript would have run to about 375,000 to 400,000 words. So, Darwin was about three-quarters finished when the arrival of Wallace's manuscript interrupted his work and spurred him to abstract the big book in the form of the *Origin*.[13]

Adding another 75,000 to 100,000 words to the big book and publishing it should not have been a more onerous task than writing and publishing an entirely new work on orchids, which itself ran to nearly 90,000 words. Why, then, did Darwin disappoint his readers by not following the *Origin* with the more comprehensive treatment of his theory?

In a review of R. C. Stauffer's 1975 publication of the big book manuscript, Stephen Jay Gould argues that Darwin did not need to publish the big book. In Gould's view, natural selection was not really the main focus of the *Origin*; rather Darwin was attempting to document the fact of evolution against creationist ideas. There is some truth to this, but Gould goes on, "We arrive then at the key point: Darwin triumphed by his documentation and convinced the world that evolution had occurred. Yet he did it with his abridgement, the *Origin*—without footnotes and without citation of sources. Since he could not have been more successful in the impact of his documentation, the longer version was clearly not necessary to achieve his result."[14]

This overstates things. *The Origin* certainly proved persuasive to many, but as we have seen, there were holdouts, including among well-informed scientists whose unqualified approval Darwin craved but had yet to secure. The big book was to be titled *Natural Selection*, and these scientifically well-informed readers of the *Origin* certainly did not view it as unnecessary. On the contrary, they had expressed that they did not think they could adequately evaluate the *Origin* without seeing all the evidence and authorities that were to be laid out in the big book.

The fact that Darwin's theory of evolution eventually prevailed among scientists, along with the pervasive Darwinian mythology, seems to have colored Gould's attempt to explain Darwin's failure to publish the big book. And Gould is not alone. Sydney Smith likewise tries to apologize for Darwin's failure to publish: "Ill health, the problem of Man, Sexual Selection, the appeal of Botanical research, excursions into family history, the continual need for revising his published works, and the final yielding to his early affection for the earthworm, consumed what energy remained after his almost daily stint of answering letters." But Smith then continues about the big book, "This text can be justly claimed as the most important of all Darwin's writings on what has come to be called evolution."[15] Clearly a text of such great importance should have taken precedence over all those other works. But it obviously didn't for Darwin.

The interesting thing about reviews of Stauffer's publication of the big book is that while basically agreeing with Smith on its importance, they provide virtually no engagement with the contents of the manuscript. Jane Oppenheimer considers Stauffer's book the publishing event of the half-century in the history of science, but she provides only a brief outline of its contents.[16] Larry Spencer, Michael Ghiselin, and M. J. S. Hodge all agree that perhaps the most important contribution of Stauffer's publication is its extensive bibliography of the sources Darwin cites (citations left out of the *Origin*).[17] This, for Ghiselin, explodes the myth that Darwin was unaware of his predecessors. Clearly having all these references and citations is a boon for modern Darwin scholars, for which they are certainly in Stauffer's debt. But citations to authorities are *exactly* what Darwin's contemporaries were yearning to see, yet he withheld them. Hodge notes that the big book contains "no great surprises or revelations" over what is contained in the *Origin*, and he focuses his review instead on tracing Darwin's thought process from his 1842 sketch up to the big book, a thought process whose logical structure was, in Hodge's view, compromised over time.[18] Hodge does not appear overly impressed with the big book and so, with other reviewers, largely ignores its contents.

I see no reason to apologize for Darwin's failure to complete and publish the big book as he promised. I would argue instead that, given the responses Darwin received to the *Origin*, he was aware of the weaknesses spotted by his critics, and may well have concluded that the big book would be unsuccessful at filling the evidentiary gaps his readers had identified in the abstract and assumed would be addressed in the big book. And, indeed, we can easily see that Darwin's unpublished manuscript does contain many of the same weaknesses his critics saw in the *Origin*.

Let's take a closer look now at the big book manuscript.

The first two chapters dealt with variation under domestication but are no longer part of the manuscript since Darwin removed them and expanded them into his 1868 monograph, *Variation of Animals and Plants under Domestication*. Chapter 3 presents an argument for Darwin's premise that all organic beings need at least occasionally to cross with other individuals of the same species, since nature abhors perpetual self-fertilization. Darwin had stated this premise in the *Origin* but provided little evidence for it. Here he does fulfill his promise to expand on his abstract with pages and pages of observations.

Things get more interesting, however, when we turn to the next several chapters, which form the heart of the big book. Would these chapters have satisfied readers of the *Origin* who were clamoring for more evidence to establish natural selection as the primary mechanism of evolutionary change?

In chapter 4, Darwin discusses variation under nature. He does give some facts documenting individual variation in nature, like variations in color, size, and spotting of some bird eggs. He also mentions the case of a monkey with extra molar teeth, and another involving antlers that occasionally appear on female deer. Additional examples continue this parade of very minor variations. But the most important part of this chapter for Darwin is to establish a relationship he believes exists between species and varieties. As Darwin recognizes, the problem is immediately apparent: no one can agree on exactly what constitutes a species. He notes the example of a British oak that some say comes in two varieties but others call two species. Or the Scotch Fir, "in which the varieties or species, call them which you please & you will have high authority for doing so, are adapted to different situations, produce different kinds of timber & are hereditary in their quality."[19]

Darwin believed that species are just strongly marked varieties and do not constitute ideal created types. And he wanted to show that large genera that contain many species also contain more varieties than small genera with few species. Why? Because "where many large trees grow, we expect to find saplings. But if we look at each species as a special act of creation, there is no apparent reason why more varieties should occur in a group having many species, than in one having few."[20] So on this view, where many varieties occur, speciation must be in the process of occurring. Of course, this is all based on the ability to distinguish species from mere varieties, a problem Darwin recognizes but then largely ignores. He instead plows ahead, poring over zoological and botanical almanacs trying to discern the ratio of varieties in large versus small genera, which he presents in a series of very technical tables. Recall (as discussed in Chapter 3) that this is where he made a major methodological error.

There was another problem. When it came to botanical almanacs, Joseph Dalton Hooker suggested to Darwin that it might well be that botanists had recorded varieties more fully in large genera, so the botanical lists were not necessarily representative of what occurs in nature. Darwin continues, "I have consulted several other botanists, & though it does not appear that they had previously thought on this point, they generally concur in this view."[21]

Darwin then consulted Asa Gray, who confessed that he did not think himself guilty of this, though he might actually have been more likely to record varieties in smaller genera. But Gray's point, far from reassuring Darwin, further undermines the credibility of the almanacs, since it reinforces the impression that botanists had not been comprehensive in their recording of varieties—some focusing more on larger genera, others on smaller genera.

Darwin was thus forced to conclude, "Now if Dr. Hooker & the others who concur with him be right, all the foregoing tables are utterly worthless; for they do not show nature's work only the imperfect handiwork of botanists."[22] In light of these methodological concerns, it is clear why Darwin would not have wanted to publish the big book with those "worthless" tables employed to carry one of his crucial articles of evidence.

Chapter 5 is titled "The Struggle for Existence." Here Darwin's concern revolves around the fecundity of most organisms—their tendency to give birth to far more progeny than can survive, leading to the enduring struggle for survival so often identified as the heart of

Darwinism. There is little difference in content between this chapter in the big book and the corresponding chapter in the *Origin*. But Darwin does double down on his failed analogy of natural selection to artificial selection when he states, "I believe such means do exist in nature, analogous, but incomparably superior, to those by which man selects & adds up trifling changes, & thus brings his pigeon or canary-bird or flower up to a preconceived standard."[23]

As he continues it becomes clear that he imbues natural selection not only with the power of foresight but also with the power to bring about perfection. He writes, "And for myself I am fully convinced that there does exist, in Nature, means of Selection, always in action & of which the perfection cannot be exaggerated." And a few lines later, "I can see no limit to the perfection of this means of Selection."[24]

If Darwin were trying to place evolution on a firmly naturalistic foundation, talk of natural selection bringing organisms up to a preconceived standard of perfection would have only undermined his project. Recall that Lyell and Hooker had charged Darwin with the deification of natural selection, and that was presumably without seeing passages like this.

Chapter 6, "On Natural Selection," is pivotal. Does Darwin in this chapter provide convincing evidence for natural selection as the main driver of evolution, evidence missing from the abstract? Here I think readers of the big book would have been greatly disappointed.

First, Darwin doubles down on his analogy between natural and artificial selection. Early in the chapter he writes:

> A sudden or great variation must rarely, some will say never, occurs in nature; but if it did, & were profitable it of course would be selected; but modifications, let them appear ever so trifling, if in the least influential on the welfare of the being, I can see no reason after the most careful consideration to doubt would tend to be preserved or selected. They would, also, tend to be inherited; & slight modification might thus be added to slight modification in any given direction useful to the animal;—just as in our domestic animals & plants modifications useful to man have been added together & rendered permanent by artificial selection.[25]

A few pages later we find a whole section subtitled "Comparison of Nature's Selection with Man's Selection," followed by another section ("Principle of Divergence") where Darwin seeks light "as in all other cases, by looking to our domestic productions."[26] By constantly highlighting the intentionality and directionality of artificial selection as the most useful analogy for his understanding of natural selection, Darwin continually undermines his contention that an unplanned, undirected process could create new species.

Readers hoping to see a rich array of empirical evidence for the creative powers of natural selection would have been disappointed. The chapter instead offers more talk about artificial selection, along with various imaginary scenarios. In a section subtitled "Illustrations of the Action of Natural Selection," Darwin begins with a statement repeated verbatim in the *Origin*: "In order to make it clear how I believe natural selection acts, I must beg permission to give one or two imaginary illustrations."[27] Darwin then launches into a hypothetical discussion of how wolves who were born slightly faster would be selected, and lead to the wolf species' becoming faster and more efficient in hunting. Two pages later he says, "Lastly let us turn to nectar-feeding insects in our imaginary case."[28] And on the next page we find, "In our imaginary examples, it may be observed that natural selection can act only by the preservation & addition of infinitesimally small inherited modifications each profitable to the preserved being."[29] And again, "The view that the greatest number of organic beings (or more strictly the greatest amount of life) can be supported on any given area, by the greatest amount of their diversification is, perhaps, most plainly seen by taking an imaginary case."[30]

The imaginary case, which he credits to Henri Milne Edwards, concerns the doctrine of the division of labor, whereby a stomach will digest food better if it does not serve at the same time as a respiratory organ. And it will digest even better if it is specialized to digest either vegetable or animal matter but not both. Likewise, "It is obvious that more descendants from a carnivorous animal could be supported in any country: if some were adapted, by long continued modification through natural selection, to hunt small prey, & others large prey living either on plains or in forests."[31] Yes, animals are specialized organisms adapted to unique ecological niches. But is this brought about by natural selection? In these passages Darwin merely assumes so rather than demonstrating it.

Before long, Darwin turns from his imaginary scenarios to a discussion of the difficulties presented by his theory of natural selection. We find this curious introduction, "Having given a pretty full outline of my theory, it will be necessary to discuss as well as we can, though very imperfectly, the circumstances, favourable or contrary to natural selection."[32] This is hardly encouraging: he is well over halfway through the chapter on natural selection, and he has just described everything covered in it so far as a mere "outline"—shades of his description of the *Origin* as a "mere abstract"; yet he then characterizes what remains of the chapter not as a parade of empirical evidence in favor of natural selection's creative powers, but instead more as a conjectural section, and very imperfect, concerning circumstances favorable and unfavorable to natural selection.

On the difficulties with his theory, Darwin notes the slowness of natural selection working on triflingly small variations, knowing that his critics will see this as fatal to his theory. But Darwin responds, "I do not believe so; but the result must be judged of by the general phenomena of nature. That changes will usually be extremely slow, I fully admit; & I am convinced that a fair view of the geological history of the world accords perfectly with an extreme degree of slowness in any modification of its inhabitants."[33] But Darwin knew that this was not true. He was well aware of the sudden appearance in the geological record of new animal body plans in the Cambrian period, a phenomenon that even he believed would undermine his whole theory if an array of transitional fossils in the Precambrian deposits were never found. (They still haven't been.) Potential readers of the big book would have been familiar with the Cambrian problem, since Darwin discussed it in the *Origin*. So his contention here that the fossil record accords with his view of slow and gradual modification would have proved quite confusing to those readers. Darwin does note the difficulty of the lack of intermediate forms in the fossil record, but defers a discussion to a later chapter on paleontology (which is not part of the big book manuscript), and by way of explanation for this contrary line of evidence offers only a passing remark about the imperfection of the geological record.

He does at least discuss the dearth of intermediate forms among currently living organisms, arguing that we should expect such forms to be rare because species modifications occur very slowly and in any given area few species are undergoing modification at any one time, so few intermediate forms would be produced. He then cites the naturalist T. V. Wollaston as a supporter of the idea that intermediate forms are rare but do occur, based on Wollaston's observations of insects and land mollusks. But Darwin does not share any of Wollaston's observations. In terms of intermediate forms in plants, Darwin sought further expert opinion:

> I applied to Mr. H. C. Watson & to Dr. Asa Gray for their opinions on this head; as from their critical knowledge of the floras of Great Britain & the United States, everyone would place great confidence in their judgment. Both these botanists concur in this opinion, & Mr. Watson has given me a list of twelve intermediate varieties found in Britain which are rarer than the forms, which they connect. But both these naturalists have insisted strongly on various sources of doubt in forming any decided judgment on this head.[34]

Darwin, alas, does not discuss any of Watson's twelve examples of intermediate forms. Further, given the doubts expressed by Watson and Gray, it seems that Darwin's experts failed to provide him with the kind of confirmation he so urgently desired. Watson and Gray clearly understood the complexities of the issue in a way that Darwin seemed to ignore. Their strong doubts and Darwin's failure to cite the specific examples Wollaston and Watson shared with him could hardly be expected to inspire confidence in his argument among would-be readers of the big book.

As noted previously, one of the places in the *Origin* where Darwin apologized for not providing the long catalogue of facts he had collected concerned a discussion of the premise that "a part normally developed in any species in an extraordinary degree or manner, in comparison with the same part in allied species, tends to be highly variable." In the big book, he takes up this topic in Chapter 7, titled "Laws of Variation." We should therefore expect to find here the long catalogue of facts Darwin refers to in the *Origin*. Does Darwin deliver?

First he provides a caveat:

> I must here premise that our apparent law, which we are here going to discuss relates only to parts differing greatly from the same parts in species if not actually congenerous at least pretty closely allied: nor do I suppose that the rule is of universal application. To give an imaginary example, the wing of a Bat is a part developed in a highly remarkable manner in comparison with the front-legs of other mammals, but our law would not here apply: it would apply only to some one Bat having wings developed in an extraordinary degree, or manner, compared with other closely allied Bats.[35]

This caveat will necessarily reduce the number of cases of this phenomenon. Second, Darwin states, "I must remark that the cases implying *extraordinary* development cannot be very frequent; & secondly that it is very difficult to collect facts of this kind."[36] With these admissions the catalogue of facts appears to be getting shorter. Third, Darwin considers that his rule will be more apparent among plants than among animals. So he reached out once again to Hooker for his expert opinion. After careful consideration, Hooker informed Darwin that "though some facts seem to countenance the rule, yet quite as many or more are opposed to it." According to Hooker, plants are so variable that it "is difficult to form a judgment on the degrees of variability."[37] Suddenly, Darwin's rule does not seem to be much of a rule at all.

And what of the long catalogue of facts alluded to in the *Origin*? After all the caveats, Darwin provides ten examples. They concern things like variability in the size of the tusk in the male narwhal, the horny points on the wing-tips of waxwings, the forked tale of the chimney swallow, the size of the beak in the oystercatcher, the long legs of the long-legged plover, and the size and curvature of the bill of the crossbill. I leave it to readers to judge whether this suffices to pay off the promised long catalogue of facts said to demonstrate the considerable creative powers of natural selection.

In Chapter 8, Darwin considers difficulties with his theory. First up is the wing of the bat. How could something like this develop through a long series of trifling modifications? Darwin responds, "We cannot answer this question even by conjectures. The earliest known, Eocene Bat apparently was as perfect, as one of the present day: if our geological records really make any approach to perfection, this would be a fatal objection."[38] Of course, as always Darwin will go on to discount the geological evidence. But his admission here flatly contradicts his earlier statement that the fossil record is in accordance with his view of natural selection as a slow, gradual process. Readers of the big book would have been unlikely to find this contradiction reassuring.

Or take the similar case of the flying squirrel. Darwin argues that the ability to glide a little further would be an adaptive modification. Hence, "I can see no difficulty in the means of gliding through the air in squirrels having been perfected through natural selection from a mere flattened brush-like tail to a wide flank membrane."[39] Maybe Darwin can see no difficulty in this, but he neglects to provide any actual empirical evidence that the gliding feature was created by natural selection working on a series of small random variations.

Now, given that William Harvey and others reacted with a hearty laugh to Darwin's example of a bear transforming into a whale, Darwin probably would not have wanted to publish the following paragraph from the big book regarding the effects of changed habits:

> To take one more extreme case, that of the Black Bear seen by Hearn: if its habit of catching small crustaceans by swimming with widely open mouth became, from the crustaceans being always present with the loss perhaps of other prey, highly important for its sustenance, then as slight variations in the size & shape of the mouth would almost certainly occur during millions of generations, some of these would certainly aid ever so little individuals in this

> strange way of fishing; & these individuals, as all cannot possibly live, would have a better chance of living, & thus such slight variations would be continually added up through natural selection, till an animal, which we should think monstrous, was produced, thoroughly aquatic & with a mouth perhaps proportionally as large as that of a whale. Who would not think it monstrously improbable, if he had never heard of a whale, that so gigantic an animal could subsist by sifting with its huge mouth the minutest animals from the waters of the sea![40]

Knowing the ridicule he had received over the shorter bear-to-whale example appearing in the *Origin*, Darwin could well have anticipated that this expanded speculative scenario would have engendered still greater ridicule. The leap from the observation of a single bear swimming with an open mouth to a fully aquatic creature that, like a whale, filter feeds as its sole source of subsistence demonstrates nothing more than the fertility of Darwin's imagination; it says little about nature.

Next up in the big book is Darwin's discussion of how the eye might have evolved, the problem that Darwin so famously said gave him a cold shudder. To evaluate the possibility that eyes could evolve gradually via natural selection, Darwin says we ought to compare the eyes of currently existing organisms with the eyes of their lineal progenitors so that we could document the various stages of the evolving eye. Fair enough. But then Darwin admits, "This is impossible; & all that we can do, is to look at the eyes of all existing animals within each great class, as a guide for judging how far a transition from one stage of perfection to another stage is possible."[41] Readers of the big book would have expected much more than the mere laying out of hypotheticals. They would have expected to see actual evidence. They would have been disappointed.

Interestingly, Darwin continues by arguing that our difficulty in accepting the evolution of the eye by natural selection stems from our tendency to compare the eye to the microscope or telescope, beautiful instruments that have been produced "by the long-continued efforts of the highest human intellects." So we naturally infer that the eye would also be the product of intelligence. But for Darwin, this is presumptuous. "Have we any right to suppose that the Creator works by the same means as man?" he asks. He, of course, answers in the negative and then goes into a long discourse about how a light-sensitive patch of tissue could be slowly honed over the course of millennia into the complex eye. "Let this process go on for millions on millions of years, & during each year on millions of individuals of many kinds," he opines, "and may we not believe that a living optical instrument might be formed, as much superior to one of glass, as the works of the Creator are to those of Man."[42] Perhaps Darwin could believe this. But could he demonstrate it with physical evidence? He provides none.

One final difficulty Darwin faces in this chapter is the origin of neuter insects. If they do not reproduce, how can their characteristics be inherited by future generations? Darwin responds, "Grave as these several difficulties are, do they overwhelm our theory? Let us turn to our best guide the process of selection by man in our domestic productions."[43] Darwin then observes that in artificial selection man selects the individual he approves of, except in the case of a cabbage or radish that he finds especially flavorful. Here he can't select the excellent radish to breed into the next generation because he has eaten it! But he can sow seed from the same stock and thereby perpetuate the flavorful radish in a process that Darwin terms "family selection." This then becomes his argument for the development of neuter insects: "This principle of selection, namely not of the individual which cannot breed, but of the family which produced such individual, has I believe been followed by nature in regard to the neuters among social insects."[44] That is, if a population of ants that produced neuters also produced individuals with other adaptive characteristics, those with the adaptive characteristics would be selected. And some of them would also be neuters.

But the neuters would still not be able to pass the neuter characteristic down to the next generation. Faced with this difficulty, Darwin holds onto his claim by way of a partial retreat: "No doubt the process of selection would be retarded in an extreme degree by its action being indirect,—that is on the family alone; the individuals themselves born with any useful variation never leaving offspring."[45] As in so many places in the big book manuscript, Darwin creates imaginative scenarios about how things may have happened, only to turn around and admit to daunting, and in some cases insuperable, difficulties inherent in his imaginative scenarios.

Chapter 9 of the big book concerns hybrid fertility and sterility and adheres closely to the corresponding chapter in the *Origin*. But Chapter 10 on instincts is more interesting. Darwin begins, "My belief is, that, like corporeal structures, the mental faculties & instincts of animals in a state of nature sometimes vary slightly; & that such slight modifications are often inherited."[46] It is fine for Darwin to believe this, but can he demonstrate it empirically? To his credit, Darwin recognizes the difficult truth that instincts do not fossilize. Documenting the slow and gradual evolution of an instinct over time is virtually impossible. Furthermore, there is the problem of distinguishing behaviors that are truly instinctive from those acquired by habit or imitation. In this regard, Darwin relates examples gained from his physician father of children whose parents died in their infancy who nevertheless seem to have inherited "all sorts of the slightest particularities."[47] Darwin then gives the following curious example:

> I will give one such case, which I myself have witnessed & can vouch for its perfect accuracy; namely that of a child who as early as between her fourth and fifth years, when her imagination was pleasantly excited & at no other time, had a most peculiar & irresistible trick of rapidly moving her fingers laterally, with her hands placed by the side of her face; & her father had precisely the same trick under the same frame of mind & which was not quite conquered even in old age; in this instance there could not possibly have been any imitation.[48]

The example is doubly weak. The four- or five-year-old child would have been easily old enough to have picked up this mannerism by observing her father, whom Darwin himself notes continued this action into old age. Also, how would touching one's face in such a way when excited increase one's fitness so that this instinct would serve as one link in a long series of "accumulated results through natural selection of slight & profitable modifications of other instincts?"[49] Darwin seems to be grasping at straws here.

Undeterred by these difficulties, Darwin sums up his discussion of instincts thus:

> Bearing in mind the facts given on the acquirement, through the selection of self-originating tricks or modifications of instinct, or through training & habit, aided in some slight degree by imitation, experience & intelligence, of hereditary actions & dispositions in our domesticated animals; & their parallelism (subject to being less true) to instincts of animals in a state of nature: bearing in mind that in a state of nature instincts do certainly vary in some slight degree: bearing in mind how very generally we find in allied but distinct animals a gradation in the more complex instincts, which shows that it is at least possible that a complex instinct might have been acquired by successive steps; & which moreover generally indicates, according to our theory, the actual steps by which the instinct has been acquired, in as much as we suppose allied animals to have branched off at different stages of descent from a common ancestor, & therefore to have retained, more or less unaltered, the instincts of the several lineal ancestral forms of any one species; bearing all this in mind, together with the certainty that instincts are as important to an animal as is their generally correlated structure, & that in the struggle for life under changing conditions, slight modifications of instinct could hardly fail occasionally to be profitable to individuals, I can see no overwhelming difficulty on our theory.[50]

If one both accepts and bears in mind all the things that Darwin exhorts us to bear in mind in this convoluted sentence, undoubtedly one could accept the possibility that instincts have evolved over time via natural selection. But Darwin requires his readers to accept an awful lot on faith in order to accept the possibility of animal instincts having evolved over time via natural selection.

This argument, so rich in speculation, is far more rhetorical than scientific. Perhaps sensing the shaky ground he's on, Darwin shifts, in the chapter's final passage, to an essentially theological argument for the evolutionary origin of instincts: "It may not be logical, but to my imagination, it is far more satisfactory to look at the young Cuckoo ejecting its foster-brothers,—the larvae of the Ichneumonidae feeding within the live bodies of their prey—cats playing with mice, otters & cormorants with living fish, not as instincts specially given by the Creator, but as very small parts of one general law leading to the advancement of all organic beings,—Multiply, Vary, let the strongest forms by their strength Live & the weakest forms Die."[51] Darwin simply could not bring himself to consider the possibility of intentionality in the development of instinctual behaviors that appeared to him so abhorrent. There was evil in nature that he would not ascribe to the Creator, and he saw no alternative but mindless evolution. Thus, he was bound by his philosophical bias to argue for the origin of instinct by natural selection despite the clear evidentiary difficulties such an argument encountered. This may have been a more satisfactory argument to Darwin's imagination, but whether it was actually true seems to have been less important than its role in providing him with personal comfort.

When Darwin *was* presented with contrary evidence, as we have already seen, he simply dismissed its importance. Again, in the instinct chapter, Darwin writes that "it has been said that fishes migrate that birds & other animals may prey on them; this is impossible on our theory of the natural selection of self-profitable modifications of instinct. But I have met with no facts, in support of this belief worthy of consideration."[52] Darwin cites both Linnaeus and a Prof. Alison for this curious phenomenon, but rather than engage with Linnaeus and Alison in detail, he simply dismisses the matter as not worthy of consideration on the basis that such an explanation is impossible on the theory of natural selection, a theory Darwin had not yet established as true.

Interestingly, Darwin's Alison reference is to an entry on instinct in Robert Bentley Todd's *Cyclopedia of Anatomy and Physiology*.[53] There Alison does not specifically reference the fish example cited by Darwin, but he does classify some instincts as existing for the benefit not necessarily of the organism that possesses them, but for another organism or for nature as a whole. Such cases posed no difficulty for

Alison, since he understood instincts as contrivances designed by a creator, not as capacities evolved by natural selection.

In any case, Darwin was never going to be able to satisfy his readers with mere imaginary scenarios about how natural selection might work in hypothetical situations. His readers were expecting hard evidence. But despite his many earlier comments building up expectations, the big book was sorely lacking in this regard.

To be fair to Darwin, rigorously documenting the action of natural selection is an extraordinary challenge. One would need to follow an entire population of organisms over many generations, counting how many progeny each organism produces and correlating this with the variations they display to document that organisms better adapted actually do out-reproduce the others. (And how would one judge this, aside from the circular method of deeming those that survived and reproduced to be the better adapted?) One could not have expected this level of detailed evidence from Darwin, but at the same time, one cannot fault his readers for desiring something more than imaginary scenarios about how natural selection might be supposed in theory to act in nature.

The readers of *The Origin of Species*, regarding the work as only an abstract, believed that Darwin possessed good empirical evidence for his theory that he simply was unable to fit in the shorter work. After all, Darwin told them as much. They therefore looked with great anticipation to the publication of the promised big book. But had Darwin published the big book, these readers would have had good reason to be disappointed, for the decisive evidence missing from the *Origin* was also missing in it. Darwin apparently recognized this. Abandoning the idea of publishing the big book, he decided to take a different tack. He had been studying the anatomy of orchid flowers for some time, and the thought must have dawned on him that perhaps his readers would view his orchid research as providing a more convincing argument for the power of natural selection than the big book. It was an interesting strategy, but one that would ultimately fail, and in the most ironic of ways.

7. Darwin the Botanist

On May 15, 1862, Darwin published *On the Various Contrivances by which British and Foreign Orchids Are Fertilised by Insects, and on the Good Effects of Intercrossing*. In January of that year, he had written to Asa Gray, "I have been ill with influenza (indeed we all have, for there have been 15 in bed in my household) & this has lost me 3 whole weeks, & delayed my little Orchid Book.—I fear that you expect in this opusculus much more than you will find—I look at it as a hobby-horse, which has given me great pleasure to ride."

Darwin, as we see, is dusting off a cherished talking point, that of downplaying in his letters the significance of a soon-to-be-published book. *The Origin of Species* was a mere abstract; the orchid book, just a pleasurable hobby distracting him from his real species work. And like *The Origin*, the orchid book made much larger claims for itself.

In the orchid book's introduction, Darwin writes, "The object of the following work is to show that the contrivances by which Orchids are fertilised, are as varied and almost as perfect as any of the most beautiful adaptations in the animal kingdom; and, secondly, to show that these contrivances have for their main object the fertilisation of the flowers by the pollen of another flower." Then he comes to the point:

> In my volume "On the Origin of Species" I have given only general reasons for my belief that it is apparently a universal law of nature that organic beings require an occasional cross with another individual; or, which is almost the same thing, that no hermaphrodite fertilises itself for a perpetuity of generations. Having been blamed for propounding this doctrine without giving ample facts, for which I had not, in that work, sufficient space, I wish to show that I have not spoken without having gone into details.[1]

So, according to Darwin, his orchid book was meant to fill in a specific evidentiary lacuna in the *Origin*, providing empirical confirmation for the proposition stated in the *Origin* that cross-fertilization is a necessity.

What Darwin's readers would not know is that the unpublished manuscript of his big book dealt with this very topic of crosses in a chapter titled "On the Possibility of All Organic Beings Occasionally Crossing." Darwin could have addressed this lacuna by simply publishing the big book, and in doing so he would have provided a far broader treatment of the subject. This chapter in the big book is full of examples of cross-fertilization in many kinds of organisms. The orchid book, in contrast, deals with only a single type of organism. Darwin could not hope to establish the need for cross-fertilization as a general law of nature by studying only one kind of organism.

As we will soon see, Darwin was less than transparent about the true purpose of the orchid book. He had another trick up his sleeve. But before we learn exactly what it was, we should observe how Darwin talked about his orchid book to his correspondents. In true Darwinian fashion, Darwin's false modesty engine went into overdrive as he alerted his correspondents to his orchid work.

On February 9, 1862, Darwin wrote to his publisher, John Murray: "I know not **in the least**, whether the Book will sell. If it prove a dead failure, I shall hold myself to a large extent responsible for having tempted you to publish with your eyes shut.—Perhaps there may be enough enthusiasts to prevent a dead failure."

Five days later he confided to his son William, "Whether my little Book has been worth writing, I know no more than the man in the moon." And then on March 7, he wrote to Hooker, "You will be disappointed in my little book: I have got to hate it, though the subject has fairly delighted me: I am an ass & always fancy at the time that others will care for what I care about: I am convinced its publication will be bad job for Murray."

Darwin seemed obsessed with lowering expectations about the value of his orchid work. But if he truly viewed it as so suspect in value, why did he put aside his big book on species to publish it?

Interestingly, as late as 1861 Darwin was still not committed to publishing his orchid research, for on September 28, he wrote to Hooker begging him to send as many specimens of orchids as he could. Didn't Darwin already have all those specimens? He explains to Hooker, "I never thought of publishing separately & therefore did not keep specimens in spirits." Darwin's decision to publish a separate monograph on orchids was an afterthought, so he had not preserved his orchid specimens after analyzing them. Now he needed them as the basis for woodcuts to illustrate his monograph, and Hooker, due to his position at the Royal Gardens at Kew, was his best source of getting orchid specimens fast.

As he neared publication, the self-flagellation continued. On March 11, Darwin wrote to his German correspondent H. G. Bronn. Darwin reported that he had made little progress on the big book because of being tempted away by other subjects. Then he reported on what he had been working on:

> In about a month's time I shall publish a little book on the Fertilisation of Orchids & on their Homologies,—of which I will send you a copy, as a mark of my sincere gratitude, for I do not suppose that the subject will interest you—I may add that if M. Schweizerbart should like to publish (but this is very improbable) a translation I would try & procure stereotype plates of the several woodcuts at no expense beyond the casting[.] But I doubt whether the Book would be worth translating though it contains I believe some new and curious facts.

On April 26, Darwin was back reporting to his son William, "Today, thank Heavens, I finished last revise of my accursed little orchid-Book, of which a copy shall be sent to you when it is out, but it will be stiff reading." It is difficult to understand how Darwin could report to Gray on the one hand that his orchid work was a hobby that gave him great pleasure, and then turn around and call his orchid book accursed. Neither is likely the whole truth.

On the May 15 publication day of the orchid book, Darwin wrote to Hooker, "You will not have time at present to read my orchid book: I never before felt half so doubtful about anything which I published: when you read it, do not fear 'punishing' me, if I deserve it."

But three days later, he had received some good news, and wrote again to Hooker: "You have pleased me much by what you say in regard to Bentham & Oliver approving of my book; for I had got a sort of nervousness & doubted whether I had made an egregious fool of myself, & concocted pleasant little stinging remarks for Reviews,—such as 'Mr. Darwin's head seems to have been turned by a certain degree of success, & he thinks that the most trifling observations are worth publication.'"

George Bentham was the president of the Linnean Society and Daniel Oliver was a professor of botany at University College, London. Their apparent approval carried some weight with Darwin (but see below). Darwin thus reported to Asa Gray on June 10: "The subject interested me, I know, beyond its real value; but I had lately got to think that I had made myself a complete fool by publishing in a semi-popular form. Now I shall confidently defy the world. I have heard that Bentham & Oliver approve of it; but I have heard the opinion of no one else, whose opinion is worth a farthing."

We see echoes here of Darwin's reaction to responses to the *Origin*: value the positive responses and ignore the negative. Fortunately for Darwin, the orchid book, as we will soon see, elicited overwhelmingly positive reviews, but not exactly in the way that Darwin hoped.

On May 23, Alfred Russel Wallace weighed in on the orchid book: "Many thanks for your most interesting book on the *Orchids*. I have read it through most attentively & really have been quite as much *staggered* by the wonderful adaptations you shew to exist in them as by the *Eye* in animals or any other complicated organs. I long to get into the country & have a look at some orchids guided by your *new lights*." (Emphasis in original.)

Despite Wallace's positive response, Darwin still replied to him the next day, "I am glad you approve of my little Orchid Book; but it has not been worth, I fear, the 10 months it has cost me: it was a hobby horse & so beguiled me." Similarly, Darwin replied to the news of Oliver's approval on June 8 with, "I am glad that you have read my orchis book & seem to approve of it; for I never published anything which I so much doubted whether it was worth publishing & indeed I still doubt."

As late as September 20, 1862, after the orchid book had been on the market for four months and was garnering praise in the botanical world, Darwin was still wallowing in self-effacement, writing to his cousin William Darwin Fox:

> I am *much* pleased & somewhat surprised at your liking my orchid-book: the Botanists praise it beyond its deserts, but hardly anyone, not a Botanist, except yourself, as far as I know, has cared for it. The subject interested me much, & was written almost by accident; for it was half written as a mere paper & then I found it too long, & thought I would risk publishing it separately. What you say about it, is very pleasant; for at one time I agreed with Lyell that I was an ass to publish it.

All this hand-wringing about the value of the orchid book and Darwin's reticence to publish it is disingenuous. As I will show, Darwin had a clear purpose for his orchid work and believed it would effectively meet the aims he had for it; but for reasons we will soon see, he wished to be coy about those aims, so he engaged in this almost pitiful display of self-flagellation as a distraction.

What was Darwin's true purpose? His friend Asa Gray hit upon it in a July 3 letter to Darwin: "I have just received and glanced at Bentham's address, and am amused to see how your beautiful *flank*-movement with the Orchid-book has nearly overcome his opposition to the Origin."

Apparently, Bentham had viewed the contrivances documented by Darwin whereby orchids ensure cross-fertilization by insects as providing the evidence for natural selection missing from the *Origin*. Darwin responded to Gray on July 23: "Of all the carpenters for knocking the right nail on the head, you are the very best: no one else has perceived that my chief interest in my orchid book, has been that it was a 'flank movement' on the enemy."

Darwin knew very well why he decided to publish his orchid book instead of completing and publishing the big book on species. The big book would not have addressed the criticisms leveled at the *Origin* by Darwin's "enemies." With the orchid book, Darwin tried to outflank those enemies by laying before them a detailed description of the exquisite contrivances found in orchids—thus hoping his readers would themselves draw the natural conclusion and see in these adaptations the power of natural selection at work. Perhaps they would then view his argument in the *Origin* in a new and more favorable light. The orchid book was in a sense a sneak attack on Darwin's adversaries—when they were expecting one thing (the big book) he put before them another (the orchid book). The orchid book was far more than a mere hobbyhorse of dubious scientific value. It might actually be Darwin's most important publication as it laid out in exquisite detail in a way no one else had ever done the unique anatomy and physiology of each orchid species and their correlation with various pollinators. As he wrote to John Murray on September 24, 1861, "I think this little volume will do good to the Origin."

So, was Darwin's flank movement successful? Before considering this, a more detailed assessment of Bentham's reaction is in order. A series of letters exchanged between Darwin and Bentham in 1863 sheds considerable doubt on whether Bentham really had warmed up to Darwin's species theory as much as Gray seemed to think. Bentham had asked Darwin for information about published reviews of the *Origin* for his anniversary address as president of the Linnean Society. Darwin responded on April 15, "I have run my eye over the Reviews & Notices on the Origin (amounting to about 90!) & very few are worth your notice." Bentham replied to Darwin on April 21: "For though I do not go so far as Jos. Hooker in the thorough adoption of all your hypotheses, and though I fully agree with John Mill and other such experienced logicians in the appreciation of your arguments still I do not feel competent to enter into the lists and argue upon the very limited observations I have myself made."

This disappointed Darwin and he responded to Bentham the next day: "You must allow me to differ in toto from you when you say you are not up to treat the whole subject. I cannot believe this, from what I hear of your Systematic knowledge."

A month later (May 21), Bentham called on that systematic knowledge to explain to Darwin his hesitations about natural selection. Bentham was troubled by the existence in the fossil record of organisms that do not seem to change over time. "It is too much for me to suppose that Natural Selection has had no opportunity for acting upon these when others which appear to have been in similar circumstances have by her agency altered so much that the common origin of northern and southern representatives is difficult to recognise." For Bentham, the observed immutability of a large number of species continued to haunt him, so he informed Darwin, "I feel that I am one of your converts but I cannot satisfy myself that I am right at all points, and therefore cannot go all lengths with you."

The very next day saw Darwin writing back to Bentham with an attempt at a solution to Bentham's concern. He expressed his gratitude at how far Bentham had gone with him and then addressed the problem:

> The objection, which you well put, of certain forms remaining unaltered through long time & space, is no doubt formidable in appearance & to a certain extent in reality according to my judgment.—But does not the difficulty rest much on our silently assuming that we know more than we do? I have literally found nothing so difficult as to try & always remember our ignorance. I am never weary when walking in any new adjoining district or country of reflecting how absolutely ignorant we are why certain old plants are not there present, & other new ones are & others in different proportions.

Once again, Darwin failed to accept evidence contrary to his theory as possible evidence against it. Whatever didn't fit was just due to our ignorance, rendering his theory essentially unfalsifiable. Darwin then concludes this letter with, "When we descend to details, we can prove that no one species has changed: nor can we prove that the supposed changes are beneficial which is the groundwork of the theory. Nor can we explain why some species have changed & others have not." I doubt Bentham found this response reassuring. He was prepared to go along with Darwin; he just needed to see evidence.

Reactions to the Orchid Book

We return to the question: Did the orchid book succeed as a flank movement? Gray thought it succeeded with Bentham. However, it seems not to have succeeded with Gray himself. In the same letter where he describes the orchid book as a flank movement, he writes, "If you grant an intelligent designer anywhere in Nature, you may be confident that he has something to do with the 'contrivances' in your Orchids." In other words, for his money, the many ingenious contrivances among orchids were just that, the work of an intelligent designer.

Gray was not alone. George Dickie was a Scottish botanist and Lecturer at King's College, Aberdeen. On May 30, 1862, he shared his reaction to the orchid book with Darwin: "I have read your work with much satisfaction, & while subscribing to your remarks—page 28—respecting adaptations, I frankly confess that I cannot comprehend how they can be explained by 'natural selection' or what relation they have to that view."

Dickie refers here to Darwin's discussion of *orchis pyramidalis* or the pyramidal orchid. Darwin had written, "As in no other plant, or indeed in hardly any animal, can adaptations of one part to another, and of the whole to other organised beings widely remote in the scale of nature, be named more perfect than those presented by this Orchis, it may be worth while briefly to sum them up."[2] Darwin then details all the exquisite adaptations characteristic of this most complex of orchids. It is visited by both diurnal and nocturnal moths and butterflies, and thus has both beautiful violet flowers to attract the diurnal fertilizers and a strong foxy odor to attract nocturnal fertilizers; the sepal and petals form a hood that protects the anthers and the stigmatic surface from the weather; it is organized so that the nectar can be sucked only slowly by the moths and butterflies that frequent the flower, allowing time for pollen transfer to their bodies for transport to another flower. Darwin describes these and many other exquisite details too numerous to reproduce here. Dickie was obviously impressed with all this, but failed to see how something so seemingly designed could be accounted for by the process of natural selection.

Many reviews of the orchid book struck a similar note, hailing the work as perhaps Darwin's most important scientific contribution, but a contribution not in support of his theory in the *Origin*. An anonymous reviewer wrote in the *Sheffield Daily Telegraph*:

> As a valuable addition to our knowledge of the structure and habits of this exceedingly beautiful and singular order of plants, we warmly commend the book to the notice of such of our readers as may be interested in the investigation. But here our commendation must cease. This is the first installment of those facts which have been so long promised, and which we were assured would supply abundant proofs of the truth of Mr. Darwin's assertions with regard to the "origin of species" by means of "*natural selection*," or the preservation of favoured races in the struggle for life. So far as the settlement of that question is concerned, we see no reason for thinking that the present volume will at all help Mr. Darwin in establishing, to the satisfaction of our more experienced Naturalists, his favourite theory. The notion of the origin of species by natural selection, we must, therefore, still continue to regard as an ingenious mistake—incorrect in its facts—unscientific in its method, and mischievous in its tendency.[3]

Another anonymous reviewer in the *Annals and Magazine of Natural History* agreed:

> It is Mr. Darwin's object in the present work to clear up the mystery hanging over the process of impregnation in the Orchids, in order to apply the results thus obtained to the support of certain opinions advanced in his book on the 'Origin of Species.' In the practical part of his task, the explanation of the mode of fertilization, it seems to us that he is completely successful; but whether the arguments deduced therefrom on the general question be equally valid, is another affair.[4]

After disagreeing with Darwin's law that nature abhors perpetual self-fertilization, the reviewer continued, "Apart from this theory and that of 'natural selection,' which we cannot think is much advanced by the present volume, we must welcome this work of Mr. Darwin's as a most important and interesting addition to botanical literature."[5]

Other reviewers went well beyond merely questioning the connection between the orchid book and natural selection. R. Vaughan entered this discussion in a review appearing in the *British Quarterly Review*: "No one acquainted with even the very rudiments of botany will have any difficulty in understanding the book before us, and no one without such acquaintance need hesitate to commence the study of it. For, in the first place, it is full of the marvels of Divine handiwork."[6]

Darwin's pigeon-fancier friend, William Tegetmeier, thought that believers in the doctrine of secondary causes and those who followed the natural theology doctrine of William Paley could both find support for their views in the orchid book. In fact, he commented, the latter "may find in its pages new and marvellous instances of design, by the aid of which he may seek to repel the ardent assailants."[7] The *British and Foreign Medico-Chirurgical Review* weighed in, "To those whose delight it is to dwell upon the manifold instances of intelligent design which everywhere surround us, this book will be a rich storehouse."[8] And the *Saturday Review* responded to the question of how cross-fertilization is assured in orchids with, "By contrivances so wonderful and manifold, that, after reading Mr. Darwin's enumeration of them, we feel a certain awe steal over the mind, as in presence of a new revelation of the mysteriousness of creation."[9]

Similarly, G. D. Campbell, the Duke of Argyll, believed the orchid book illustrated "in no ordinary degree the beautiful adaptations which are seen in plants, and is calculated to exalt our ideas of the wonder-working Jehovah."[10] And Darwin's seeming reticence to ascribe the contrivances in orchids to a divine designer met with disapproval from an anonymous reviewer in the *Literary Churchman*: "We thank Mr. Darwin for putting before us so clearly these wonderful details of the workings of Nature, and so for helping us to admire God in His works.... But we regret to find Mr. Darwin slow in ascribing to Him alone to whom praise is due, the wonders at which even he stands aghast."[11]

Review after review of Darwin's orchid book sounded the same theme. Darwin had provided evidence not for natural selection, but for natural theology.

As the noted Anglican priest and Cambridge professor Charles Kingsley would put it some twelve years later in his *Westminster Sermons,* Darwin's orchid book was "a most valuable addition to natural Theology."[12] And Henry Griffiths, in the year Darwin died (1882) would write, "In his fascinating work on '*The Various Contrivances by which British and Foreign Orchids are Fertilized by Insects,*' Dr. Darwin seems to have exhausted his vocabulary, in emphasizing the notion of design."[13]

And then there was this from M. J. Berkeley in the *London Review*: "Most certainly, so far from justifying anyone in considering the author as heretofore as a heathen man or an heretic for the enunciation of his theory, the whole series of the Bridgewater Treatises will not afford so striking a set of arguments in favour of natural theology as those which he has displayed."[14]

Francis Henry Egerton, the 8th Earl of Bridgewater, had funded in his will the development of a series of treatises designed to demonstrate the power, wisdom, and goodness of God as manifested in creation. Eight treatises were published between 1833 and 1836. If Darwin believed anything about his species work, its purpose was (in popular imagination at least) to counteract this central aim of the Bridgewater Treatises. But Berkeley read Darwin's orchid book as surpassing these treatises in providing evidence for God's guiding intelligence in the design of the organic world.

Surely nothing could be further from Darwin's aim in writing the orchid book. But maybe not. Darwin had written to his publisher, John Murray, on September 21, 1861, to feel out Murray on the possibility of publishing the orchid book. In this letter Darwin surprisingly wrote, "The facts are new & have been collected during 20 years & strike me as curious. Like a Bridgewater Treatise the chief object is to show the perfection of the many contrivances in Orchids."

Darwin here seems to suggest that his orchid book might actually make a contribution to natural theology. I have never seen this letter of Darwin cited in any other literature about him. But as we will see shortly, it may well represent Darwin's real feelings about his orchid work.

None of the reviewers of the orchid book, with the possible exception of Charles Kingsley, were close associates of Darwin. What would associates like Joseph Hooker or Asa Gray, both trained botanists, have to say about *Orchids*?

Hooker wrote an extensive review laid out over three editions of the *Gardeners' Chronicle* where he enumerated in almost as much detail as Darwin himself the exquisite adaptations for cross-fertilization characteristic of different genera of orchids. Hooker began, "Ever since the publication of the 'Origin of Species,' the public have waited impatiently for the promised 'pièces justificatives,' by which its author himself announced that the theory propounded in that work must stand or fall."[15] According to Hooker, some accepted Darwin's theory without all the facts and evidence due to their own work or a previous leaning toward Lamarck. Others awaited the appearance of detailed observations before drawing a final conclusion. Hooker then continues:

> Such being the case, the appearance of the present work, which is not professedly put forth as a prop to Mr. Darwin's hypothesis, will be regarded by many as a disappointment; but on the other hand, by those interested in the study to which it relates, and by a still larger number who condemn the "Origin" while they admire its author, his return with undiminished powers of observation to cautious induction from positive facts, will be welcomed with acclamation.[16]

Hooker seems here to tactfully and tacitly admit that the orchid book did not serve as an adequate follow-up to the *Origin*, even though those who condemned the *Origin* might find the book of great importance.

This interpretation is reinforced in what follows. Hooker asserts that Darwin had been most successful in two of his three objectives.

First, he showed that orchids are fertilized exclusively by insects, and though the flowers are hermaphrodite, they are fertilized by the pollen of other flowers. Second, Darwin demonstrated that the study of organic beings can be just as interesting to those who hold to the action of secondary laws as to those who view the fine details of structure as being the result of the action of the Creator. But, "Whether... his third object, that of supporting his hypothesis of the origin of species by natural selection, is attained, will no doubt lead to much diversity of opinion."[17]

But what was Hooker's opinion? He is noncommittal: "Upon this point we have earnestly and assiduously laboured to arrive at an unprejudiced opinion, feeling pretty well assured that this great subject must be treated in Mr. Darwin's forthcoming volumes very much as it is here."[18] In other words, the final assessment of Darwin's theory of natural selection would need to await the publication of the big book on speciation by natural selection, which Hooker clearly still expected. The orchid book at best laid out a method for how to approach the subject through the process of detailed observation. It did not, however, itself prove the wonder-working powers that Darwin had ascribed to natural selection.

Gray, not surprisingly, was more transparent. He ends an extensive ten-page review with, "We cannot close without an expression of gratitude to Mr. Darwin for having brought back teleological considerations into botany."[19] Gray complains that botany and zoology had become too morphological, too concerned with the forms of living organisms to the detriment of their function. And correcting this imbalance was, in his view, the importance of the orchid book:

> In this fascinating book on the fertilization of Orchids, and in his paper explaining the meaning of dimorphism in hermaphrodite flowers, Mr. Darwin,—who does not pretend to be a botanist—has given new eyes to botanists, and inaugurated a new era in the science. Hereafter teleology must go hand in hand with morphology, functions must be studied as well as forms, and useful ends presumed, whether ascertained or not, in every permanent modification of every organ. In all this we *faithfully* believe that both

> natural science and natural theology will richly gain, and equally gain, whether we view each varied form as original, or whether we come to conclude, with Mr. Darwin, that they are derived;—the grand and most important inference of *design in nature* being drawn from the same data, subject to similar difficulties, and enforced by nearly the same considerations, in the one case as in the other.[20]

Darwin may have introduced his orchid book as a flank movement on the enemy, designed to provide the evidence for natural selection missing from both the *Origin* and his unfinished big book manuscript, but in fact it did the opposite. And as his note to his publisher, John Murray, indicates, there were at least moments when Darwin was well aware of this.

The aid and comfort the book lends to natural theology is substantive. Darwin richly explores a variety of ingenious orchid features and nowhere offers a plausible explanation of how natural selection working on random variations might have constructed them in the absence of purposive ingenuity. Further, the term "contrivances," found in the book's title and then repeated at least a dozen times throughout the work, seems to support natural theology. A contrivance, by definition, is something un-natural—the product of artifice. As the Cambridge Dictionary puts it, a contrivance is "the act of intentionally arranging for something to happen by clever planning, or something that is arranged in this way," or alternately, "a clever device or object that has been invented for a particular purpose."[21] Thus, it would seem that if the exquisite adaptations in orchids are "contrivances," they must be something produced by an intentional agent.

The father of natural theology, William Paley, had used the term "contrivance" in this way in his own work. Darwin, on the other hand, wrote in his autobiography, "The old argument of design in nature, as given by Paley, which formerly seemed to me so conclusive, fails, now that the law of natural selection has been discovered."[22] But there is more than his frank letter to Murray to suggest that Darwin was conflicted on this point.

In the orchid book, Darwin wrote, "In my examination of Orchids, hardly any fact has struck me so much as the endless diversity of structure,—the prodigality of resources,—for gaining the very same end, namely, the fertilisation of one flower by the pollen of another. The fact to a certain extent is intelligible on the principle of natural selection."[23] He never walks this back in the book, but there is this curious feature of the work: near the beginning of the book he writes, "The object of the following work is to show that the contrivances by which Orchids are fertilised, are as varied and almost as perfect as any of the most beautiful adaptations in the animal kingdom,"[24] and then he makes frequent reference in the remainder of the book to the *perfection* of the contrivances in orchids.

Why is this curious? Dov Ospovat has argued that early on in Darwin's career, the Victorian naturalist believed in the perfection of adaptations due to his grounding in Paleyan natural theology. But according to Ospovat, due to the influence of Malthus, Darwin later gave up on the idea of perfect adaptation, preferring to view adaptation as merely relative, as natural selection mindlessly adapts certain organisms to their environment slightly better than others, but never in a way that could be construed as perfect.[25] Yet in the orchid book, Darwin does appeal to the idea of perfection. This suggests that as late as 1862, he had not fully divested himself of the influence of natural theology. Darwin, it would seem, had more in common with William Paley than he likely would have admitted.

After Orchids

With the orchid book in print, Darwin was free to return to the big book on species, with its promised evidence for the creative powers of natural selection working on random variations. Instead he expanded just the first two chapters into a two-volume monograph dealing with variation under domestication. So, no macroevolution, and no natural selection. Just artificial selection in pursuit of new breeds.

On September 20, 1862, he told his cousin Fox, "As soon as I get home, if we all can but keep well, I must return to variation under domestication." A month later he was writing to Gray, "Now that we are home again, I have begun dull steady work on 'Variation under Domestication'; but alas & alas pottering over plants is much better sport." He did, however, complete his book on variation under domestication, publishing this monograph in 1868. That domestic animals and plants vary is undeniable, and Darwin could provide numerous empirical observations to support it. But the rest of his promised big book—especially the parts dealing with the action of natural selection—remained an unpublished afterthought.

Yet people still wanted to see it. On July 6, 1868, Darwin wrote to Alphonse de Candolle:

> You ask me when I shall publish on the "Variation of Species in a State of Nature." I have had the MS. for another volume almost ready during several years, but I was so much fatigued by my last book that I determined to amuse myself by publishing a short essay on the "Descent of Man."... Now this essay has branched out into some collateral subjects, and I suppose will take me more than a year to complete. I shall then begin on "Species", but my health makes me a very slow workman.[26]

Here Darwin admits to the near-completion of his species manuscript, but, he says, due to fatigue from publishing the *Variation of Plants and Animals under Domestication*, he has decided to dabble in a short essay about human evolution. That short essay turned into the 300,000-word *Descent of Man and Selection in Relation to Sex* published in 1871. If Darwin was truly too fatigued to complete an almost completed manuscript, where did he find the energy to publish his massive work on human evolution and sexual selection? Once again, Darwin makes excuses for the delay in publication of his highly anticipated big book on speciation by natural selection. While he indicates to Candolle his desire to get back to it after the human evolution book, he never did. Darwin ultimately abandoned the project, and did so because, I would submit, he knew he could not make a convincing empirical case for the creative powers he had claimed for natural selection.

During the balance of his career, Darwin would amuse himself with the study of insectivorous and climbing plants, emotions and facial expressions in humans and apes, and earthworms. Though he viewed these subjects as connected to his evolutionary work, Darwin, counter to the widespread Darwinian mythology of today, never established the theory of evolution by natural selection in any empirically convincing way.

Up until publication of *The Origin of Species* in 1859, Darwin believed he was on the verge of a revolutionary new theory in natural history that would bring him fame and establish him as one of the leading men of science. Yet his confidence that he could actually pull this off flagged, and he dragged his feet until being goaded into publication by Lyell and by the prospect of losing priority when Wallace's manuscript arrived from Southeast Asia. Darwin downplayed expectations by informing his readers that the *Origin* was a mere abstract of a larger work on species that he hoped to publish shortly after the *Origin.* But when the criticisms of the abstract came in and Darwin realized his big book would not effectively address those criticisms, he abandoned the idea of publishing the big book and turned instead to orchids.

He hoped that documenting the amazing variety of exquisite adaptations for cross-fertilization in orchids would convince readers of the ability of natural selection to drive the evolution of new species. But this largely backfired when many of Darwin's readers, including even some leading scientists at least partially sympathetic to his evolutionary project, hailed the orchid book as supplying evidence not for natural selection but for natural theology and design in nature.

The man whose name is today synonymous with naturalistic evolutionary theory and natural selection knew, it would seem, that he couldn't find and present the crucial confirming evidence for his theory in his own lifetime. The notion that he did so, and that the decades following his death were a mere mopping-up operation, is the mythology. The reality is very different, and the tell is that Darwin, a master bluffer, never showed his hand. The big book would wait a century before it appeared, and when it did, the very lacuna that existed in the *Origin* was to be found in the big book. Where cogent confirming evidence for the creative powers of natural selection were called for, there was instead only talk of geographical distribution, microevolution of domesticated breeds via artificial selection, and imaginative just-so stories about bears evolving into whales and such.

Persons chiefly concerned with scientific truth and with little interest in historical accuracy might, of course, shrug all this off, concluding that while Darwin may have failed to deliver the confirming evidence, undoubtedly the scientific research over the next several decades succeeded spectacularly. I would argue that this too is mythology.

I addressed this in some detail in my previous book, *The Mystery of Evolutionary Mechanisms: Darwinian Biology's Grand Narrative of Triumph and the Subversion of Religion*, where I traced the development of a grand narrative of Darwinian triumph throughout the historical development of evolutionary biology. I point readers there for an extended treatment of the subject. But the final chapter of the present book will provide a quick flyover of the growing problems facing modern evolutionary theory, problems that, taken together, suggest that it is a paradigm in profound crisis, even if still borne along by the sort of institutional inertia that historian of science Thomas Kuhn ably described in *The Structure of Scientific Revolutions*.

The final chapter also will take a look at how the distortions of Darwinian mythology have influenced issues of race, gender, and our understanding of the fundamental nature of reality.

8. Demythologizing Darwin

As previous chapters show, Darwinian mythology has significantly distorted our view of the person and work of a fascinating and enigmatic Victorian figure. Charles Darwin, for all his astute observational work, did not solve the riddle of the origin of species. But the prevailing view that he did, or that he at least laid a firm empirical foundation for the solution, has overridden attempts to encounter Darwin on more nuanced historical terms. This final chapter will seek to rescue other aspects of Darwin and his work from the distorting influence of Darwinian mythology. This includes Darwin's views on slavery and race, gender and sexual selection, and the fundamental nature of scientific inquiry, the latter having been negatively influenced by the prevailing Darwinian mythology. On all these points, the Darwinian mythology has stunted authentic scientific development by perpetuating certain ideological commitments in the guise of science, with potentially harmful social consequences.

Darwin on Slavery

Slavery had been abolished in England before Darwin was born, and he hailed from a long line of strong abolitionists, especially on his mother's side; many members of the Unitarian Wedgwood family were active members of abolitionist movements. It is not surprising then to find that Darwin himself had a strong aversion to slavery. This is confirmed in the *Journal of Researches* where Darwin describes his horror at encountering slavery in Brazil during the *Beagle* voyage:

> On the 19th of August we finally left the shores of Brazil. I thank God, I shall never again visit a slave country. To this day, if I hear a distant scream, it recalls with painful vividness my feelings, when passing a house near Pernambuco, I heard the most pitiable moans, and could not but suspect that some poor slave was being tortured, yet knew that I was as powerless as a child even to remonstrate. I suspected that these moans were from a tortured slave, for I was told that this was the case in another instance. Near Rio de Janeiro I lived opposite to an old lady, who kept screws to crush the fingers of her female slaves. I have stayed in a house where a young household mulatto, daily and hourly, was reviled, beaten, and persecuted enough to break the spirit of the lowest animal. I have seen a little boy, six or seven years old, struck thrice with a horsewhip (before I could interfere) on his naked head, for having handed me a glass of water not quite clean.[1]

Darwin continues in this passage to recount many more horrors he witnessed in slave countries. The brutality of the slave system was clearly sickening to someone so sensitive to human suffering.

Darwin's revulsion from slavery is central to the argument made by Adrian Desmond and James Moore in *Darwin's Sacred Cause* that Darwin's evolutionary work was motivated primarily by a desire to challenge the polygenist views of human origins so central to the racist worldview of creationists like Louis Agassiz. If human racial groups were each created separately by God, it was easy to argue that white people were created superior to black and brown races and represented the crowning glory of God's creation. Darwin's monogenist view, according to Desmond and Moore, challenged this notion by bringing all human racial groups together under the umbrella of descent from a common ancestor.

But as Ibram Kendi has shown, monogenism and natural selection were also employed in support of racist ideology. Evolutionists could and did argue that natural selection acting on geographically separate populations would produce varying degrees of fitness among racial groups, with Europeans, not surprisingly, representing the most evolutionarily advanced race.[2] Racism was not the property only of the polygenists. Contrary to Desmond and Moore, I see no evidence in all the narration Darwin provides in his correspondence regarding the development of his species theory that he ever explicitly or implicitly ties his species work to an anti-slavery or anti-racist agenda.[3]

One feels that, by arguing for an anti-racist agenda as the primary motivating factor in Darwin's work, Desmond and Moore have seized on a contemporary academically salient issue in order to paint Darwin and his work in a favorable light. Who wouldn't champion such a strong advocate of racial justice and reconciliation? But I fear Desmond and Moore have greatly overstated their case due to their fidelity to Darwinian mythology.[4] Darwin was a product of his time, not ours, and as we will see below, was himself thoroughly racist and, moreover, appeared to view his racist conception of different people groups as confirming evidence of his evolutionary theory.

Darwin's aversion to slavery, it would seem, was rooted not in any ideas of universal human equality, human exceptionalism, and inherent human dignity, but instead in an emotional reaction to slavery's brutality. He was famously sensitive to all forms of suffering and cruelty. In his later years, he and Emma were actively involved in anti-vivisection movements. And his Cambridge friend, John Maurice Herbert, remembered how Darwin once said he would give up shooting after coming across a bird shot the day before that was still alive and in agony. Herbert also remembers Darwin leaving a dog show for fear of watching the masters treat their dogs harshly if they disobeyed. And it is in the context of recalling Darwin's aversion to animal cruelty that Herbert also notes Darwin's aversion to slavery.[5] Darwin's squeamishness even extended to wholly humanitarian situations. He could not become a doctor because the requirement to observe surgery turned his stomach.

Desmond and Moore emphasize Darwin's positive experience with a former slave as formative for his anti-slavery views. While at Edinburgh, the teenage Darwin took taxidermy lessons in bird stuffing from a former slave who had been brought to Scotland from Guyana by a Charles Waterton. Darwin learned much from him and fondly recalled his bird-stuffing teacher in his autobiography: "By the way, a negro lived in Edinburgh, who had travelled with Waterton and gained his livelihood by stuffing birds, which he did excellently; he gave me lessons for payment, and I used often to sit with him, for he was a very pleasant and intelligent man."[6]

This was clearly a positive relationship, but we must not fall into the Darwin-could-not-have-been-racist-because-he-had-a-black-friend trap. Darwin's views on slavery and race were far more conflicted, as his views on the Civil War make clear.

As one who reviled slavery, we might expect Darwin to have sided fully with the Union cause during the war. Asa Gray, as a New Englander, was of course a staunch supporter of the Union. But letters written between Darwin, Gray, and Hooker during the Civil War years portray Darwin in a more ambiguous light. For example, Darwin wrote to Gray on January 22, 1862:

> Now for a few words on politics; but they shall be few, for we shall no longer agree, & alas & alas, I shall never receive another kind message from Mrs. Gray. I must own that the speeches & actions recently of your leading men (I regard little the newspapers), and especially the Boston Dinner have quite turned my stomach. I refer to Wilkes' being made a Hero for boarding an unarmed vessel.—to the Judges advice to him—& to your Governor triumphing at a shot being fired, right or wrong, across the bows of a British vessel. It is well to make a clean breast of it at once; & I have begun to think whether it would not be well for the peace of the world, if you were to split up into two or three nations. On the other hand I cannot bear the thought of the Slave-holders being triumphant.

Darwin here is responding to Gray's positive reaction to the Trent Affair. On November 8, 1861, Charles Wilkes, a US naval officer, captured two Confederate envoys sailing on a British mail ship, the *Trent*. The Confederate envoys had been sent by Jefferson Davis to Britain on a diplomatic mission to seek recognition of the Confederacy by Britain and to open up British markets for Southern cotton. Wilkes was not operating under official orders when he stopped the British ship and went aboard to seize the envoys. This action sparked a diplomatic crisis between the US and Britain as Britain accused the

US of violating British neutrality in the war. Clearly, Gray viewed Wilkes as a hero, while Darwin saw this action as an affront to British sovereignty. Though not wanting the slave-holding southerners to win the war, Darwin didn't seem to think ending Southern slavery worth the bloodshed required to do so.

For his part, Hooker had somewhat negative views on American democracy that Darwin at least in part appeared to share. From March 20–22, 1862, Hooker had been a guest of Edward James Herbert, the third Earl of Powis, at his Walcot Hall estate in Shropshire. He described his experience to Darwin on March 23:

> I had a very profitable stay at Walcot considering all things & came away with food for much reflection. I could not make up my mind to stay over Sunday, though kindly pressed with real English hospitality—Some of the family are very nice—all the Ladies particularly so, the Servants perfection (such Nat. selection of flunkies)—the food good and plenty.... it does one good to go to such places rarely, gives one much food for reflection & will add a chapter to my posthumous work "On the principles which regulate the development of an Aristocracy."

Hooker seemed to think that natural selection would inevitably lead to the development of a class of superior men in whom the leadership of a country ought to be entrusted while at the same time producing a class of people suited for subservience ("flunkies"). American democracy and its ideal of equality was therefore, in his view, completely inconsistent with nature.

He expressed these very views to Darwin on November 26, 1862:

> The more I reflect, the more sure I am that America will never settle until she has the equivalent of an Aristocracy (used in the best sense) wherefrom to chuse able Governors & statesmen. There is no more certain fruits of your doctrines than this—that the laws of nature lead infallibly to an aristocracy as the only security for a *settled condition of improvement*—What has prevented America having one of same sort hitherto?, but the incessant pouring in of democratic elements from the West—which has prevented the sorting of the masses, & frustrated all good effects of Natural Selection.

A month later, on December 21, Hooker told Darwin that he was reading Alexis de Tocqueville's *Democracy in America* but did not agree with it. Tocqueville assumed that democracy in America had been a success, but in Hooker's view, America had never had enough cohesion to be pronounced either a success or a failure. Regardless, Hooker could not see how democracy could resist the effects of natural selection. In his view, "a Govt must always eventually get into the hands of an individual, or family, or a class—or there is no truth in Nat: Selection."

How would Darwin respond to Hooker's use of his theory to argue against the naturalness of democracy? In his January 22 letter to Gray, Darwin seemed amused by Hooker's views: "Here is a good joke, my book on Nat. Selection, he says, has made him an aristocrat, in fact—he thinks breeding—the high breeding of the aristocracy—of the highest importance." Yet when writing to Hooker three days later, Darwin's tone had changed:

> Your notion of the aristocrats being ken-speckle,[7] & the best men of a good lot being thus easily selected is new to me & striking. The Origin having made you, in fact, a jolly old Tory, made us all laugh heartily. I have sometimes speculated on this subject: primogeniture is dreadfully opposed to selection,—suppose the first-born Bull was necessarily made by each farmer the begetter of his stock! On the other hand, as you say, ablest men are continually raised to peerage & get crossed with the older Lord-breeds—& the Lords continually select the most beautiful and charming women out of the lower ranks; so that a good deal of indirect selection improves the Lords. Certainly I agree with you, the present American row has a very toryfying influence on us all.

While Darwin objected to Hooker's characterization of the connection between natural selection and aristocracy, he nevertheless agreed that the Civil War reflected badly on the viability of American democracy. By December 24 of that year, Darwin could say to Hooker, "I like to hear your notions about America; I think Asa Gray would consider them two or three degrees more atrocious than mine. Slavery draws me one day one way & another day another way.

But certainly the Yankees are utterly detestable towards us.—What a new idea of Struggle for existence being necessary to try & purge a government! I daresay it is very true."

Despite his feelings about slavery, Darwin could not give a full-throated endorsement to the Union's attempt to defeat the slave system and save American democracy. Writing to Gray on October 16, Darwin expressed his great concern about the effects of the war: "This war of yours, however it may end, is a fearful evil to the whole world; & its evil effect will, I must think, be felt for years.—I can see already it has produced wide spread feeling in favour of aristocracy & Monarchism: no one in England will speak for years in favour of the people governing themselves."

Hooker was not so empathetic, writing to Darwin on March 10, "His (Gray's) whole letters are steeped in the most inordinate self esteem as a Yankee. He can allow of no difference of opinion, is blind to everything, & what is worse brags like the greatest bullies amongst them." Though Darwin's views on the Civil War were far more ambivalent than Hooker's, that he was unable to champion the cause of the Union to the extent that Gray did does raise questions about just how strong his anti-slavery feelings were. For if the US did split up, an outcome Darwin entertained as a possible good, slavery would have continued in the independent Confederacy.

Interestingly, despite Darwin's aversion to the slave system, some readers of the *Origin* viewed him as almost promoting it, as we see in a very brief announcement of the *Origin's* publication appearing in the *Hartford* (Connecticut) *Courant*. According to this anonymous writer, "Darwin's observations of the habits of certain ants to make slaves of the *black race* (dominant race being *red*) will gratify the South, and make Darwin a safe book to travel with in those parts."[8] On the eve of the Civil War, an American writer was able to make a direct connection between Darwin's example of slave-making ants and the American institution of slavery! I doubt Darwin would have wanted his book to be considered "safe" to travel with in the American South. Indeed, he once noted to his cousin Fox in a September 4, 1850, letter his disapproval of how Louis Agassiz's lectures about the separate creation of human racial groups brought "comfort to the slave-holding Southerns." Nonetheless, Darwin may himself have provided a similar kind of southern comfort.

Darwin on Race

Just because Darwin held anti-slavery views does not mean he was anti-racist. The man born the same day as Darwin, Abraham Lincoln, ended slavery in America but still held to the racist view that freed blacks could not effectively integrate into American society, and explored the possibility of repatriation of them to Africa. So to what extent was Darwin influenced by British racism even in the face of his anti-slavery views?

Darwin wrote to his sister Catherine during the *Beagle* voyage sometime between May and July 1833:

> I was told before leaving England, that after living in Slave countries, all my opinions would be altered; the only alteration I am aware of is forming a much higher estimate of the Negros character.—it is impossible to see a negro & not feel kindly towards him; such cheerful, open honest expressions & such fine muscular bodies; I never saw any of the diminutive Portuguese with their murderous countenances, without almost wishing for Brazil to follow the example of Hayti; & considering the enormous healthy looking black population, it will be wonderful if at some future day it does not take place.

Though registering a positive attitude toward black people and wishing for Brazil to experience a slave revolt like that which occurred in Haiti around 1800, Darwin nevertheless reinforces racist stereotypes here about black people as more emotional and possessing superior physical strength. And his comment about the murderous countenances of the Portuguese Brazilians betrays an attitude of white British superiority.

Darwin's racism shone forth in other unexpected places as well. In an October 1845 letter to Charles Lyell, Darwin relates a report he heard about lice that occur on negroes born in North America—they are larger and blacker than European lice, the latter apparently unable to live on negroes. "From some analogous statements made to me with respect to the men of the Sandwich islands," wrote Darwin, "I am inclined to believe there may be some truth in these statements." Darwin is referring to a story he was told by a whale boat's surgeon he had met during the *Beagle* voyage. The surgeon, whom Darwin describes as "a rather worthless, slightly educated man," told him that if the lice of Sandwich Islanders strayed onto the bodies of the English, the lice died within three or four days.[9] One might be suspicious of the veracity of this story given Darwin's negative evaluation of the surgeon's intellect, but Darwin concluded that the surgeon's lack of education made it less likely that the story was invented. If different racial groups harbor different parasites, as Darwin clearly wanted to believe, it would emphasize their biological differences rather than their unity.

We see another example of Darwin's racism in his casual use of the N-word. For example, Darwin's older brother Erasmus had for a time taken up with Harriett Martineau, a progressive British writer and socialite. In a November 9, 1836, letter to his sister Caroline, Darwin warns:

> Our only protection from so admirable a sister-in-law is in her working him too hard. He begins to perceive, (to use his own expression) he shall be not much better than her "nigger."—Imagine poor Erasmus a nigger to so philosophical & energetic a lady.—How pale & woe begone he will look.—She already takes him to task about his idleness—She is going some day to explain to him her notions about marriage—Perfect equality of rights is part of her doctrine. I must doubt whether it will be equality in practice. We must pray for our poor "nigger."

The sexism revealed in this passage aside, Darwin's casual use of a vulgar racialized term to refer to what he viewed as a hen-pecked brother betrays a real insensitivity to the utter seriousness of the slave system and its racist underpinnings.

And this is no isolated example. Darwin addressed a May 25, 1848, letter to his wife Emma "My dear Mammy." He then signed this letter, "Your old nigger." Charles and Emma employed the N-word as a playful term for each other, a striking display of insensitivity to the context in which this term arose, a context that produced such unspeakable violence and misery.[10] One might argue that Darwin does not employ the N-word in reference to black people in these examples, but such is not the case in a May 11, 1859, letter to Hooker regarding what Hooker felt was Darwin's obscure writing style in the *Origin*. "Thank you for telling me about obscurity of style," Darwin wrote. "But on my life no nigger with lash over him could have worked harder at clearness than I have."

How many slaves living under the lash would have loved to have had Darwin's problems! Darwin was a man of his times. And a sense of white British superiority was the order of the day.

Darwin knew that his and Emma's use of the N-word for each other was insensitive, for he occasionally employed an abbreviation for the racist epithet. For instance, he wrote to Emma on June 25, 1846, "Your very long letter of Monday has delighted me, with all the particulars about the children—how happy they seem: I will forward it to Caroline, though twice it has 'my dearest N.'"

Emma often started her letters to her husband "My Dearest N," and Darwin knew that his strongly abolitionist sister, Caroline, would find this objectionable. It should have been objectionable to Darwin too, but clearly wasn't. Charles and Emma casually employed slave system tropes in both their personal and scientific lives. Shortly before their marriage, while Darwin was in London securing a house, Emma wrote (on January 3, 1839), "I can fancy how proud you are in your big house, ordering breakfast in the front drawing room dinner in the dining room tea in the back drawing room & luncheon in the study, & occasionally looking through your window on your estate & plantations."

Emma imagines Darwin as a plantation owner! For his part, when Darwin was observing slave-making ants, he wrote to Hooker on July 13, 1858, "I have seen a migration from one nest to another of the slave-makers carrying their slaves (who are *house* & not field niggers) in their mouths." Darwin understood the world around him through the lens of the slave system that he says he so abhorred, and yet here he blithely jokes about the distinction between house and field slaves.

It is concerning the lengths Desmond and Moore go to downplay the evidence of Darwin's casual racism: "Marriage as metaphorical slavery was a tolerable joke in a family whose abolitionism was absolute, and Emma settled into calling Charles her 'nigger', while he made himself her 'happy slave.'"[11] To whom was this joke tolerable? Maybe to Desmond and Moore, but certainly not to those who experienced the horrors of slavery. There is no need to apologize for Darwin's casual racism. It is a part of who he was. And its casual nature betrays a shocking lack of awareness of his own implicit racial biases.

Darwin's casual racism became more overt in his published writings when it came to his views toward the indigenous peoples he met during the *Beagle* voyage. On a previous voyage of the *Beagle*, Captain FitzRoy had brought three captives back to England from Tierra del Fuego to civilize and Christianize them. During Darwin's voyage, the three Fuegians were returned to their homeland along with a Christian missionary to set up a missionary outpost in Tierra del Fuego and ostensibly civilize and Christianize the local population. The plan did not go well. The three Fuegians from the *Beagle* quickly reverted to their indigenous ways and the missionary had to be rescued by the *Beagle* crew for fear of his life. Darwin wrote to his sister Caroline from the Falkland Islands in April of 1833:

> We here saw the native Fuegian; an untamed savage is I really think one of the most extraordinary spectacles in the world.—the difference between a domesticated & wild animal is far more strikingly marked in man.—in the naked barbarian, with his body coated with paint, whose very gestures, whether they may be peaceible [sic] or hostile are unintelligible, with difficulty we see a fellow creature.

Darwin never denied the full humanity of indigenous peoples, but by using terms like savage and barbarian, he clearly viewed them as inherently inferior to "civilized" Englishmen.

Interestingly, Charles Kingsley wrote to Darwin on January 30, 1862, with a creative solution for why there seemed to be no intermediate forms between apes and humans as Darwin's theory would seem to predict. Kingsley pointed out that human mythology from around the world is full of such creatures, and "every myth has an original nucleus of truth." Kingsley fully believed that these mythological creatures pointed back to some real form of life intermediate between humans and apes that no longer existed (except in the form of myth) because they died out by natural selection before the superior white race.

Darwin responded on February 6, "It is a very curious subject, that of the old myths; but you naturally with your classical & old-world knowledge lay more stress on such beliefs, than I do with all my profound ignorance." Darwin didn't think much of Kingsley's solution to the human evolution problem. But Kingsley's thoughts prompted Darwin once more to comment on his view of indigenous peoples:

> That is a grand & almost awful question on the genealogy of man to which you allude. It is not so awful & difficult to me, as it seems to be most, partly from familiarity & partly, I think, from having seen a good many Barbarians. I declare the thought, when I first saw in T. del Fuego a naked painted, shivering hideous savage, that my ancestors must have been somewhat similar beings, was at that time as revolting to me, nay more revolting than my present belief that an incomparably more remote ancestor was a hairy beast.

Darwin was less troubled by the notion of descending from apes than sharing humanity with indigenous peoples! But not to worry. Darwin continued, "In 500 years how the Anglo-Saxon race will have spread & exterminated whole nations; & in consequence how much the Human race, viewed as a unit, will have risen in rank." Darwin, it would seem, saw little value in racial and ethnic diversity.

Darwin employs the "savage/civilized" dichotomy repeatedly in *The Descent of Man*, comparing different aspects of life between the two mutually exclusive groups. He speaks of comparing the "skulls of savage and civilized races,"[12] and ranks the Fuegians as "the lowest barbarians," even if he also marveled at how the three Fuegians who had been brought to England and learned a little English "resembled us in disposition and in most of our mental faculties."[13]

In contrast to Darwin, Alfred Russel Wallace could write, "The more I see of uncivilized people, the better I think of human nature, and the essential differences between civilized and savage men seem to disappear."[14] Perhaps because Wallace was a member of the British working class, and because he lived so intimately among indigenous people for so long, relying on them for the necessities of life, he was able to develop a greater appreciation for their unique ways of life than the upper-class Darwin who only observed indigenous peoples at arm's length. Wallace was much the better ethnologist than Darwin.

Darwin on Eugenics

Darwin's half-first cousin, Francis Galton, is widely considered the father of the eugenics movement that swept through America and beyond in the 1920s and resulted in programs like genetic registries and forced sterilizations, programs that directly inspired the eugenics programs of Nazi Germany.[15] Building on Darwinian reasoning, Galton held that human society could be improved through the practice of artificial selection in human populations. If only the healthiest and most intelligent people are allowed to contribute to the gene pool, human societies could eventually reach a state of near perfection. If one attended the Second International Eugenics Conference held at the American Museum of Natural History in 1921, one would have been greeted at the entrance by busts of Francis Galton and Charles Darwin. Darwin's work clearly provided the philosophical foundation for the movement.

Yes, the eugenics movement involved artificial, not natural, selection, but of course much of the evidence Darwin presented for his theory of evolutionary progress was precisely the artificial selection of domestic breeders. On the other hand, it is common to absolve Darwin of any responsibility for what was done in his name. After all, Galton did not publish the text in which he coined the term *eugenics* until 1883, a year after Darwin's death (though Darwin was familiar with Galton's earlier work *Hereditary Genius* published in 1869). So as the argument goes, Darwin cannot be blamed for ethically problematic uses of his work by others.

What were Darwin's views on the matter? In his autobiography Darwin said of his cousin, "I am inclined to agree with Francis Galton in believing that education and environment produce only a small effect on the mind of any one, and that most of our qualities are innate."[16] This comment hardly proves that Darwin would have approved of later eugenic practices, but by siding with nature in the nature versus nurture debate, he certainly agreed with the basic underpinnings of eugenic theory.

In *The Descent of Man* Darwin articulates precisely the worry at the heart of the eugenics movement, namely that civilized society tends to spare the weak and inferior, even allowing them to breed, thereby ostensibly posing a threat to the future genetic health of the civilized races. Darwin writes:

> With savages, the weak in body or mind are soon eliminated; and those that survive commonly exhibit a vigorous state of health. We civilised men, on the other hand, do our utmost to check the process of elimination: We build asylums for the imbecile, the maimed, and the sick; we institute poor laws; and our medical men exert their utmost skill to save the life of every one to the last moment. There is reason to believe that vaccination has preserved thousands, who from a weak constitution would formerly have succumbed to small-pox. Thus the weak members of civilised societies propagate their kind. No one who has attended to the breeding of domestic animals will doubt that this must be highly injurious to the race of man.[17]

Darwin points out that not only do civilized nations take care of the sick and weak, they also raise up standing armies made up of only the finest young men, who are often killed during war before they can contribute to the gene pool. The shorter and feebler men are left at home to marry and propagate their kind.[18] Moreover, "A most important obstacle in civilized countries to an increase in the number of men of a superior class has been strongly insisted on by Mr. Greg and Mr. Galton, namely, the fact that the very poor and reckless who are often degraded by vice, almost invariably marry early, whilst the careful and frugal, who are generally otherwise virtuous, marry late in life, so that they may be able to support themselves and their children in comfort."[19]

Darwin fully understood the populational effects of Galton's use of his theory. But did Darwin operationalize this understanding into any kind of eugenic policy? First, he recommends that "all ought to refrain from marriage who cannot avoid abject poverty for their children." If the prudent avoid marriage while the reckless marry, "the inferior members tend to supplant the better members of society."[20] Just like other animals, humans, according to Darwin, have reached their present high condition through the struggle for existence. In order to advance even higher, humans must remain subject to the struggle. Otherwise, they would sink into indolence, and the superior people would not out-reproduce the inferior ones. Darwin therefore calls for open competition for all men, with the best able being unrestrained by law or custom from succeeding and rearing the largest number of offspring. Thus unrestrained population growth will, given Darwin's Malthusian influence, unleash unfettered competition and struggle leading to the advancement of society. So we see that although Darwin may not have called for forced sterilization, he did connect the long-term genetic improvement of society with public policy, making him at least a proto-eugenicist.

Not surprisingly, Alfred Russel Wallace's emphasis was distinctly different from Darwin's. While Darwin was preaching unconstrained breeding of the stronger (presumably at the expense of the weaker), Wallace enumerated the characteristics of organisms that go beyond simply ensuring survival and reproduction, and held that living organisms had a sanctity all their own and should be used by humans but not abused. "To pollute a spring or a river, to exterminate a bird or beast," wrote Wallace, "should be treated as moral offences and social crimes."[21]

While the understanding of nature had increased during the nineteenth century, there had been no corresponding advancement in the reverence for nature. In Wallace's view, "never before has there been such widespread ravage of the earth's surface by destruction of native vegetation and with it much animal life." And all of this, he concludes, has come about due to personal greed:

> And what is worse, the greater part of this waste and devastation has been and is being carried on, *not* for any good or worthy purpose, but in the interest of personal greed and avarice; so that in every case, while wealth has increased in the hands of the few, millions are still living without the bare necessities for a healthy or a decent life, thousands dying yearly of actual starvation, and other thousands being slowly or suddenly destroyed by hideous diseases or accidents, directly caused in this cruel race for wealth, and in almost every case easily preventable. Yet they are *not* prevented, solely because to do so would somewhat diminish the profits of the capitalists and legislators who are directly responsible for this almost world-wide defacement and destruction, and virtual massacre of the ignorant and defenceless workers.[22]

His working-class roots gave Wallace a completely different view of the relationship between nature and political economy from the bourgeois Darwin's. Deconstructing the mythological Darwin may be a crucial piece of any attempt to address sustainability issues today. Wallace makes a far better symbol for sustainability and environmentalism than does Darwin.

Darwin, Gender, and the Theory of Sexual Selection

Darwin early recognized that natural selection could not account for all characteristics of organisms because species frequently bear characteristics that do not advance reproductive fitness or may even undermine it. The classic example is the peacock's tail. This large showy tail makes escaping from predators more difficult and thus cannot have developed through successive small variations rendering the peacock more fit. So how could such a showy ornament arise? Darwin developed the theory of sexual selection to explain the existence of such seemingly maladaptive traits.

According to Darwin, females prefer males with showy ornaments. If a peacock is born with a small variation that slightly enhances the size of its tail, he will outcompete other males for mating opportunities, passing his "larger tail" trait to more descendants. If in each generation, females prefer males with larger, showier tails, the tails will get successively larger and showier, leading to the monstrous tail we see today. Darwin employed sexual selection to explain a host of these seemingly maladaptive traits, such as the massive antlers on the Irish elk and the bright colors of many male songbirds.

In her magisterial historiography of the development of Darwin's sexual selection theory, Evelleen Richards points out how Darwin, by assigning human aesthetic sensibilities to birds, was engaging in extreme anthropomorphism even while his strategy in *The Descent of Man* was "to dehumanize the aesthetic basis of human mate choice, to give it a biological basis by extending it to animals—but animals were humanized in this exchange."[23] Darwin simply assumed that birds shared the same aesthetic sense as humans, so that we could use our own sense of the beauty of a peacock's tail to account for why peahens would prefer peacocks with showy tails for mating. Richards shows how Darwin's judgments about the aesthetic senses of birds were always deeply influenced by the aesthetic senses of Victorian society.

Moreover, in the development of his theory of evolution by sexual selection (enlisted to shore up his theory of evolution by natural selection), Darwin was enacting certain assumptions about gender and sexuality potentially inconsistent with what we find in nature. Not surprisingly, feminist theorists have begun challenging the accuracy of Darwin's sexual selection theory. But before considering those challenges, we should consider the problematic ways Darwin extended sexual selection to human gender dynamics.

In *The Descent of Man and Selection in Relation to Sex*, Darwin naturalized a fully patriarchal view of human society:

> The chief distinction in the intellectual powers of the two sexes is shewn by man's attaining to a higher eminence, in whatever he takes up, than can woman—whether requiring deep thought, reason, or imagination, or merely the use of the senses and hands. If two lists were made of the most eminent men and women in poetry, painting, sculpture, music (inclusive both of composition and performance), history, science, and philosophy, with half-a-dozen

> names under each subject, the two lists would not bear comparison. We may also infer, from the law of the deviation from averages, so well illustrated by Mr. Galton, in his work on 'Hereditary Genius,' that if men are capable of a decided pre-eminence over women in many subjects, the average of mental power in man must be above that of woman.[24]

I am sure Darwin could well have produced the comparative list of male and female accomplishment he alludes to, thus ostensibly documenting male superiority. But Darwin seems to not even consider the possibility that gender dynamics and cultural biases were the reason that women were not as eminent as men in poetry, art, music, history, science, and philosophy. As Judith Flanders notes in her book on Victorian London, "There were thousands of places to go and be amused, on and off the street, in early- and mid-Victorian London—thousands of places, that is, if one happened to be a man. Public places for women's amusement were less easy to find and, for middle- and upper-class women, they verged on the non-existent."[25]

The supposedly superior faculties of men have, according to Darwin, developed as a result of sexual selection. Since men must compete against each other for mates, the smarter, stronger men will be more successful and reproduce more. "Thus man has ultimately become superior to woman."[26] It's curious that Darwin imagines that women do not compete for the most desirable men, a view that would be touching in its naivete if it were not insulting for its depiction of women as passive, a point that we will shortly see stands at the center of criticisms of Darwin's sexual selection theory.

Now Darwin realized that brute physical competition for women no longer held for genteel Victorian men. Nevertheless, "during manhood, they generally undergo a severe struggle in order to maintain themselves and their families; and this will tend to keep up or even increase their mental powers, and, as a consequence, the present inequality between the sexes."[27]

We can see why Darwin was so concerned about his brother's dalliance with Harriet Martineau: she was a strong supporter of women's equality.

The patriarchal assumptions in Darwin's views are obvious, making room for modern theorists to take him to task. Stanford University evolutionary ecologist Joan Roughgarden does so in *Evolution's Rainbow: Diversity, Gender, and Sexuality in Nature and People*. An expert on population genetics, Roughgarden cites hundreds of peer-reviewed papers documenting the diversity of gender expression in organisms, examples that complicate the simplistic framework for Darwin's sexual selection theory. Especially when it comes to female mate choice, there are far more complex reasons for why any given female bird, even among species with colorful males, chooses any particular male than an aesthetic desire for showy ornaments. Roughgarden provides the following summary of the extensive research she cites on female mate choice:

> Thus Darwin was fundamentally on the wrong track in his conceptualization of female choice. Sand gobies and alpine accentors show that dominant males don't have any better genes than subordinate males, according to any known metric (such as the weight and vitality of the nestlings). Sand gobies and peacock wrasses demonstrate that females choose males not for their great genes but for the likelihood of actually delivering on their promise of parental care: females are looking to avoid deadbeats. Alpine accentors and tree swallows suggest that females may choose males to distribute the probability of paternity so as to balance the incentive for a male to provide parental care with the danger to her nest from other males.
>
> Damselflies reveal that females may tune their gendered presentation to control the number of male advances. Female wattled starlings, hooded warblers, reindeer, and other females with male ornaments suggest that gendered symbolism may also be tuned among vertebrates to regulate the frequency of male advances.[28]

Add to this the example of male seahorses performing all the domestic chores—as well as many other confounding examples that could be offered—and the complexity of gender expression and mate choice in nature becomes glaringly apparent.

Thus Roughgarden asks, "Does social life in animals consist of discreetly discerning damsels seeking horny, handsome, healthy warriors?"[29] Of course not, she insists. It is simply not true that males are always promiscuous while females are coy and choosy. Gender dynamics are so diverse that the idea of females choosing males for their showy ornaments simply cannot be maintained. Yet, despite the evidence to the contrary, this continues to be the story told in all the textbooks and biology classes, which has implications for how fluidity in gender expression is viewed more generally.

Roughgarden writes, "I appreciate the gravity of discrediting a discipline's master text. However, I doubt that the factual difficulties in Darwin's theory of sexual selection can be easily smoothed over. I also believe that this theory has promoted social injustice and that overall we'd be better off both scientifically and ethically if we jettisoned it."[30]

So, once again we see that Darwin was a product of his times and that his scientific work was deeply influenced by the social mores of a patriarchal Victorian society.

In addition to *Evolution's Rainbow*, Roughgarden has also published *The Genial Gene*, a direct response to Richard Dawkins's best-selling *The Selfish Gene*. Roughgarden employs the mathematics of game theory (often used to model economic behavior) to show that there is far more cooperation in the natural world than the ruthless competition central to Darwinian thinking. Though Roughgarden never explicitly disavows Darwin's theory of natural selection in the same way that she has sexual selection, her concept of social selection presents a challenge to the tendency to view competition and struggle as uniquely fundamental to evolutionary mechanisms.

Another voice criticizing sexual selection theory belongs to University of Rhode Island evolutionary anthropologist Holly Dunsworth. She challenges the deeply entrenched story attributing size differences between men and women to sexual selection. Men must compete for breeding opportunities with women, and bigger, stronger men presumably would be more successful at attracting a mate, thus passing those "larger" genes to their progeny. Over time, men would naturally become on average larger than women. At the same time, women would evolve wider pelvises due to men preferring sexual partners with wider hips for giving birth to bigger babies.

But this is mere storytelling, As Dunsworth notes, what we actually know is that size differences between men and women are largely dictated by differing hormone levels. Boys and girls grow roughly at the same rate up until age 13. But with the onset of puberty, greater estrogen production in girls causes long bone growth plates to fuse, while boys continue to grow at a faster rate. Hormone differences also play a role in the widening of the pelvis in women. As for dominance and competition, they can be better understood as a consequence of greater size in men, and of differing hormone levels, rather than as the cause of men's greater size.

Dunsworth's hope is that "an updated answer to why there are sex differences in the human skeleton," a more nuanced one that takes into account such considerations, "is less likely to be interpreted to justify cultural conceptions of masculinity, femininity, and rigid binaries of sex and gender with 'human nature.'"[31]

The influence of Darwinian mythology still resides in Dunsworth's article, however, as she deftly assures her readers that she is not completely discrediting Darwin's sexual selection theory—even as she most certainly does. Alas, it seems that even Darwin's feminist critics must continue to genuflect to the man in order to be taken seriously in the scientific community.

Darwinian Mythology and the Search for Scientific Truth

A particularly egregious effect of Darwinian mythology is that it distorts our standard of what constitutes authentic science. The general belief that Darwin provided an empirically verified foundation for evolutionary biology obscures how uncertain our understanding of the process of evolution really is. The deeply entrenched nature of what I called in my previous book the "grand narrative of Darwinian triumph" leads to a dismissal of any criticisms of Darwin or natural selection as unworthy of serious attention. Critics of Darwin are dismissed as anti-scientific and unable or unwilling to accept the core theory of the biological sciences due, supposedly, to their religious biases. Critics of Darwin and Darwinism are, in short, seen as backwards and uninformed. Truth be told, establishment biologists have been very successful at pushing this narrative of Darwinian triumph, a narrative that developed primarily for the purpose of "scientizing" biology as it emerged from its associations with nineteenth-century religiously informed natural history. Darwin made it possible for biology to emerge as a purely naturalistic science without any taint of higher teleology or design. Or as Richard Dawkins famously put it, "Darwin made it possible to be an intellectually fulfilled atheist."[32]

None of this, of course, is true. That Darwin essentially solved the origin of species is a powerful myth, to be sure. But it is still just a myth. Some of the most important scientists of the later nineteenth and early twentieth centuries were critics of Darwinism.

One of the fathers of early genetics, Thomas Hunt Morgan, a Nobel Laureate, regularly taught a class on criticisms of Darwin during his first teaching post at Bryn Mawr College in the 1890s. And one of the most influential and pioneering geneticists of the early twentieth century, Richard Goldschmidt, never accepted that natural selection working on small variations could produce new species. That he is treated with contempt in biological circles today is a function of his vigorously questioning the Darwinian paradigm. And keep in mind that Goldschmidt was attempting to place evolutionary theory on a firmer evidential footing, not reject it wholesale—yet his criticisms of Darwinian theory were nevertheless enough to place him beyond the pale.

Another Nobel Prize-winning geneticist, Barbara McClintock, raised the uncomfortable prospect of cellular and genomic intelligence, a prospect that would upend the notion that evolution proceeds as an algorithmic process of randomly produced variation and natural selection with no overarching direction or goal. It challenges, in other words, the Darwinian formulation that Daniel Dennett famously termed a "universal acid," one that has driven purpose from biology and, in the process, eaten away at any notion that there is any larger purpose to existence.[33] These are just a few of the historical figures who challenged Darwinian evolution on scientific grounds. More recent critics are just as scientifically informed.

No fair-minded person could read the books of Lehigh University biochemist Michael Behe, such as *Darwin's Black Box* and *The Edge of Evolution*,[34] and not come away impressed with both the scientifically substantive criticisms of Darwinism and the arguments for intelligent design. The idea of irreducible complexity—that some biochemical systems, characterized by the functional integration of many essential parts, could not have evolved in a blind and gradual stepwise fashion—is often disparaged by mainstream evolutionists. But I am unaware of any research demonstrating that natural selection has in fact evolved any functionally integrated systems, like the bacterial flagellum or the blood clotting cascade. Until that is demonstrated, the existence of irreducible complexity in biological systems remains a cogent scientific argument against Darwinism.

Even highly decorated scientists like Marcos Eberlin have declared their support for intelligent design in recent years. Eberlin, a chemist, is a member of the Brazilian Academy of Sciences, the founder of the Thomson Mass Spectrometry Laboratory, winner of the 2005 Brazilian National Order of Scientific Merit, and the 2016 winner of the prestigious Thomson Medal. In his book, *Foresight: How the Chemistry of Life Reveals Planning and Purpose*, Eberlin demonstrates that, given our current understanding of chemistry, it is difficult to conceive how biological systems could form as a result of an unguided naturalistic process.[35] The book was endorsed by Nobel Laureate scientists.

We should also consider the work of Stephen Meyer, especially his book *Darwin's Doubt: The Explosive Origin of Animal Life and the Case for Intelligent Design*.[36] Meyer analyzes the well-known Cambrian explosion, whereby the fossil record documents the sudden (geologically speaking) appearance of more than a dozen new animal body plans without any long period of evolutionary divergence leading up to this amazing level of biological disparity. As we have seen, Darwin was aware of this phenomenon and viewed it as potentially fatal to his theory, but hoped that new fossil discoveries in the future would save him. As Meyer shows, they haven't.

What is significant about Meyer's work, however, is his recognition of the importance of information in biological systems. Biological systems run on coded information like DNA sequences, guided by the genetic code, to build higher-level biological "software," strings of precisely sequenced amino acid "letters" that form a host of precisely configured protein machines. The rather sudden appearance of new complex animal body plans in the Cambrian era would have required the explosive appearance of an extraordinary amount of new biological information.

Where did all this novel information come from? As Meyer points out, the origin of coded information, such as human language and computer code, can always be traced back to intelligent minds. In fact, there are no examples of a purely natural process ever producing coded information. None. So if coded information stands at the heart of biological organisms, this information must also have its origin in an intelligent mind. This is Meyer's far more developed argument in a nutshell. Suffice here to say that, for my money, this is the strongest argument not only against the power of natural selection to evolve biological complexity but in favor of intelligent design.

There is also this: information has to come from somewhere, but information is not a physical entity. It can be conveyed in a material carrier (e.g., ink on paper, a thumb drive, the sound waves of a human voice), but the information itself is immaterial, evidenced by the fact that the same information can be conveyed by radically different material substrates. Information is ultimately immaterial and therefore is much more naturally understood as a property of mind rather than matter.

Of course, the issue of the origin of biological information also raises the question of the origin of life itself, since even the simplest cell is bursting with coded information. Most readers will probably have seen in their high school or college biology textbook the image of the famous Miller-Urey experiment from the 1950s. Put some gasses together simulating what was then believed to constitute the atmosphere of the early Earth, run an electric discharge through them to simulate lightening, and out pop a few simple amino acids. We have solved the question of how life emerged from non-life in a natural way, right? Not so fast. Laboratory experiments designed to demonstrate how life emerged on the early Earth continue unabated, but the results are barely any better than what Miller and Urey produced decades ago. Producing a few amino acids in a flask is orders of magnitude removed from producing anything resembling a living cell.

Recently, an internationally distinguished Rice University synthetic organic chemist, James Tour, has highlighted the many problems plaguing origin-of-life research. As he explains, in what little progress these researchers have made in synthesizing some of the building blocks of life (but again, still not even close to synthesizing life from non-life), laboratory investigators neglect to accurately simulate prebiotic conditions on the early Earth. They use chemical compounds bought from industrial suppliers that are far more concentrated and pure than what would be found in nature; they shield their experiments from the degrading effects of solar radiation or free oxygen; and they manipulate the chemical reactions in ways that ironically demonstrate the opposite of what they intend.[37]

Meyer takes the argument a step further: if producing life in the laboratory requires repeated intelligent interference by these researchers, then it stands to reason that the origin of life on Earth also required an infusion of intelligence.[38]

These are only a few examples of many that give the lie to the charge that critics of Darwin and Darwinism are necessarily anti-science or motivated by religious bias. Some highly decorated scientists find Darwin's theory wanting. But their criticisms have been so marginalized as to undermine the development of authentic scientific inquiry on questions about the origin and evolution of life. Richard Dawkins, for example, who once held the position of Professor of the Public Understanding of Science at Oxford University, has done considerably more to stifle scientific inquiry and understanding on the matter of biological origins than to advance it; and he has done so precisely by his dismissive attitude toward anyone who criticizes Darwin.

Critical inquiry is the engine of scientific discovery. But interview just about any science professor today who has dared to publicly question evolutionary theory. Whole academic careers have been derailed.

Consider the case of Eric Hedin, a former physics professor at Ball State University who had taught a popular honors course, "Boundaries of Science," that introduced students to some of the evidence for design in cosmology and biochemistry. Pressure from outside atheist groups like the Freedom from Religion Foundation led the university to cancel his course.[39]

Then there is Günter Bechly, a paleontologist and internationally recognized expert on fossil insects who, after long accepting the Darwinian story, dared to question it and to consider the scientific evidence for intelligent design. He was forced out of his position as curator at the State Museum of Natural History in Stuttgart, Germany.

A final example: Cuban-American Guillermo Gonzalez, a young astronomer with an enviable record of peer-reviewed publication whose work had even been featured on the cover of *Scientific American*. Gonzalez was forced out of the astronomy department at Iowa State University for co-authoring a book called *The Privileged Planet*, which pointed to evidence of intelligent design in the fine tuning of Earth and the cosmos for both life and scientific discovery. Leading the charge was an atheist religion professor at the university. (You can't make this stuff up.)

These kinds of egregious violations of academic freedom abound. Yet, ironically, the founding text of the deeply entrenched Darwinian theory was viewed by its own author as nothing more than an abstract devoid of much of the evidence and references on which the theory propounded in it is supposedly based. But no one is told this in a biology textbook. Instead, biology textbooks continue to perpetuate what Jonathan Wells has termed "icons of evolution," famous images used to convince readers of the truth of Darwinian evolution without any discussion of the complexities and problems they create for Darwinism. These icons include things like industrial melanism in the peppered moth, Darwin's finches, Haeckel's embryos, Darwin's tree of life, and the aforementioned Miller-Urey experiment.

Showing that the color morphs of peppered moths changed frequency during industrialization in England is hardly a strong piece of evidence for natural selection's ability to create new biological complexity. After all, the darker- and lighter-colored moths already existed. The finches of the Galapagos may undergo changes in beak size related to changes in climate. But the beak sizes return to their previous state when the climate switches back, so there is no net change over time. Haeckel's embryo drawings, purportedly showing that embryonic stages among different species recapitulate evolutionary history, are known to be highly inaccurate, which begs the question of why textbooks continue to use century-old hand drawings when modern technology would allow for the use of digital photographs. (The obvious explanation is that accurate photographs would not be as convincing since Haeckel's drawings greatly exaggerate the similarities.) Then, too, there is that original icon of evolution, Darwin's tree of life, but good luck finding an introductory high school or college biology textbook noting how the Cambrian explosion, as well as phenomena like horizontal gene transfer, suggest a very different picture of life's history on Earth.[40] These textbook icons perpetuate Darwinian mythology at the expense of accurate science.

These icons are part of a larger Darwinian mythology, one that obscures the truth painstakingly explored in the present book and documented over and over in the Darwinian correspondence, namely that *The Origin of Species* is only an imperfect abstract of a larger work that later would fill in the crucial missing evidence, a larger work on natural selection that Darwin delayed and delayed and never published. This larger book only appeared a century later and then only as a historical artifact, wholly lacking in the evidence that Darwin promised his big book would deliver.

James Shapiro of the University of Chicago (and a former student of Barbara McClintock), while maintaining a safe distance from proponents of intelligent design, is one biologist unafraid to ask critical questions about Darwin's work. Shapiro coined the term Natural Genetic Engineering (NGE) to highlight all the ways that modern biochemistry and molecular biology challenge the Darwinian paradigm.[41] Another Darwinian critic is decorated Oxford University physiologist Denis Noble, who coined the term *biological relativity* to note how all levels of organismal structure play into and contribute to the evolutionary process, not just the genome.[42] Shapiro and Noble demonstrate that viewing evolution as a process primarily driven by random variation and natural selection within populations of organisms is an extremely narrow view. Evolution is far more than mere population genetics.

Recently, Shapiro and Noble teamed up to author a paper titled "What Prevents Mainstream Evolutionists Teaching the Whole Truth about How Genomes Evolve?" They begin:

> It is often taken for granted that the fundamental problems of evolutionary biology were solved on the basis of random mutations and natural selection by Charles Darwin and his 20th Century followers who formulated the so-called "Modern Synthesis" of Darwinism and Mendelian genetics. However, that comfortable assumption is inconsistent with a large body of research over more than a century that has documented more biologically complex processes at work in evolution.[43]

Shapiro and Noble point to processes like symbiogenesis, the role of viruses in transporting genetic material, horizontal DNA transfers, natural genetic engineering, organismal stress responses that activate intrinsic genome reorganization, and macroevolution by genome restructuring. They also challenge the assumption that DNA is a faithful replicator of genetic information that operates only in one direction, from DNA out to the synthesis of proteins—Francis Crick's well-known Central Dogma of molecular biology. This assumption is undermined by evidence that the genome acts as a highly formatted and integrated Read-Write database rather than a Read-Only Memory. These complexities of molecular biology are all well documented and well known. But according to Shapiro and Noble, they are usually ignored in discussions of evolution. The title of their paper asks why this is. Unfortunately, they do not attempt to answer the very "why" question they pose, content to merely document all the evidence challenging standard evolutionary theory.

This "why" question was central to my 2019 book, *The Mystery of Evolutionary Mechanisms.* I showed there that because the deeply entrenched Darwinian framework of evolutionary biology serves to place biology on a purely materialistic foundation as a proper natural science, any attempt to challenge it as insufficient opens the door to the possibility of some sort of guidance, direction, or even intelligence central to the evolutionary process. And once this is conceded, biology is seen as bleeding over into religion, leaving its status as a purely natural science in question. But this is an ideological or worldview objection, not one based on the evidence. Science should be about following the evidence.

Breaking down the edifice of Darwinian mythology, then, is important to reclaiming authentic scientific inquiry. Questioning Darwin and Darwinism (including neo-Darwinism) is not a negation of science, but rather its fulfillment. Many of the questions being raised today about the sufficiency of Darwinian evolution simply couldn't be asked without knowledge of the dizzying complexity of life at the cellular and molecular levels. It is the deeply entrenched Darwinian mythology that actually serves as a major deterrent to a proper airing of these questions, and thus a major deterrent to scientific advancement.

The threatening nature of an evolutionary model not entirely reducible to simple variation and selection is well demonstrated by a situation that played out in the pages of the *Journal of Theoretical Biology* in 2020. Two Scandinavian scientists, Steinar Thorvaldsen (Tromso University) and Ola Hössjer (Stockholm University), published a paper titled "Using Statistical Methods to Model the Fine-tuning of Molecular Machines and Systems." Taking their cues from discussions occurring today within cosmology about the fine tuning of the universe, Thorvaldsen and Hössjer argue that molecular systems in living organisms demonstrate similar kinds of fine tuning. Thorvaldsen and Hössjer's paper is a mathematically sophisticated argument for the concept of intelligent design; and the work of well-known intelligent design proponents like Michael Behe, William Dembski, Douglas Axe, and others are featured throughout the paper. Even the well-known intelligent design concept of irreducible complexity is analyzed in depth and endorsed as meaningful. The paper's intelligent design foundation is plain for anyone to see. So how did a paper overtly endorsing the widely ridiculed idea of intelligent design end up in a peer-reviewed biology journal?

The editors clearly thought the paper made a significant contribution to biology and sent it out for peer review. The peer reviewers must have agreed, and so the paper was published. This touched off a firestorm of criticism toward the journal for publishing a paper so favorable to intelligent design, an idea derided as religiously motivated pseudo-science by establishment biologists. How, critics wanted to know, could the editors and peer reviewers have possibly let such a worthless piece of research into the journal, a move that would only serve to embolden these pseudo-scientific quacks? The backlash was so severe that the editors published a disclaimer several months later, disingenuously commenting:

> The *Journal of Theoretical Biology* and its co-Chief Editors do not endorse in any way the ideology of nor reasoning behind the concept of intelligent design. Since the publication of the paper it has now become evident that the authors are connected to a creationist group (although their addresses are given on the paper as departments in bona fide universities). We were unaware of this fact while the paper was being reviewed. Moreover, the keywords "intelligent design" were added by the authors after the review process during the proofing stage and we were unaware of this action by the authors. We have removed these from the online version of this paper. We believe that intelligent design is not in any way a suitable topic for the *Journal of Theoretical Biology*.[44]

This disclaimer, of course, does not pass the smell test. First, the professors listed their university affiliations because they were in fact professors at those universities. Also, as noted, the paper is so shot through with intelligent design thinking and references to leading intelligent design thinkers that no one reading the paper could miss it. Clearly, the editors and peer reviewers thought that scientific evidence for intelligent design in biology *was* an appropriate topic for the journal, the editors making an about-face only after the angry backlash.

This affair powerfully demonstrates just how worried the biological establishment is about biology losing its foundation in Darwinian naturalism. Nothing less than the professional status of biologists is believed to be at stake. Unfortunately, the evidence is not on their side, as the editors of the *Journal of Theoretical Biology* could plainly see. The dazzling intricacy of life at the cellular and molecular levels, demonstrated so beautifully by biologists over the last half century, cries out for an explanation that Darwinian materialism cannot provide, a fact that was apparent to Darwin's contemporaries in reviewing his book on orchids, and is all the more apparent more than 150 years of scientific progress later. Living organisms are a wonder whose origin cannot be reduced to algorithmic processes alone.

In 2014, Nita Sahai, a chemist and origin-of-life researcher at the University of Akron, spoke at an origin-of-life symposium held at Case Western Reserve University in Cleveland. At one point, where she was impressing on the audience the complexity involved in laboratory modeling of the steps needed toward the origin of life from non-life, Sahai noted how the various components involved (nucleotides, amino acids, clays, etc.) need to be intelligently de—. Her voice broke off without completing the word. Realizing what she'd almost said, she sheepishly corrected herself: "No, not intelligent design." Then at the prompting of an audience member, she rephrased: "carefully select." She then went on to describe how the various elements must be carefully selected by the chemist in the lab to create a viable sequence of steps toward the origin of life. It seems that Sahai knew she could not utter the dreaded "i" term without serious blowback, yet it is clearly what she intended to say.[45] Moreover, as noted above, careful selection is part and parcel of intelligent design, and intelligent design is precisely what the origin-of-life experimenters were contributing to the process in the lab, suggesting that life could not have emerged by a purely undirected physical process.

Resituating Darwin

The time has come to return Darwin to his proper place in the history of ideas. The 1859 publication of his abstract, *The Origin of Species*, indeed touched off a significant controversy in Britain, Europe, and America. And the rise of Darwinism in the first half of the twentieth century, leading to the development of the neo-Darwinian synthesis, is an important historical narrative with wide-ranging implications. No one can or should ignore Darwin and his impact on modern science and society. He is a highly influential historical figure.

But being an influential figure in the history of science doesn't mean that Darwin's case for his theory was necessarily a robust one, or even that the theory is true. As Evelleen Richards reminds us, "There is no need to minimize, rationalize, or indeed, valorize those aspects of his thinking that do not mesh with present-day values, or might be seen to jeopardize Darwin's iconic standing. The history of science, as historians well know, is no place for icons, however dazzling their stature."[46]

As for *The Origin of Species*, as we have seen, it was a mere abstract of a larger work that Darwin decided never to publish. And if not for the goading of Charles Lyell and the surprise letter that arrived at Down House from Alfred Russel Wallace in the summer of 1858, containing the theory of natural selection in brief, even the abstract might never have seen the light of day. Further, the abstract was produced by an indecisive, anxiety-ridden, chronically ill amateur naturalist lucky enough to be born into high-class Victorian society, affording him the opportunity to rub shoulders with the scientific elites of his day without the pressure and time commitment involved in holding an academic appointment (or any other paying job). And this amateur naturalist made frequent methodological errors in both his geological and biological work.

Wallace, for his part, was the better and more experienced observational naturalist, and was largely free of the racial prejudices that characterized Darwin's outlook. And Wallace ultimately concluded that while natural selection could explain some things, creative intelligence was surely required to explain many others in origin biology, most notably that most exceptional of curiosities, the human mind.

There is simply no longer any principled reason to continue holding up *The Origin of Species* as a masterwork, or the modern form of

Darwin's theory as sacrosanct. To do so hinders any attempt to advance our scientific understanding of the actual causes for the origin and diversity of life. We should not be so hindered, even if the picture that emerges inconveniently fails to cooperate with our philosophical biases in favor of material causation as the only valid form of scientific explanation.

A little historical perspective is in order here. The modern requirement for scientific work to adhere to the tenets of methodological naturalism has not always characterized science, nor must it continue to do so in the future. Copernicus's main reason for revolutionizing our view of the structure of the cosmos was his religiously inspired aesthetic sensibility that the creator God he believed in would never have created the ad hoc monstrosity the Ptolemaic system had become.[47] Copernicus had no decisive empirical evidence for his model: the Ptolemaic system worked as well as his in accounting for observations and making predictions. But Copernicus's religiously informed hypothesis led him to search for a more elegant model of the solar system, one that turned out to be right.

Likewise, eighteenth-century Scottish astronomer James Ferguson used explicitly religious arguments to hypothesize that the stars he saw in the night sky represented bodies like our sun encircled by their own planetary systems.[48] Ferguson could not know that more than two centuries later, technology would develop that would allow us to observe extra-solar planets and prove him right.

And then there is Isaac Newton, widely regarded as perhaps the greatest scientist who ever lived, who was convinced that one could not account for the orderly movements of heavenly bodies apart from the action of an intelligent agent.[49] As Stephen Meyer notes, there is a myth, propagated by atheists such as astronomer Neil deGrasse Tyson, according to which Newton was puzzled as to why the planets of our solar system remained in their orbits when they should long ago have tugged each other into disarray. Newton, so the myth goes, shrugged and explained it by saying God must tinker with the planetary orbits from time to time to set things right. Newton is then lambasted for lazily committing the so-called God-of-the-gaps fallacy instead of patiently waiting for a fully materialistic explanation. But as Meyer explains, the story is a gross distortion.

In reality, Newton invoked God as the source of the orderly laws of nature that guide the planets, and was rightly convinced that the planets, once in their orbits around the sun, could be expected to remain so without repeated fiddling from God.[50] "Newton thought that God was responsible on an ongoing basis for the mathematical regularities evident in nature, not fixing irregularities or rectifying instabilities," Meyer writes. "His *Mathematical Principles of Natural Philosophy* sought to use mathematics to describe the orderly concourse of nature as a way of demonstrating the rationality of God, the divine geometer."[51]

These are but three of countless examples that could be invoked supporting what is a commonplace among historians of science: namely that modern science was born from the soil of theism, with the conviction that nature was the rational work of a rational designer playing a crucial role in fostering scientific exploration. The dogma of methodological materialism, which if strictly followed would disallow attributing even the fine-tuned laws of nature to God, came later.

As for Darwin, he did make significant contributions to the science of his day. Given his great gift for detailed observation and the encyclopedic nature of his collections of facts and observations, Darwin did the scientific community service with his comprehensive monograph on barnacles and with some of his botanical work—especially the orchid book. These remain important milestones in systematic description. But as to his species theory, even Darwin could say to Asa Gray on June 18, 1857, in the midst of writing his big book, "It is extremely kind of you to say that my letters have not bored you very much, & it is almost *incredible* to me, for I am quite conscious that my speculations run quite beyond the bounds of true science." We would do well today to take Darwin at his word.

Chronological Index of Letters Cited

All letters are keyed to Frederick Burkhardt, ed., *The Correspondence of Charles Darwin* (Cambridge, UK: Cambridge University Press, 1985–1999).

1820s

Darwin to Susan Darwin (March 27, 1826) 1:37

1830s

Darwin to William Darwin Fox (April 7, 1831) 1:120
Darwin to Caroline Darwin (April 28, 1831) 1:121
John Stevens Henslow to Darwin (August 24, 1831) 1:128
Darwin to Caroline Darwin (March 30/April 12, 1833) 1:302
Darwin to Catherine Darwin (May 22–July 14, 1833) 1:311
Darwin to Susan Darwin (April 23, 1835) 1:445
Darwin to Caroline Darwin (April 29, 1836) 1:494
Darwin to John Stevens Henslow (July 9, 1836) 1:499
Darwin to Caroline Darwin (November 9, 1836) 1:518
Darwin to John Stevens Henslow (October 14, 1837) 2:30
Darwin to William Darwin Fox (June 15, 1838) 2:91
Darwin to Charles Lyell (August 9, 1838) 2:95
Darwin to George Robert Waterhouse (August 1838–1840) 2:93
Emma Wedgwood to Darwin (January 3, 1839) 2:157
Darwin to William Darwin Fox (October 24, 1839) 2:234

1840s

Darwin to William Darwin Fox (January 25, 1841) 2:279
Darwin to Louis Agassiz (March 1, 1841) 2:284
Darwin to Charles Maclaren (November 15–December, 1842) 2:341
Darwin to Joseph Dalton Hooker (January 11, 1844) 3:1
Darwin to Henry Denny (June 3, 1844) 3:38
Darwin to Emma Darwin (July 5, 1844) 3:43
Darwin to Leonard Horner (August 29, 1844) 3:54
Darwin to Leonard Jenyns (October 12, 1844) 3:67
Darwin to Leonard Jenyns (November 25, 1844) 3:84
Darwin to Joseph Dalton Hooker (March 31, 1845) 3:165
Darwin to Joseph Dalton Hooker (September 10, 1845) 3:252
Darwin to Charles Lyell (October 8, 1845) 3:258
Darwin to Emma Darwin (June 25, 1846) 3:326
Darwin to Leonard Horner (August 17-September 7, 1846) 3:333
Darwin to James Clark Ross (June 27, 1847) 4:53
Darwin to Bernhard Studer (July 4, 1847) 4:53
Darwin to Joseph Dalton Hooker (July 19, 1847) 4:55
Darwin to Joseph Dalton Hooker (May 10, 1848) 4:139
Darwin to Emma Darwin (May 25, 1848) 4:146
Darwin to Emma Darwin (May 27, 1848) 4:147
Darwin to John Stevens Henslow (July 2, 1848) 4:155
Darwin to Susan Darwin (March 19, 1849) 4:224
Darwin to Charles Lyell (June 14-28, 1849) 4:239
Darwin to Charles Lyell (September 2, 1849) 4:251
Darwin to Joseph Dalton Hooker (October 12, 1849) 4:268

1850–1854

Joseph Dalton Hooker to Darwin (April 6, 1850) 4:327
Darwin to William Darwin Fox (September 4, 1850) 4:353
Erasmus Alvey Darwin to Darwin (April 25, 1851) 5:27
Darwin to George Robert Waterhouse (September 8, 1852) 5:97
Darwin to William Darwin Fox (October 24, 1852) 5:99
Joseph Dalton Hooker to Darwin (November 4, 1853) 5:164

Darwin to Joseph Dalton Hooker (March 26, 1854) 5:186
Darwin to Joseph Dalton Hooker (September 7, 1854) 5:214

1855

Darwin to Joseph Dalton Hooker (April 24, 1855) 5:319
Darwin to William Darwin Fox (May 7, 1855) 5:325
Darwin to Joseph Dalton Hooker (May 11, 1855) 5:328
Darwin to Joseph Dalton Hooker (May 15, 1855) 5:329
Darwin to *Gardeners' Chronicle* (May 26, 1855) 5:337
Darwin to Miles Joseph Berkeley (June 12, 1855) 5:353
Asa Gray to Darwin (June 30, 1855) 5:363
Darwin to John Stevens Henslow (July 2, 1855) 5:364
Darwin to William Erasmus Darwin (November 29, 1855) 5:508

1856

Darwin to John Maurice Herbert (January 2, 1856) 6:1
Darwin to George Henry Kendrick Thwaites (March 8, 1856) 6:54
Darwin to Syms Covington (March 9, 1856) 6:55
Charles Lyell to Darwin (May 1–2, 1856) 6:89
Darwin to Charles Lyell (May 3, 1856) 6:99
Darwin to Joseph Dalton Hooker (May 9, 1856) 6:106
Darwin to Joseph Dalton Hooker (May 11, 1856) 6:108
Darwin to William Darwin Fox (June 8, 1856) 6:135
Darwin to Samuel Pickworth Woodward (July 18, 1856) 6:189
Darwin to Joseph Dalton Hooker (August 5, 1856) 6:200
Victor de Robillard to Darwin (September 20, 1856) 6:518
Darwin to William Darwin Fox (October 3, 1856) 6:237
Hewett Cottrell Watson to Darwin (November 10, 1856) 6:265
Darwin to Joseph Dalton Hooker (November 11–12, 1856) 6:266
Darwin to Joseph Dalton Hooker (December 10, 1856) 6:304

1857

William Henry Harvey to Darwin (January 3, 1857) 6:316
Darwin to William Darwin Fox (February 22, 1857) 6:346

Victor de Robillard to Darwin (February 26, 1857) 6:520
Darwin to Joseph Dalton Hooker (April 29, 1857) 6:384
Darwin to Asa Gray (June 18, 1857) 6:412
Darwin to Joseph Dalton Hooker (July 14, 1857) 6:428
Darwin to John Lubbock (July 14, 1857) 6:430
Darwin to Asa Gray (July 20, 1857) 6:431
Darwin to Asa Gray (September 5, 1857) 6:445
Darwin to Thomas Henry Huxley (September 26, 1857) 6:456
Darwin to William Darwin Fox (October 30, 1857) 6:476
Darwin to Joseph Dalton Hooker (November 21, 1857) 6:488
Darwin to Asa Gray (November 29, 1857) 6:491
Darwin to George Bentham (December 1, 1857) 6:494

1858

Darwin to John Stevens Henslow (January 25, 1858) 7:10
Darwin to William Darwin Fox (February 28, 1858) 7:39
Darwin to Syms Covington (May 18, 1858) 7:95
Darwin to Charles Lyell (June 18, 1858) 7:107
Darwin to Charles Lyell (June 25, 1858) 7:117
Darwin to Joseph Dalton Hooker (June 29, 1858) 7:121
Charles Lyell and Joseph Dalton Hooker to the Linnean Society (June 30, 1858) 7:122
Darwin to Joseph Dalton Hooker (July 5, 1858) 7:127
Darwin to William Darwin Fox (July 6, 1858) 7:129
Darwin to Joseph Dalton Hooker (July 13, 1858) 7:129
Darwin to John Phillips (September 1, 1858) 7:153
Darwin to Thomas Campbell Eyton (October 4, 1858) 7:161
Alfred Russel Wallace to Joseph Dalton Hooker (October 6, 1858) 7:166
Darwin to Joseph Dalton Hooker (December 24, 1858) 7:220

1859

Darwin to John Phillips (January 21, 1859) 7:237
Darwin to Joseph Dalton Hooker (January 23, 1859) 7:238

Thomas Henry Huxley to Darwin (November 23, 1859) 7:390
Darwin to Charles Lyell (November 23, 1859) 7:391
Adam Sedgwick to Darwin (November 24, 1859) 7:396
Darwin to Thomas Henry Huxley (November 25, 1859) 7:398
Darwin to Charles Lyell (November 25, 1859) 7:400
Henry Holland to Darwin (December 10, 1859) 7:418
Darwin to Charles Lyell (December 10, 1859) 7:421
Joseph Dalton Hooker to Darwin (December 12, 1859) 7:425
Darwin to Francis Galton (December 13, 1859) 7:427
Darwin to François Jules Pictet de la Rive (December 24, 1859) 7:448
Darwin to William Darwin Fox (December 25, 1859) 7:449

1860

Leonard Jenyns to Darwin (January 4, 1860) 8:13
Darwin to Leonard Jenyns (January 7, 1860) 8:25
Darwin to Charles Lyell (January 14, 1860) 8:35
Darwin to Baden Powell (January 18, 1860) 8:39
Asa Gray to Darwin (January 23, 1860) 8:46
Darwin to Charles Griffin & Co. (January 29, 1860) 8:56
Charles James Fox Bunbury to Darwin (January 30, 1860) 8:58
Darwin to Asa Gray (February 8, 1860) 8:74
George Henry Kendrick Thwaites to Darwin (February 14, 1860) 8:86
François Jules Pictet de la Rive to Darwin (February 19, 1860) 8:95
Darwin to Samuel Pickworth Woodward (March 6, 1860) 8:122
Darwin to Joseph Prestwich (March 12, 1860) 8:129
Darwin to François Jules Pictet de la Rive (April 1, 1860) 8:137
Darwin to Asa Gray (April 3, 1860) 8:140
Darwin to Charles Lyell (April 10, 1860) 8:153
Darwin to Alfred Russel Wallace (May 18, 1860) 8:219
Darwin to Asa Gray (May 22, 1860) 8:223
Darwin to Charles Lyell (June 6, 1860) 8:242
Darwin to Charles Lyell (June 14, 1860) 8:253
Charles Lyell to Darwin (June 15, 1860) 8:255
Darwin to Charles Lyell (June 17, 1860) 8:258
Joseph Dalton Hooker to Darwin (July 2, 1860) 8:270

Darwin to Joseph Dalton Hooker (July 2, 1860) 8:272
Darwin to Asa Gray (July 3, 1860) 8:273
Darwin to Asa Gray (July 22, 1860) 8:298
Darwin to John Murray (August 3, 1860) 8:309
William Henry Harvey to Darwin (August 24, 1860) 8:322
Darwin to William Henry Harvey (September 20–24, 1860) 8:370
William Henry Harvey to Darwin (October 8, 1860) 8:415
Heinrich Georg Bronn to Darwin (October 13 [or 15], 1860) 8:547

1861

Darwin to Alexander Goodman More (March 8, 1861) 9:49
Darwin to Cuthbert Collingwood (March 14, 1861) 9:53
Darwin to Frederick Wollaston Hutton (April 20, 1861) 9:96
Darwin to Joseph Dalton Hooker (April 23, 1861) 9:98
Darwin to Thomas Wilson St. Clair Davidson (April 30, 1861) 9:107
Robert Edmund Grant to Darwin (May 16, 1861) 9:127
Darwin to John Frederick William Herschel (May 23, 1861) 9:135
Henry Fawcett to Darwin (July 16, 1861) 9:204
Darwin to Henry Fawcett (July 20, 1861) 9:212
Darwin to Charles Lyell (July 20, 1861) 9:212
Darwin to Asa Gray (July 21, 1861) 9:213
Darwin to Charles Lyell (August 1, 1861) 9:225
Darwin to Thomas Francis Jamieson (September 6, 1861) 9:255
Darwin to Charles Lyell (September 6, 1861) 9:256
Darwin to Asa Gray (September 17, 1861) 9:267.
Darwin to John Murray (September 21, 1861) 9:272
Darwin to John Murray (September 24, 1861) 9:278
Darwin to Joseph Dalton Hooker (September 28, 1861) 9:283
Darwin to George Bentham (November 26, 1861) 9:352
Alfred Russel Wallace to Darwin (November 30, 1861) 9:356

1862

Darwin to Asa Gray (January 22, 1862) 10:40
Darwin to Joseph Dalton Hooker (January 25, 1862) 10:47

Charles Kingsley to Darwin (January 31, 1862) 10:62
Darwin to Charles Kingsley (February 6, 1862) 10:71
Darwin to John Murray (February 9, 1862) 10:76
Darwin to William Erasmus Darwin (February 14, 1862) 10:79
Asa Gray to Darwin (February 18, 1862) 10:86
Searles Valentine Wood to Darwin (February 18, 1862) 10:88
Darwin to Joseph Dalton Hooker (March 7, 1862) 10:102
Joseph Dalton Hooker to Darwin (March 10, 1862) 10:104
Heinrich Georg Bronn to Darwin (Before March 11, 1862) 10:644
Darwin to Heinrich Georg Bronn (March 11, 1862) 10:111
Joseph Dalton Hooker to Darwin (March 23, 1862) 10:126
Darwin to Joseph Dalton Hooker (April 9, 1862) 10:147
Thomas Gold Appleton to Darwin (April 24, 1862) 10:165
Darwin to William Erasmus Darwin (April 26, 1862) 10:170
Darwin to Joseph Dalton Hooker (May 15, 1862) 10:195
Darwin to Joseph Dalton Hooker (May 18, 1862) 10:208
Alfred Russel Wallace to Darwin (May 23, 1862) 10:217
Darwin to Alfred Russel Wallace (May 24, 1862) 10:218
Darwin to George Dickie (May 30, 1862) 10:225
Alphonse de Candolle to Darwin (June 13, 1862) 10:649
Darwin to Daniel Oliver (June 18, 1862) 10:236
Darwin to Asa Gray (June 10-20, 1862) 10:239
Darwin to Joseph Dalton Hooker (June 11, 1862) 10:245
Darwin to Joseph Dalton Hooker (June 23, 1862) 10:270
Darwin to Joseph Dalton Hooker (June 30, 1862) 10:283
Asa Gray to Darwin (July 2–3, 1862) 10:291
Darwin to Asa Gray (July 23–4, 1862) 10:330
Darwin to William Erasmus Darwin (August 2–3, 1862) 10:348
Margaret Susan Wedgwood to Darwin (August 4, 1862) 10:351
William Erasmus Darwin to Darwin (August 5, 1862) 10:356
George Howard Darwin to Darwin (August 5, 1862) 10:358
Margaret Susan Wedgwood to Darwin (August 6, 1862) 10:359
Alfred Russel Wallace to Darwin (August 8, 1862) 10:360
Darwin to Alfred Russel Wallace (August 20, 1862) 10:371
Darwin to Asa Gray (August 21, 1862) 10:373

Darwin to John Lubbock (September 2, 1862) 10:387
Darwin to John Lubbock (September 3, 1862) 10:392
Darwin to Asa Gray (September 3–4, 1862) 10:389
Philip Gidley King to Darwin (September 16, 1862) 10:413
Darwin to William Darwin Fox (September 20, 1862) 10:421
Darwin to Hugh Falconer (October 1, 1862) 10:439
Darwin to John Murray (October 7, 1862) 10:448
Darwin to Asa Gray (October 16, 1862) 10:470
Darwin to John Lubbock (October 23, 1862) 10:481
Darwin to Joseph Dalton Hooker (November 10–12, 1862) 10:513
Darwin to Hugh Falconer (November 14, 1862) 10:524
Joseph Dalton Hooker to Darwin (November 26, 1862) 10:569
Joseph Dalton Hooker to Darwin (December 21, 1862) 10:618
Darwin to Joseph Dalton Hooker (December 24, 1862) 10:624

1863

James Dwight Dana to Darwin (February 5, 1863) 11:116
Darwin to Thomas Henry Huxley (February 26, 1863) 11:180
Darwin to Joseph Dalton Hooker (March 5, 1863) 11:200
Darwin to Charles Lyell (March 12–13, 1863) 11:222
Darwin to George Bentham (April 15, 1863) 11:316
George Bentham to Darwin (April 21, 1863) 11:344
Darwin to George Bentham (April 22, 1863) 11:347
Darwin to Joseph Dalton Hooker (May 9, 1863) 11:393
Darwin to Asa Gray (May 11, 1863) 11:402
George Bentham to Darwin (May 21, 1863) 11:426
Darwin to George Bentham (May 22, 1863) 11:432

1871

Darwin to Joseph Dalton Hooker (February 1, 1871) 19:53

Biographical Register

Agassiz, Alexander (1835–1910)—Zoologist, oceanographer, and mining engineer. Son of Louis Agassiz.

Agassiz, Louis (1807–73)—Zoologist, Professor of Natural History, Neuchatel, Switzerland, 1832–46. Professor of Natural History, Harvard University, 1848–73. Founded Museum of Comparative Zoology at Harvard University, 1859. Helped found the National Academy of Sciences, 1863.

Alison, William Pulteney (1790–1859)—Professor of Medicine, Edinburgh University, 1822–42.

Appleton, Thomas Gold (1812–84)—Writer, artist, and patron of the fine arts. Brother-in-law to Henry Wadsworth Longfellow.

Bates, Henry Walter (1825–92)—Entomologist. Traveled to Amazon with Alfred Russel Wallace, 1848–50. President, Entomological Society of London, 1868–69 and 1878.

Bentham, George (1800–84)—Botanist. President of the Linnean Society of London, 1861–74.

Berkeley, Miles Joseph (1803–89)—Clergyman and botanist. Editor, *Journal of the Royal Horticultural Society*, 1866–77. Expert on British fungi.

Brent, Bernard Philip (d. 1867)—Pigeon fancier who studied pigeon breeding in France and Germany.

Bronn, Heinrich Georg (1800–62)—Paleontologist. Professor of Natural Science, Heidelberg University, 1833. Translated the first German edition of *The Origin of Species*.

Buckland, William (1784–1856)—Geologist and clergyman. Professor of Minerology, Oxford University, 1813; Reader in Geology, 1819–49. President of the Geological Society of London, 1824–5.

Bunbury, Charles James Fox (1809–86)—Botanist. Collected plants in South America, 1833–4 and in South Africa, 1838–9.

Campbell, George Douglas (Duke of Argyll) (1823–1900)—Chancellor of St. Andrews University, 1851. President of the Royal Society of Edinburgh, 1861.

Candolle, Alphonse de (1806–93)—Botanist, lawyer, and politician. Professor of Botany and Director of the Botanic Gardens, Geneva from 1835.

Collingwood, Cuthbert (1826–1908)—Naturalist, Lecturer in Botany, Royal Infirmary Medical School, Liverpool, 1858–66. Surgeon and naturalist on expeditions of HMS *Rifleman* and HMS *Serpent* in China seas.

Condorcet, Nicolas de (1743–94)—Philosopher and mathematician. Scholar of Enlightenment rationalism. Honorary member, American Philosophical Society.

Covington, Syms (1816–61)—Charles Darwin's assistant on the *Beagle.* Settled in Australia in 1839.

Dana, James Dwight (1813–95)—Geologist and zoologist. Professor of Natural History, Yale University, 1856–64. Professor of Geology and Minerology, Yale University, 1864–90.

Darwin, Anne Elizabeth (1841–51)—Charles Darwin's daughter. Died in childhood of infectious disease.

Darwin, Charles Waring (1856–8)—Charles Darwin's son. Died in childhood of scarlet fever.

Darwin, Emily Catherine (1810–66)—Charles Darwin's sister. Married Charles Langton.

Darwin, Emma (1808–96)—Wife and first cousin of Charles Darwin. Daughter of Josiah Wedgwood II.

Darwin, Erasmus (1731–1802)—Charles Darwin's grandfather. Physician, botanist, and poet. Developed an evolutionary theory in his *Zoonomia.*

Darwin, Erasmus Alvey (1804–81)—Charles Darwin's brother. Graduated Edinburgh University with a medical degree but never practiced.

Darwin, Francis (1848–1925)—Charles Darwin's son. Collaborated with his father on botanical papers. Lecturer in Botany at Cambridge University, 1884; reader, 1888–1904. Knighted in 1913.

Darwin, George Howard (1845–1912)—Charles Darwin's son. Mathematician. Plumian Professor of Astronomy and Experimental Philosophy, Cambridge University, 1883–1912.

Darwin, Henrietta Emma (1843–1927)—Charles Darwin's daughter. Married Richard Buckley in 1871.

Darwin, Leonard (1850–1943)—Charles Darwin's son. Military engineer. President, Royal Geographical Society of London, 1908–11. Member of the Eugenics Education Society, 1911–28.

Darwin, Robert Waring (1766–1848)—Charles Darwin's father. Physician with a large practice in Shrewsbury.

Darwin, Susan Elizabeth (1803–66)—Charles Darwin's sister. Never married. Lived entire life at family home in Shrewsbury.

Darwin, Susannah Wedgwood (1765–1817)—Charles Darwin's mother. Married Robert Waring Darwin in 1796.

Darwin, William Erasmus (1839–1914)—Charles Darwin's son. Partner in Southampton and Hampshire Bank. Chairman of the Southampton Water Company. Amateur photographer.

Davidson, Thomas Wilson St. Clair (1817–85)—Artist and paleontologist. Fellow of the Geological Society of London.

Denny, Henry (1803–71)—Entomologist and expert on parasitic insects.

Dickie, George (1812–82)—Botanist. Lecturer in Botany, Queen's College, Aberdeen, 1839–49. Professor of Natural History, Queen's College, Belfast, 1849–60.

Egerton, Francis Henry (1756–1829)—8th earl of Bridgewater. Commissioned the Bridgewater Treatises to illustrate the goodness of God manifested in the creation.

Elwin, Whitwell (1816–1900)—Clergyman and writer. Editor of the *Quarterly Review*, 1853–60.

Eyton, Thomas Campbell (1809–80)—Naturalist. Friend of Charles Darwin's at Cambridge University. Built a museum of bird skins and skeletons in Shropshire.

Falconer, Hugh (1808–65)—Paleontologist and botanist. Superintendent of botanical gardens in India, 1832–42. Professor of Botany, Calcutta Medical College, 1848–55. Vice President of the Royal Society, 1865.

Fawcett, Henry (1833–84)—Statesman. Professor of Political Economy, Cambridge University, 1863.

FitzRoy, Robert (1805–65)—Naval officer, hydrographer, meteorologist. Commander of the HMS *Beagle*, 1828–36. Governor of New Zealand, 1843–5.

Fox, William Darwin (1805–80)—Clergyman. Charles Darwin's second cousin. Attended Cambridge University with Darwin. Breeder of domestic animals.

Galton, Francis (1822–1911)—Charles Darwin's half-first cousin. Statistician. Researched heredity and founded the eugenics movement.

Godwin, William (1756–1836)—Journalist, political philosopher, novelist. Proponent of anarchism. Father of Mary Shelley.

Gould, John (1804–81)—Ornithologist. Taxidermist to the Zoological Gardens of London, 1826–81. Described Darwin's bird specimens from the *Beagle* voyage.

Grant, Robert Edmund (1793–1874)—Physician and zoologist. Professor of Comparative Anatomy and Zoology, University College, London, 1827–74.

Gray, Asa (1810–88)—Botanist. Fisher Professor of Natural History, Harvard University, 1842–88. Regent of the Smithsonian Institution, 1874–88.

Gully, James Manby (1808–83)—Physician. Founded hydropathic establishment at Malvern in 1842.

Harvey, William Henry (1811–66)—Botanist. Colonial Treasurer in Cape Town, 1836–42. Professor of Botany, Trinity College, Dublin, 1856–66.

Henslow, John Stevens (1796–1861)—Clergyman, botanist, and minerologist. Professor of Minerology, Cambridge University,

1822–7; Professor of Botany, 1825–61. Recommended Darwin for the *Beagle* voyage.

Herbert, Edward James (1818–91)—3rd Earl of Powis. Conservative M. P., 1843–8.

Herbert, John Maurice (1808–82)—County Court judge, South Wales, 1847–82.

Herschel, John Frederick William (1792–1871)—Astronomer, mathematician, chemist. Astronomer in Cape of Good Hope, 1834–8.

Holland, Henry (1788–1873)—Physician. Attended to Prince Albert and Queen Victoria. President of the Royal Institution of Great Britain, 1865–73.

Hooker, Joseph Dalton (1817–1911)—Botanist. Assistant Director of the Botanical Gardens at Kew, London, 1855–65; Director, 1865–85. Visited Antarctica on expedition led by James Clark Ross, 1839–43. Traveled to Himalayas, 1847–50. Knighted, 1877.

Horner, Leonard (1785–1864)—Geologist. Founder of the Edinburgh School of Arts. President of the Geological Society of London, 1846 and 1860–2. Father-in-law of Charles Lyell.

Humboldt, Alexander von (1769–1859)—Naturalist, geographer, world traveler.

Hutton, Frederick Wollaston (1836–1905)—Geologist and army officer. Professor of Biology and Geology, Canterbury University College of the University of New Zealand, 1890–3.

Huxley, Thomas Henry (1825–95)—Zoologist. Assistant surgeon on the HMS *Rattlesnake*, 1846–50. Hunterian Professor, Royal College of Surgeons of England, 1863–9. President of the Royal Society of London, 1883–5.

Jamieson, Thomas Francis (1829–1913)—Geologist. Lecturer at the University of Aberdeen, 1862. Fellow of the Geological Society of London.

Jenyns, Leonard (1800–93)—Naturalist and clergyman. Brother-in-law of John Stevens Henslow. Described fish specimens from the *Beagle* voyage.

King, Philip Gidley (1817–1904)—Midshipman on the HMS *Beagle*, 1831–6. Settled in Australia and worked in the mining industry.

Kingsley, Charles (1819–75)—Author and clergyman. Lecturer in English Literature, Queen's College, London, 1848–9. Professor of Modern History, Cambridge University, 1860–9.

Lamarck, Jean-Baptiste (1744–1829)—Naturalist. Held botanist positions at the Jardin du Roi, Paris, 1788–93. Propounded a theory of evolutionary development.

Linnaeus, Carolus (1707–78)—Botanist and zoologist. Professor of Botany, University of Uppsala, 1741–2. Reformed scientific nomenclature.

Lubbock, John (1834–1913)—Banker, politician, naturalist. Neighbor to Charles Darwin in the village of Downe. M. P., 1870 and 1874.

Lyell, Charles (1797–1875)—Geologist. President of the Geological Society of London, 1835–6 and 1849–50. Professor of Geology, King's College, London, 1831. Knighted in 1848.

Maclaren, Charles (1782–1866)—Geologist. Editor of *Scotsman*, 1820–48.

Malthus, Thomas Robert (1766–1834)—Clergyman and political economist. Professor of History and Political Economy, East India Company College, Haileybury, 1805–34. Authored *An Essay on the Principle of Population*, 1798.

Martineau, Harriet (1802–76)—Author, traveler, and advocate for woman's equality. Friend of Erasmus Alvey Darwin.

Mill, John Stuart (1806–73)—Philosopher and political economist. Administrator, East India Company, 1823-58.

More, Alexander Goodman (1830–95)—Naturalist. Studied flora of Ireland. Curator, Dublin Natural History Museum, 1881–7.

Murray, John (1808–92)—Publisher and author of guidebooks. Publisher of *The Origin of Species* and other of Darwin's works.

Oliver, Daniel (1830–1916)—Botanist. Professor of Botany, University College, London, 1861–88.

Owen, Richard (1804–92)—Comparative anatomist. Hunterian Professor of Comparative Anatomy and Physiology, Royal College of Surgeons of England, 1836–56. Superintendent of the natural history departments of the British Museum, 1850–84.

Paley, William (1743–1805)—Clergyman and philosopher. Author of *Natural Theology or Evidences of the Existence and Attributes of the Deity*, 1802.

Peacock, George (1791–1858)—Lowndean Professor of Geometry and Astronomy, Cambridge University, 1837.

Phillips, John (1800–74)—Geologist. Professor of Geology, King's College, London, 1834–40. Professor of Geology, Oxford University, 1860–74.

Pictet de la Rive, François Jules (1809–72)—Zoologist and paleontologist. Professor of Zoology, University of Geneva, 1835.

Powell, Baden (1796–1860)—Clergyman and writer on optics. Vicar of Plumstead, Kent, 1821–7. Professor of Geometry, Oxford University, 1827–60.

Prestwich, Joseph (1812–96)—Geologist. Professor of Geology, Oxford University, 1874–88.

Robillard, Victor de (Dates unknown)—Resident of Mauritius. Member of the Natural History Society of Mauritius.

Ross, James Clark (1800–62)—Naval officer and polar explorer. Led expedition to Antarctica, 1839–43.

Schweizerbart, Christian Friederich (1805–79)—Publisher. Published a German translation of *The Origin of Species.*

Sedgwick, Adam (1785–1873)—Geologist and clergyman. Woodwardian Professor of Geology, Cambridge University, 1818–73. President, Geological Society of London, 1829–31.

Spencer, Herbert (1820–1903)—Philosopher. Sub-editor of the *Economist*, 1848–53. Author of numerous papers on evolution, philosophy, and the social sciences.

Studer, Bernhard (1794–1887)—Geologist. Professor of Geology and Minerology, University of Berne, 1834–73.

Tegetmeier, William Bernhard (1816–1912)—Pigeon fancier and expert on poultry. Secretary of the Apiarian Society of London.

Thwaites, George Henry Kendrick (1811–82)—Botanist and entomologist. Superintendent of the Peradeniya Botanical Gardens, Ceylon, 1849; Director, 1857–80.

Tocqueville, Alexis de (1805–59)—Political writer. Visited the United States in 1831–2. Wrote *Democracy in America*, 1834.

Todd, Robert Bentley (1809–60)—Physician. Professor of Physiology at King's College, London, 1836–53.

Wallace, Alfred Russel (1823–1913)—Naturalist. Collector in the Amazon rainforest, 1848–52. Collector in the Malay Archipelago, 1854–62. Developed a theory of natural selection independent of Charles Darwin.

Waterhouse, George Robert (1810–88)—Naturalist. Founder of the Entomological Society of London, 1833. Curator of the Zoological Society of London, 1836–43. Described Darwin's mammalian and entomological specimens from the *Beagle* voyage.

Waterton, Charles (1782–1865)—Naturalist and traveler.

Watson, Hewett Cottrell (1804–81)—Botanist. Collected plants in the Azores, 1842.

Wedgwood, Caroline Sarah (Darwin) (1800–88)—Charles Darwin's sister. Married first cousin Josiah Wedgwood III.

Wedgwood, Hensleigh (1803–91)—Philologist and lawyer. Charles Darwin's brother-in-law and first cousin.

Wedgwood, Margaret Susan (1843–1937)—Charles Darwin's niece. Daughter of Caroline Wedgwood and Josiah Wedgwood III. Mother of Ralph Vaughan Williams.

Whewell, William (1794–1866)—Mathematician. Philosopher of Science. Professor of Minerology, Cambridge University, 1828–32.

Wilberforce, Samuel (1805–73)—Clergyman. Chaplain to Prince Albert. Bishop of Oxford, 1845–69.

Wilkes, Charles (1798–1877)—U. S. naval officer and explorer. Sparked the "Trent Affair" in 1861 as commander of the *San Jacinto.*

Wollaston, Thomas Vernon (1822–78)—Entomologist and conchologist. Fellow of the Linnean Society and the Cambridge Philosophical Society. Published *On the Variation of Species* in 1856.

Wood, Searles Valentine (1798–1880)—Geologist. Solicitor in London, 1851–65.

Woodward, Samuel Pickworth (1821–65)—Naturalist. Professor of Geology and Natural History, Royal Agricultural College, 1845.

Endnotes

Introduction

1. R. C. Stauffer, ed., *Charles Darwin's Natural Selection: Being the Second Part of His Big Species Book Written from 1856 to 1858* (Cambridge, UK: Cambridge University Press, 1975). The first two chapters dealing with variation under domestication are missing from the manuscript because Darwin expanded them into his 1868 publication *Variation of Animals and Plants under Domestication.*
2. In a letter to Asa Gray, July 23–4, 1862. See further discussion in Chapter 7.
3. English translations of letters written by French and German scholars are from the Burkhardt collection.
4. Charles Darwin, *The Voyage of the Beagle* [1839] (New York: P. F. Collier & Son, 1909), 382.

1. Piercing the Veil of Darwinian Mythology

1. Daniel Dennett, *Darwin's Dangerous Idea: Evolution and the Meaning of Life* (New York: Simon & Schuster, 1995), 21.
2. Janet Browne, *Darwin's Origin of Species: A Biography* (New York: Atlantic Monthly Press, 2006), 1.
3. Adrian Desmond and James Moore, *Darwin's Sacred Cause: Race, Slavery, and the Quest for Human Origins* (Chicago: University of Chicago Press, 2009), xv.
4. Ernst Mayr, "Evolution and God," *Nature* 248 (1974): 285.
5. Michael T. Ghiselin, *The Triumph of the Darwinian Method* (Chicago: University of Chicago Press, 1969), 1.
6. John Bowlby, *Charles Darwin: A New Life* (New York: W. W. Norton, 1990), 1.
7. Francis Darwin, ed., *The Life and Letters of Charles Darwin* (London: John Murray, 1887), 3: 98.
8. Browne, *Darwin's* Origin, 79.
9. See Bowlby, *Charles Darwin,* 333, 335.
10. James T. Costa, *Darwin's Backyard: How Small Experiments Led to a Big Theory* (New York: W. W. Norton, 2017), 75–76.

11. Frederick Burkhardt, ed., *Charles Darwin's Letters: A Selection 1825–1859* (Cambridge, UK: Cambridge University Press, 1996), title page.
12. Burkhardt, *Letters*, x.
13. Stephen Buranyi, "Do We Need a New Theory of Evolution?" *Guardian*, June 28, 2022.
14. Nicholas H. Barton, "The 'New Synthesis,'" *Proceedings of the National Academy of Sciences* 119, no. 30 (July 18, 2022), https://doi.org/10.1073/pnas.2122147119.
15. Massimo Pigliucci and Gerd Müller, eds., *Evolution: The Extended Synthesis* (Cambridge, MA: MIT Press, 2010).
16. Douglas H. Erwin and James W. Valentine, *The Cambrian Explosion: The Construction of Animal Biodiversity* (Greenwood Village, CO: Roberts and Company, 2013).
17. Simon Conway Morris, *From Extraterrestrials to Animal Minds: Six Myths of Evolution* (Conshohocken, PA: Templeton Press, 2022). See also *Life's Solution: Inevitable Humans in a Lonely Universe* (Cambridge, UK: Cambridge University Press, 2003).
18. Denis Noble, *Dance to the Tune of Life: Biological Relativity* (Cambridge, UK: Cambridge University Press, 2016).
19. James A. Shapiro, *Evolution: A View from the 21st Century* (Upper Saddle River, NJ: FT Press Science, 2011).
20. Janet Browne, "Reflections on Darwin Historiography," *Journal of the History of Biology* 55 (2022): 381–393, https://doi.org/10.1007/s10739-022-09686-5.
21. See Ralph Colp, *To Be an Invalid: The Illness of Charles Darwin* (Chicago: University of Chicago Press, 1977) and "More on Darwin's Illness," *History of Science* 38 (2000): 219–236. Child psychologist John Bowlby (*Charles Darwin: A New Life*) relates Darwin's symptoms to stress and anxiety stemming from the early death of his mother and a father who himself was emotionally compromised over the loss of his wife.
22. Unless otherwise noted, letters cited in this book are taken from Frederick Burkhardt et al., eds., *The Correspondence of Charles Darwin, Vols. 1 –11 and 19* (Cambridge, UK: Cambridge University Press), and can easily be located based on the date and addressee of the letter. In addition, an index of letters cited, arranged chronologically, appears in the back matter of the present book.
23. "Geologize" was a verb used by Darwin to describe traveling to observe and study geological formations.
24. Charles Darwin, *Variation of Animals and Plants under Domestication* [1868] (London: John Murray, 1905), 2.
25. Peter B. Medawar, "Darwin's Illness," *Annals of Internal Medicine* 61 (1964): 785.
26. Janet Browne, *Charles Darwin: The Power of Place* (New York: Knopf, 2002), 97.
27. Browne, *The Power of Place*, 385.
28. At least Hooker was willing to travel with his wife to other countries. There is no evidence that Darwin ever took Emma anywhere outside England!
29. A bacterial infection causing a skin rash similar to cellulitis.
30. Nora Barlow, ed., *The Autobiography of Charles Darwin, 1809–1882* (London: Collins, 1958), 119.

2. Darwin the Geologist

1. Nora Barlow, ed., *The Autobiography of Charles Darwin, 1809–1882* (London: Collins, 1958), 28.
2. Barry G. Gale, *Evolution without Evidence: Charles Darwin and the "Origin of Species"* (Albuquerque, NM: University of New Mexico Press, 1982), 146.
3. Francis Darwin, "Reminiscences of My Father's Everyday Life," circa 1884, *Darwin Online*, CUL-DAR140.3.1, paragraph 45A, http://darwin-online.org.uk. A catalogue of Darwinian manuscripts is available at that site.
4. Charles Darwin, *Journal of Researches* (London: Ward, Lock & Co., 1891), 295.
5. Charles Maclaren, review of *Coral Reefs* by Charles Darwin, *Scotsman*, October 29 and November 9, 1842.
6. This letter is cited in Francis Darwin, ed. *More Letters of Charles Darwin* (London: John Murray, 1903), 2: 198.
7. André W. Droxler and Stéphan J. Jorry, "The Origin of Modern Atolls: Challenging Darwin's Deeply Ingrained Theory," *Annual Review of Marine Science* 13 (2021): 537–73.
8. "Darwin's Theory about Coral Reef Atolls Is Fatally Flawed," *Science Daily*, October 13, 2020, https://www.sciencedaily.com/releases/2020/10/201013105811.htm.
9. Charles Lyell, *The Antiquity of Man* [1863] (London: J. M. Dent & Sons, 1914), 200.
10. Darwin wrote on page 17 of his 1838 Glen Roy notebook, "I did not look carefully for Marine remains." Darwin Online, CUL-DAR130, http://darwin-online.org.uk/content/frameset?pageseq=17&itemID=CUL-DAR130.-&viewtype=side.
11. Lyell, *Antiquity*, 206.
12. Darwin, *Researches*, 308.
13. Martin Rudwick, "Darwin and Glen Roy: A 'Great Failure' in Scientific Method?" *Studies in the History and Philosophy of Science* 5 (1974):176.
14. Rudwick, "Darwin and Glen Roy," 176.
15. This would square with Ruth Barton's contention that for Hooker, "Expertise counted far more than gentlemanly status of the conventional kind." See *The X Club: Power and Authority in Victorian Science* (Chicago: University of Chicago Press, 2018), 44.
16. A hazardous situation. Hooker encountered many trials during his travels in the Himalayas.
17. Darwinism may not be as fruitful a heuristic as it is often billed. National Academy of Sciences member Philip Skell "asked more than 70 eminent researchers if they would have done their work differently if they had thought Darwin's theory was wrong. The responses were all the same: No." He reports and reflects on those findings in Philip S. Skell, "Why Do We Invoke Darwin?" *The Scientist*, August 2005, available at https://www.discovery.org/a/2816/.
18. Darwin Online, CUL-DAR6.14, http://darwin-online.org.uk/content/frameset?pageseq=1&itemID=CUL-DAR6.14&viewtype=side.

19. Francis Darwin, ed., *The Life and Letters of Charles Darwin* (London: John Murray, 1887), 1: 346.
20. Darwin, *Life and Letters*, 315.

3. Darwin the Experimenter

1. Charles Darwin, *The Foundation of the Origin of Species: Two Essays Written in 1842 and 1844*, ed. Francis Darwin (Cambridge, UK: Cambridge University Press, 1909), http://darwin-online.org.uk/content/frameset?pageseq=1&itemID=F1556&viewtype=text.
2. Charles Darwin, *Journal of Researches* [1839] (London: Ward, Lock & Co., n.d.), 362–363.
3. R. C. Stauffer, ed., *Charles Darwin's Natural Selection: Being the Second Part of His Big Book Written from 1856 to 1858* (Cambridge, UK: Cambridge University Press, 1975), 257.
4. Frank J. Sulloway, "Darwin and His Finches: The Evolution of a Legend," *Journal of the History of Biology* 15 (1982): 32.
5. See Elizabeth Hennesey, "Mythologizing Darwin's Islands" in *Darwin, Darwinism, and Conservation in the Galapagos Islands: The Legacy of Darwin and its New Applications* (Cham, Switzerland: Springer, 2017), 65–90.
6. Thomas Robert Malthus, *An Essay on the Principle of Population* [1798] (New York: Norton, 1976), 9.
7. Gillian Beer, "Darwin's Reading and the Fictions of Development" in *The Darwinian Heritage*, ed. David Kohn (Princeton, NJ: Princeton University Press, 1986), 553.
8. Paul Johnson, *Darwin: Portrait of a Genius* (New York: Penguin, 2012), 48.
9. Charles Darwin, *The Origin of Species*, 6th ed. [1872] (New York: Modern Library, 1950), 74.
10. Darwin raised pigeons for crossbreeding experiments but had a rather humorous attitude toward others who did the same. He wrote to his son William on November 29, 1855: "I am going up to London this evening & I shall start quite late, for I want to attend a meeting of the Columbarian Society, which meets at 7 oclock near London Bridge. I think I shall belong to this Society where, I fancy, I shall meet a strange set of odd men.—Mr. Brent was a very queer little fish; but I suppose Mamma told you about him; after dinner he handed me a clay pipe, saying, 'here is your pipe' as if it was a matter of course that I should smoke.—Another odd little man (N. B. all Pigeon Fanciers are little men, I begin to think)...." Darwin was not a little man, likely standing more than six feet tall. But as a pigeon fancier himself, would he not have counted as one of these odd men?
11. Darwin, *Origin*, 29.
12. Darwin, *Origin*, 39.
13. Darwin, *Origin*, 82. This quote is from the sixth and final edition of the *Origin*, where Darwin had adopted Herbert Spencer's phrase "survival of the fittest," a phrase Darwin had not used until the fifth edition of the *Origin*.

14. Alfred Russel Wallace, "On the Tendency of Varieties to Depart Indefinitely from the Original Type," *Journal of the Proceedings of the Linnean Society (Zoology)*, 3 (1858): 61.
15. Darwin, *Origin*, 20.
16. W. R. Church, review of *On the Origin of Species*, by Charles Darwin, *Guardian*, February 8, 1860, 135.
17. T. V. Wollaston, review of *On the Origin of Species*, by Charles Darwin, *Annals and Magazine of Natural History* 5 (1860): 132.
18. Darwin, *Origin*, 305.
19. Darwin, *Origin*, 308.
20. Darwin, *Origin*, 365.
21. Darwin, *Origin*, 334.
22. See Cornelius G. Hunter, *Darwin's God: Evolution and the Problem of Evil* (Eugene, OR: Wipf & Stock, 2019). Hunter shows that Darwin's God-wouldn't-have-done-it-that-way argument is central to his theory. Darwin's theory, according to Hunter, is more theological than scientific.
23. Letter cited in Frederick Burkhardt et al., eds., *The Correspondence of Charles Darwin* (Cambridge, UK: Cambridge University Press, 1990), 6:365n2.
24. Latin for "I have sinned."
25. Charles Darwin, "On the Action of Sea-Water on the Germination of Seeds," *Gardeners' Chronicle & Agricultural Gazette* 10 (March 7, 1857), 155.
26. An island 130 miles southwest of Mauritius known today as Réunion.
27. A style is a filament that supports a flower's stigma, the female reproductive organ of the flower that receives pollen from the male organ, the anther, which sits atop the stamen. Darwin was interested in how the different anatomical layouts of the reproductive organs of flowers would influence fertilization.
28. Johnson, *Darwin: Portrait of a Genius*, 120.
29. Charles Darwin, *The Different Forms of Flowers on Plants of the Same Species* [1877] (London: John Murray, 1892), 1.
30. Unsigned review of *The Different Forms of Flowers on Plants of the Same Species*, by Charles Darwin, *John Bull*, 1877, 618.

4. Writing *The Origin of Species*

1. John van Wyhe, "Mind the Gap: Did Darwin Avoid Publishing His Theory for Many Years?," *Notes & Records of the Royal Society* 61 (2007): 177–205.
2. In a letter written to George Bentham, president of the Linnean Society, on November 26, 1861, Darwin reflects on his earlier work as secretary of the Geological Society and says, "I always protested against an abstract appearing when the paper itself might appear."
3. James T. Costa, *Darwin's Backyard: How Small Experiments Led to a Big Theory* (New York: Norton, 2017), 106.

4. For more on Darwin's use of "Abstract" in the original title of the *Origin*, see Koen B. Tanghe, "*On the Origin of Species*: The Story of Darwin's Title," *Notes & Records* 73 (2019): 83–100.
5. Robert J. Richards, *Darwin and the Emergence of Evolutionary Theories of Mind and Behavior* (Chicago: University of Chicago Press, 1987), 160.

5. Reacting to *The Origin of Species*

1. The Latin phrase "nunc dimittis" comes from the Gospel of Luke 2:29–32 where Simeon, upon looking upon the baby Jesus, utters the words "Now, let your servant depart in peace."
2. Darwin had already expressed these frustrations to Huxley on February 26, 1863: "I am fearfully disappointed at Lyell's excessive caution in expressing any judgment on Species or origin of man."
3. Charles Lyell, *The Antiquity of Man* [1863] (London: J. M. Dent & Sons, 1914), 394.
4. Alfred Russel Wallace, *The World of Life: A Manifestation of Creative Power, Directive Mind and Ultimate Purpose* (London: Chapman and Hall, 1911), 185.
5. Wallace, *World of Life*, 278.
6. "Nature does not make jumps."
7. See Thomas Henry Huxley, "The *Origin of Species*" in *Darwiniana Essays* (New York: Appleton, 1896), 74. See also the discussion in Thomas M. Lessl, *Rhetorical Darwinism: Religion, Evolution, and the Scientific Identity* (Waco, TX: Baylor University Press, 2012), 210.
8. The reference is to John Wilkins's 1638 publication of *The Discovery of a World in the Moon* in which he proposed the possibility that the moon might be inhabited by some type of creature and that humans might be able to invent a way to fly to the moon.
9. Sedgwick's reaction certainly got Darwin's attention, for on November 25 he wrote to T. H. Huxley, "I have had a kind yet slashing letter against me from poor old Sedgwick, who has laughed till his sides ached at my Book."
10. This passage, found on p. 165 of the first edition of the *Origin*, is quoted in Frederick Burkhardt et al., *The Correspondence of Charles Darwin* (Cambridge, UK: Cambridge University Press, 1985), 7:400n2.
11. Charles Darwin, *The Origin of Species*, 6th ed. [1872] (New York: Modern Library, 1950), 131. Interestingly, in a November 25, 1859, letter to Lyell, in which Darwin thanked Lyell for his comments on the pre-publication copy of the *Origin*, Darwin wrote, "I will leave out the Whale & Bear." Thus Lyell seems to have been among those who found it ridiculous.
12. Dana is referring to his 1863 publication *Manual of Geology*.
13. This is why Niles Eldridge and Stephen J. Gould offered the theory of punctuated equilibria in the 1970s. They recognized that the fossil record simply does not demonstrate a slow gradual process of modification, but rather sudden (geologically speaking) emergence of new species amid long periods of stasis. See Niles Eldredge and Stephen J. Gould, "Punctuated Equilibria: An Alternative to

Phyletic Gradualism" in *Models in Paleobiology* (San Francisco: Freeman Cooper, 1972), 82–115. See also Jeffrey H. Schwartz, *Sudden Origins: Fossils, Genes, and the Emergence of Species* (New York: Wiley, 1999).

14. Charles Darwin, "The Doctrine of Heterogeny and Modification of Species," *Athenaeum* (April 25, 1863): 554.
15. William Harvey, "Darwin on the Origin of Species," *Gardeners' Chronicle & Agricultural Gazette*, February 18, 1860, 145–146.
16. Joseph Dalton Hooker, "The Monstrous Begonia frigida at Kew, in Relation to Mr. Darwin's Theory of Natural Selection," *Gardeners' Chronicle & Agricultural Gazette*, February 25, 1860, 170–171.
17. A. Dewitte et al. note that "Polyploidy may play a significant role in Begonia diversification as evidenced by the wide range of chromosome number across various species." See "The Origin of Diversity in Begonia: Genome Dynamism, Population Processes, and Phylogenetic Patterns" in *The Dynamical Processes of Biodiversity: Case Studies in Evolution and Spatial Distribution* (Edinburgh, UK: InTech, 2011), 37. For how modern supporters of Darwin handle the inconvenient fact of polyploidy, see Robert F. Shedinger, *The Mystery of Evolutionary Mechanisms: Darwinian Biology's Grand Narrative of Triumph and the Subversion of Religion* (Eugene, OR: Cascade, 2019), 159–64.
18. Burkhardt, *Correspondence*, 8: 595.
19. Burkhardt, *Correspondence*, 8: 595.
20. Richard England, "Censoring Huxley and Wilberforce: A New Source for the Meeting that the *Athenaeum* 'Wisely Softened Down,'" *Notes and Records* 71 (2017): 379.
21. England, "Censoring Huxley," 381.
22. Burkhardt, *Correspondence*, 8: 596.
23. John Bowlby, *Charles Darwin: A New Life* (Cambridge, MA: Harvard University Press, 1990), 354.
24. William Irvine, *Apes, Angels, and Victorians: The Story of Darwin, Huxley, and Evolution* (New York: McGraw-Hill, 1955), 272.
25. Samuel Wilberforce, review of *The Origin of Species*, by Charles Darwin, *Quarterly Review* (1860): 256.
26. Wilberforce, review of *The Origin,* 233.
27. Wilberforce, review of *The Origin,* 237.
28. Wilberforce, review of *The Origin,* 238.
29. Wilberforce, review of *The Origin,* 240.
30. In chapter 10 of the *Origin*, under the subtitle "On the Sudden Appearance of Groups of Allied Species in the Lowest Known Fossiliferous Strata," Darwin wrote, "The case at present must remain inexplicable; and may be truly urged as a valid argument against the views here entertained." Darwin, *Origin*, 254.
31. Wilberforce, review of *The Origin,* 245.
32. Precambrian deposits do show signs of primitive life. But the long gradual succession from these primitive forms up to the complex animals of the Cambrian explosion continue to be absent from Precambrian deposits. See Douglas H. Erwin and

James W. Valentine, *The Cambrian Explosion: The Construction of Animal Biodiversity* (Greenwood Village, CO: Roberts, 2013); Stephen C. Meyer, *Darwin's Doubt: The Explosive Origin of Animal Life and the Case for Intelligent Design* (New York: HarperOne, 2013); and David Klinghoffer, ed., *Debating Darwin's Doubt: A Scientific Controversy that Can No Longer Be Denied* (Seattle, WA: Discovery Institute Press, 2015).

33. Wilberforce, review of *The Origin,* 250.
34. Wilberforce, review of *The Origin,* 250.
35. See letters of Darwin to Asa Gray (July 22, 1860) and to A. R. Wallace (May 24, 1862).
36. W. C. Wilson, review of *The Origin of Species*, by Charles Darwin, *Methodist Quarterly Review* 43 (1861): 627.
37. Wilson, review of *The Origin,* 614.
38. Wilson, review of *The Origin,* 615.
39. Wilson, review of *The Origin,* 618.
40. Wilson, review of *The Origin,* 622.
41. Wilson, review of *The Origin,* 623.
42. Wilson, review of *The Origin,* 624.
43. Wilson, review of *The Origin,* 627.
44. Burkhardt, *Correspondence*, 10: 691.
45. Burkhardt, *Correspondence,* 10: 694.
46. Burkhardt, *Correspondence*, 10: 694.
47. Burkhardt, *Correspondence*, 10: 695.
48. Burkhardt, *Correspondence,* 10: 695. This author was likely influenced by Richard Owen's *Edinburgh Review* article on the *Origin*, for there Owen argues that Darwin left "the determination of the origin of species very nearly where the author found it." See Richard Owen, review of *The Origin of Species*, by Charles Darwin and other works, *Edinburgh Review* 111 (April 1860): 494.

6. Darwin's Unfinished Book under the Microscope

1. Charles Darwin, *The Origin of Species*, 6th ed. [1872] (New York: Modern Library, 1950), 11.
2. Darwin, *Origin*, 38. It's worth noting that while Darwin made superficial stylistic adjustments to this statement between the first and sixth editions, he did not delete this claim even as late as the 1872 (sixth) edition quoted here, suggesting that even at this point he still hoped to produce the big book with its "long catalogue of dry facts" in support of the creative powers of natural selection; or at least he could not bring himself to correct the public's expectations on this point.
3. Darwin, *Origin*, 112. Emphasis in original.
4. Darwin, *Origin*, 52.
5. Darwin, *Origin*, 119.
6. Darwin, *Origin*, 75.

7. John R. Leifchild, review of *On the Origin of Species*, by Charles Darwin, *Athenaeum* 1673 (November 19, 1859): 660.
8. Unsigned review of *On the Origin of Species*, by Charles Darwin, *Spectator*, November 26, 1859, 1210.
9. J. Crawfurd, review of *On the Origin of Species*, by Charles Darwin, *Examiner*, December 3, 1859, 772.
10. W. C. Wilson, review of *On the Origin of Species*, by Charles Darwin, *Methodist Quarterly Review* 43 (Oct. 1861): 605.
11. Richard Owen, review of *On the Origin of Species*, by Charles Darwin and other works, *Edinburgh Review* 111, April 1860, 494.
12. Darwin's journal is catalogued as DAR 158.1 and is available at www.darwin-online.org.uk.
13. Darwin wrote to T. C. Eyton on October 4, 1858, reporting that his species book was too great for him, but that it was three-fourths complete.
14. Stephen Jay Gould, "Darwin's 'Big Book,'" *Science* 188 (1975): 824–26.
15. Sydney Smith, review of *Charles Darwin's Natural Selection*, edited by R. C. Stauffer, *The New Phytologist* 76 (1976): 183.
16. Jane Oppenheimer, review of *Charles Darwin's Natural Selection*, edited by R. C. Stauffer, *The Quarterly Review of Biology* 51 (1976): 93–94.
17. Larry T. Spencer, review of *Charles Darwin's Natural Selection*, edited by R. C. Stauffer, *BioScience* 27 (1977): 361; Michael Ghiselin, review of *Charles Darwin's Natural Selection,* edited by R. C. Stauffer, *Systematic Zoology* 24 (1975): 391–92; M. J. S. Hodge, "The Structure and Strategy of Darwin's 'Long Argument,'" *British Journal for the History of Science* 10 (1977): 237–46.
18. Hodge, "The Structure and Strategy of Darwin's 'Long Argument,'" 244.
19. R. C. Stauffer, ed., *Charles Darwin's Natural Selection: Being the Second Part of His Big Book Written from 1856 to 1858* (Cambridge, UK: Cambridge University Press, 1975), 118.
20. Stauffer, *Charles Darwin's Natural Selection*, 146.
21. Stauffer, *Charles Darwin's Natural Selection*, 161.
22. Stauffer, *Charles Darwin's Natural Selection*, 161.
23. Stauffer, *Charles Darwin's Natural Selection*, 175.
24. Stauffer, *Charles Darwin's Natural Selection*, 175.
25. Stauffer, *Charles Darwin's Natural Selection*, 216.
26. Stauffer, *Charles Darwin's Natural Selection*, 227.
27. Stauffer, *Charles Darwin's Natural Selection*, 220. The statement appears in the *Origin* on page 70.
28. Stauffer, Charles Darwin's *Natural Selection*, 222.
29. Stauffer, Charles Darwin's *Natural Selection*, 223.
30. Stauffer, *Charles Darwin's Natural Selection*, 233.
31. Stauffer, *Charles Darwin's Natural Selection*, 233.
32. Stauffer, *Charles Darwin's Natural Selection*, 251.
33. Stauffer, *Charles Darwin's Natural Selection*, 262.

34. Stauffer, *Charles Darwin's Natural Selection*, 268.
35. Stauffer, *Charles Darwin's Natural Selection*, 307.
36. Stauffer, *Charles Darwin's Natural Selection*, 308. Emphasis in original.
37. Stauffer, *Charles Darwin's Natural Selection*, 308.
38. Stauffer, *Charles Darwin's Natural Selection*, 340.
39. Stauffer, *Charles Darwin's Natural Selection*, 342.
40. Stauffer, Charles Darwin's Natural Selection, 346.
41. Stauffer, *Charles Darwin's Natural Selection*, 350.
42. Stauffer, *Charles Darwin's Natural Selection*, 352.
43. Stauffer, *Charles Darwin's Natural Selection*, 369.
44. Stauffer, *Charles Darwin's Natural Selection*, 370.
45. Stauffer, *Charles Darwin's Natural Selection*, 370.
46. Stauffer, Charles Darwin's *Natural Selection*, 467.
47. Stauffer, Charles Darwin's *Natural Selection*, 481.
48. Stauffer, Charles Darwin's *Natural Selection*, 481.
49. Stauffer, Charles Darwin's *Natural Selection*, 479.
50. Stauffer, Charles Darwin's *Natural Selection*, 526.
51. Stauffer, Charles Darwin's *Natural Selection*, 527.
52. Stauffer, Charles Darwin's *Natural Selection*, 520.
53. See W. P. Alison, "Instinct" in Robert B. Todd, ed., *The Cyclopedia of Anatomy and Physiology* (London: Longman, 1847), 3: 1–29.

7. Darwin the Botanist

1. Charles Darwin, *The Various Contrivances by which Orchids Are Fertilised by Insects, and the Good Effects of Intercrossing* (London: John Murray, 1862), 1–2.
2. Darwin, *Orchids*, 28-29.
3. Unsigned review of *Orchids*, by Charles Darwin, *Sheffield Daily Telegraph*, August 5, 1862, 6.
4. Unsigned review of *Orchids*, by Charles Darwin, *Annals and Magazine of Natural History* (November 1862): 384.
5. Unsigned review of *Orchids*, by Charles Darwin, *Annals*, 388.
6. R. Vaughan, review of *Orchids*, by Charles Darwin, *British Quarterly Review* 36 (July 1862): 244.
7. W. B. Tegetmeier, review of *Orchids*, by Charles Darwin, *Welda's Register of Facts and Occurrences* (August 1862): 39.
8. Unsigned review of *Orchids*, by Charles Darwin, *British and Foreign Medico-Chirurgical Review* 30 (October 1862): 313.
9. Unsigned review of *Orchids*, by Charles Darwin, *Saturday Review*, October 18, 1862, 486.
10. G. D. Campbell, review of *Orchids*, by Charles Darwin, *Edinburgh New Philosophical Magazine* n.s. 16 (1862): 285.

11. Unsigned review of *Orchids*, by Charles Darwin, *Literary Churchman*, July 16, 1862.
12. Quoted in Frederick Burkhardt, ed., *The Correspondence of Charles Darwin* (Cambridge, UK: Cambridge University Press, 1997), 10:635n9.
13. Henry Griffith, review of *Orchids*, by Charles Darwin, *in Faith: The Life-root of Science, Philosophy, Ethics, and Religion* (1882): 118.
14. M. J. Berkeley, review of *Orchids*, by Charles Darwin, *London Review*, June 14, 1862, 553.
15. Joseph Dalton Hooker, review of *Orchids* by Charles Darwin, *Gardeners' Chronicle & Agricultural Gazette*, August 23, 1862, 789.
16. Hooker, review of *Orchids*, August 23, 1862, 789.
17. Hooker, review of Orchids, *Gardeners' Chronicle & Agricultural Gazette*, September 27, 1862, 910.
18. Hooker, review of *Orchids*, September 27, 1862, 910.
19. Asa Gray, review of *Orchids*, by Charles Darwin, *American Journal of Science & Arts* 2nd ser. 34 (1862): 428.
20. Gray, review of *Orchids*, 429.
21. "Contrivance," *Cambridge Dictionary*, last accessed October 2023, https://dictionary.cambridge.org/us/dictionary/english/contrivance.
22. Nora Barlow, *The Autobiography of Charles Darwin*, 1809–1882 (London: Collins, 1958), 87.
23. Darwin, *Orchids*, 349.
24. Darwin, *Orchids*, 1.
25. See Dov Ospovat, *The Development of Darwin's Theory: Natural History, Natural Theology, and Natural Selection, 1838–1859* (Cambridge, UK: Cambridge University Press, 1981).
26. Francis Darwin, ed., *The Life and Letters of Charles Darwin* (London: John Murray, 1887), 3: 98.

8. Demythologizing Darwin

1. Charles Darwin, *Journal of Researches* [1839] (London: Ward, Lock & Co., 1891), 469.
2. Ibram X. Kendi, "Reigning Assimilationists and Defiant Black Power: The Struggle to Define and Regulate Racist Ideas" in *New Perspectives on the Black Intellectual Tradition*, eds. Keisha N. Blain, Christopher Cameron, and Ashley D. Farmer (Evanston, IL: Northwestern University Press, 2018), 162.
3. Darwin does draw out implications of his theory for human racial groups later in his *Descent of Man*. But this was long after he had already developed his species theory.
4. Desmond and Moore have not only overstated their case, but also constructed it via a highly problematic misrepresentation of the primary sources, as I have shown in a series of 2023 articles at *Evolution News and Science Today*: "'Sacred Cause'? Reconsidering Charles Darwin as Abolitionist," March 16, 2023, https://evolutionnews.org/2023/03/sacred-cause-reconsidering-charles-darwin-as-abolitionist/; "Fact

Check: Imagining Darwin's Abolitionism," March 17, 2023, https://evolutionnews.org/2023/03/fact-check-imagining-darwins-abolitionism/; "Darwin and Agassiz: An Imaginary Picture," March 18, 2023, https://evolutionnews.org/2023/03/darwin-and-agassiz-an-imaginary-picture/; "Darwin and the 'Eyre Affair': A Speculative Tale," March 20, 2023, https://evolutionnews.org/2023/03/darwin-and-the-eyre-affair-a-speculative-tale/; and "A Failed Attempt to Turn Darwin into Wilberforce," March 22, 2023, https://evolutionnews.org/2023/03/a-failed-attempt-to-turn-darwin-into-wilberforce/.

5. J. M. Herbert's remembrances are catalogued at Darwin Online, http://darwin-online.org.uk/content/frameset?viewtype=text&itemID=CUL-DAR112.B57-B76&pageseq=1.
6. Nora Barlow, ed., *The Autobiography of Charles Darwin, 1809–1882* (London: Collins, 1958), 51.
7. Conspicuous.
8. Unsigned review of *On the Origin of Species*, by Charles Darwin, *Hartford Courant*, May 31, 1860.
9. See Darwin's June 3, 1844, letter to the entomologist and expert in parasitic insects, Henry Denny.
10. Shortly after their marriage, Emma wrote to Charles, "I am rather afraid my own dear Nigger will think I have forgotten my promise not to bother him." See Barlow, *Autobiography*, 237.
11. Desmond and Moore, *Sacred Cause*, 137.
12. Charles Darwin, *The Descent of Man and Selection in Relation to Sex* [1871] (New York: Modern Library, 1950), 436.
13. Darwin, *Descent*, 445.
14. Alfred Russel Wallace, *My Life: A Record of Events and Opinions* (London: Chapman & Hall, 1905), 1: 368.
15. See Richard Weikart, *From Darwin to Hitler: Evolutionary Ethics, Eugenics, and Racism in Germany* (New York: Palgrave Macmillan, 2004) and *Darwinian Racism: How Darwinism Influenced Hitler, Nazism, and White Nationalism* (Seattle, WA: Discovery Institute Press, 2022).
16. Barlow, *Autobiography*, 43.
17. Darwin, *Descent,* 501.
18. Darwin, *Descent,* 502.
19. Darwin, *Descent,* 505.
20. Darwin, *Descent*, 919.
21. Alfred Russel Wallace, *The World of Life: A Manifestation of Creative Power, Directive Mind, and Ultimate Purpose* (London: Chapman and Hall, 1911), 279.
22. Wallace, *Life,* 279.
23. Evelleen Richards, *Darwin and the Making of Sexual Selection* (Chicago: University of Chicago Press, 2017), 440.
24. Darwin, *Descent*, 873. In writing to John Murray on September 21, 1861, about the possibility of publishing his orchid book, Darwin noted, "The subject of

propagation is interesting to most people, & is treated in my paper so that any woman could read it."

25. Judith Flanders, *The Victorian City: Everyday Life in Dickens' London* (New York: St. Martin's Griffin, 2012), 347.
26. Darwin, *Descent,* 874.
27. Darwin, *Descent,* 875.
28. Joan Roughgarden, *Evolution's Rainbow: Diversity, Gender, and Sexuality in Nature and People* (Berkeley, CA: University of California Press, 2004), 125.
29. Roughgarden, *Evolution's Rainbow*, 167.
30. Roughgarden, *Evolution's Rainbow*, 164.
31. Holly M. Dunsworth, "Expanding the Evolutionary Explanations for Sex Differences in the Human Skeleton," *Evolutionary Anthropology* 29 (2020): 14.
32. Richard Dawkins, *The Blind Watchmaker* (New York: Norton, 1986), 287.
33. Daniel C. Dennett, *Darwin's Dangerous Idea: Evolution and the Meaning of Life* (New York: Simon & Schuster, 1995), 63.
34. See Michael J. Behe, *Darwin's Black Box: The Biochemical Challenge to Evolution* (New York: Free Press, 1996) and *The Edge of Evolution: The Search for the Limits of Darwinism* (New York: Free Press, 2007).
35. Marcos Eberlin, *Foresight: How the Chemistry of Life Reveals Planning and Purpose* (Seattle, WA: Discovery Institute Press, 2019).
36. See Stephen C. Meyer, *Darwin's Doubt: The Explosive Origin of Animal Life and the Case for Intelligent Design* (New York: HarperOne, 2013).
37. James M. Tour, "We're Still Clueless about the Origin of Life," in *The Mystery of Life's Origin: The Continuing Controversy*, eds. Charles B. Thaxton et al. (Seattle, WA: Discovery Institute Press, 2020), 323–358.
38. Stephen C. Meyer, "Evidence of Intelligent Design in the Origin of Life," in *The Mystery of Life's Origin: The Continuing Controversy*, eds. Charles B. Thaxton et al. (Seattle, WA: Discovery Institute Press, 2020), 415–470.
39. See Eric Hedin, *Canceled Science: What Some Atheists Don't Want You to See* (Seattle, WA: Discovery Institute Press, 2021).
40. See Jonathan Wells, *Icons of Evolution: Science or Myth?* (Washington DC: Regnery, 2000) and *Zombie Science: More Icons of Evolution* (Seattle, WA: Discovery Institute Press, 2017). For a detailed analysis of the effect of Darwinian mythology on industrial melanism in the peppered moth, see Robert F. Shedinger, *The Mystery of Evolutionary Mechanisms: Darwinian Biology's Grand Narrative of Triumph and the Subversion of Religion* (Eugene, OR: Cascade, 2019), 117–128.
41. See James A. Shapiro, *Evolution: A View from the 21st Century* (Upper Saddle River, NJ: FT Press Science, 2011).
42. See Denis Noble, *Dance to the Tune of Life: Biological Relativity* (Cambridge, UK: Cambridge University Press, 2016).
43. James Shapiro and Denis Noble, "What Prevents Mainstream Evolutionists Teaching the Whole Truth about How Genomes Evolve?" *Progress in Biophysics and Molecular Biology* 165 (2021): 140.

44. Editorial disclaimer, *Journal of Theoretical Biology* 506 (2020): 110456.
45. Nita Sahai, "The Origins of Life: From Geochemistry to Biochemistry," Case Western Reserve University, *YouTube*, October 28, 2014, video, https://youtu.be/CeVk9yC0_vk?si=pvuh-EBbADYDuJcG&t=2915, 48:35–49:17.
46. Richards, *Sexual Selection*, 535.
47. See Bruce Wrightsman, "The Legitimation of Scientific Belief: Theory Justification by Copernicus" in *Scientific Discovery: Case Studies*, ed. T. Nickles (Dordrecht: Reidel, 1980), 51–66.
48. See Michael J. Crowe, "Astronomy and Religion (1780–1915): Four Case Studies Involving Ideas of Extraterrestrial Life," *Osiris* 16 (2001): 212.
49. See Stephen Snobelen, "'God of gods, and Lord of lords:' The Theology of Isaac Newton's General Scholium to the *Principia*," *Osiris* 16 (2001): 173.
50. Stephen C. Meyer, *Return of the God Hypothesis: Three Scientific Discoveries That Reveal the Mind behind the Universe* (New York: HarperOne, 2021), 426–429.
51. Meyer, *Return of the God Hypothesis*, 429.

Bibliography

Alison, W. P. "Instinct." In *The Cyclopedia of Anatomy and Physiology, Vol. 3*, edited by Robert B. Todd, 1–29. London: Longman, Brown, Green, Longmans & Roberts, 1847.

Annals and Magazine of Natural History. Unsigned review of *The Various Contrivances by which Orchids Are Fertilised by Insects*, by Charles Darwin. (November 10, 1862): 384–388.

Barlow, Nora, ed. *The Autobiography of Charles Darwin, 1809–1882*. London: Collins, 1958.

Barton, Nicholas H. "The 'New Synthesis.'" *Proceedings of the National Academy of Sciences* 119, no. 30 (July 18, 2022).

Barton, Ruth. *The X Club: Power and Authority in Victorian Science*. Chicago: University of Chicago Press, 2018.

Beer, Gillian. "Darwin's Reading and the Fictions of Development." In *The Darwinian Heritage*, edited by David Kohn, 543–580. Princeton: Princeton University Press, 1986.

Behe, Michael J. *Darwin's Black Box: The Biochemical Challenge to Evolution*. New York: Free Press, 1996.

———. *The Edge of Evolution: The Search for the Limits of Darwinism*. New York: Free Press, 2007.

Berkeley, M. J. Review of *The Various Contrivances by which Orchids Are Fertilised by Insects*, by Charles Darwin. *London Review*, June 14, 1862, 553–554.

Bowlby, John. *Charles Darwin: A New Life*. New York: W. W. Norton, 1990.

Browne, Janet. *Charles Darwin: The Power of Place*. New York: Knopf, 2002.

———. *Darwin's Origin of Species: A Biography*. New York: Atlantic Monthly Press, 2006.

———. "Reflections on Darwinian Historiography." *Journal of the History of Biology* 55 (2022): 381–393.

Buranyi, Stephen. "Do We Need a New Theory of Evolution?" *Guardian*, June 28, 2022.

British and Foreign Medico-Chirurgical Review. Unsigned review of *The Various Contrivances by which Orchids Are Fertilised by Insects*, by Charles Darwin. 30 (October 1862): 312–318.

Burkhardt, Frederick, ed. *Charles Darwin's Letters: A Selection 1825–1859*. Cambridge, UK: Cambridge University Press, 1996.

———. *The Correspondence of Charles Darwin, Vols. 1–11*. Cambridge, UK: Cambridge University Press, 1985–1999.

Campbell, G. D. Review of *The Various Contrivances by which Orchids Are Fertilised by Insects*, by Charles Darwin. *Edinburgh New Philosophical Magazine* n.s. 16 (1862): 277–285.

Church, W. R. Review of *On the Origin of Species*, by Charles Darwin. *Guardian*, February 8, 1860, 134–135.

Colp, Ralph. *To Be an Invalid: The Illness of Charles Darwin*. Chicago: University of Chicago Press, 1977.

———. "More on Darwin's Illness." *History of Science* 38 (2000): 219–236.

Costa, James T. *Darwin's Backyard: How Small Experiments Led to a Big Theory*. New York: W. W. Norton, 2017.

Crawfurd, J. Review of *On the Origin of Species*, by Charles Darwin. *Examiner*, December 3, 1859, 772–773.

Crowe, Michael J. "Astronomy and Religion (1750–1915): Four Case Studies Involving Ideas of Extraterrestrial Life." *Osiris* 16 (2001): 209–226.

Dawkins, Richard. *The Blind Watchmaker*. New York: Norton, 1986.

Darwin, Charles. "On the Action of Sea-Water on the Germination of Seeds." *Gardeners' Chronicle & Agricultural Gazette* 10. March 7, 1857, 155.

———. *The Descent of Man and Selection in Relation to Sex*. [1871] New York: Modern Library, 1950.

———. *The Different Forms of Flowers on Plants of the Same Species.* [1877] London: John Murray, 1892.

———. "The Doctrine of Heterogeny and Modification of Species." *Athenaeum: Journal of Literature, Science, and the Fine Arts* 1852 (April 25, 1863): 554–555.

———. *Journal of Researches.* [1839] London: Ward, Lock & Co, 1891. After 1905 this book was titled *The Voyage of the Beagle.*

———. *On the Origin of Species*, 6th ed. [1872] New York: Modern Library, 1950.

———. *Variation of Animals and Plants under Domestication.* [1868] London: John Murray, 1905.

———. *The Various Contrivances by which Orchids Are Fertilised by Insects and the Good Effects of Intercrossing.* [1862] 2nd ed. New York: D. Appleton, 1877.

Darwin, Francis, ed. *The Life and Letters of Charles Darwin*, 3 vols. London: John Murray, 1887.

——— and Albert Charles Seward, eds. *More Letters of Charles Darwin*, 2 vols. London: John Murray, 1903.

Dennett, Daniel. *Darwin's Dangerous Idea: Evolution and the Meaning of Life.* New York: Simon & Schuster, 1995.

Desmond, Adrian and James Moore. *Darwin's Sacred Cause: Race, Slavery, and the Quest for Human Origins.* Chicago: University of Chicago Press, 2009.

Dewitte, A. et al. "The Origin of Diversity in Begonia: Genome Dynamism, Population Processes, and Phylogenetic Patterns." In *The Dynamical Processes of Biodiversity: Case Studies in Evolution and Spatial Distribution*, 27–52. Edinburgh: InTech, 2011.

Droxler, André W. and Stéphan J. Jorry. "The Origin of Modern Atolls: Challenging Darwin's Deeply Ingrained Theory." *Annual Review of Marine Science* 13 (2021): 537–573.

Dunsworth, Holly M. "Expanding the Evolutionary Explanations for Sex Differences in the Human Skeleton." *Evolutionary Anthropology* 29 (2020): 108–116.

Eberlin, Marcos. *Foresight: How the Chemistry of Life Reveals Planning and Purpose.* Seattle, WA: Discovery Institute Press, 2019.

Editorial Disclaimer. *Journal of Theoretical Biology* 506 (2020): 110456.

Eldredge, Niles and Stephen J. Gould. "Punctuated Equilibria." In *Models in Paleobiology*, 82–115. San Francisco: Freeman Cooper, 1972.

England, Richard. "Censoring Huxley and Wilberforce: A New Source for the Meeting that the *Athenaeum* 'Wisely Softened Down.'" *Notes and Records* 71 (2017): 371–384.

Erwin, Douglas H. and James W. Valentine. *The Cambrian Explosion: The Construction of Animal Biodiversity*. Greenwood Village, CO: Roberts and Company, 2013.

Flanders, Judith. *The Victorian City: Everyday Life in Dickens' London*. New York: St. Martin's Griffin, 2012.

Gale, Barry G. *Evolution without Evidence: Charles Darwin and the "Origin of Species."* Albuquerque, NM: University of New Mexico Press, 1982.

Ghiselin, Michael T. *The Triumph of Darwinian Method*. Chicago: University of Chicago Press, 1969.

———. Review of *Charles Darwin's Natural Selection*, edited by R. C. Stauffer. *Systematic Zoology* 24 (1975): 391–92.

Gould, Stephen Jay. "Darwin's 'Big Book.'" *Science* 188 (1975): 824–826.

Gray, Asa. Review of *The Various Contrivances by which Orchids Are Fertilised by Insects*, by Charles Darwin. *American Journal of Science & Arts*, 2nd ser. 34 (1862): 138–144; 419–429.

Griffith, Henry. Review of *The Various Contrivances by which Orchids Are Fertilised by Insects*, by Charles Darwin. In *Faith: The Life-root of Science, Philosophy, Ethics, and Religion*, 118–119. London: Elliot Stock, 1882.

Hartford Courant. Unsigned review of *On the Origin of Species*, by Charles Darwin. May 31, 1860, 2.

Harvey, W. H. "Darwin on the Origin of Species." *Gardeners' Chronicle & Agricultural Gazette*. February 18, 1860, 145–46.

Hedin, Eric. *Canceled Science: What Some Atheists Don't Want You to See*. Seattle, WA: Discovery Institute Press, 2021.

Hennesey, Elizabeth. "Mythologizing Darwin's Islands." In *Darwin, Darwinism, and Conservation in the Galapagos Islands: The Legacy of Darwin and its New Applications*, 65–90. Cham, Switzerland: Springer, 2017.

Hodge, M. J. S. "The Structure and Strategy of Darwin's 'Long Argument.'" *British Journal for the History of Science* 10 (1977): 237–46.

Hooker, Joseph Dalton. "The Monstrous Begonia frigida at Kew, in Relation to Mr. Darwin's Theory of Natural Selection." *Gardeners' Chronicle & Agricultural Gazette*, February 25, 1860, 170–171.

———. Review of *The Various Contrivances by which Orchids Are Fertilised by Insects*, by Charles Darwin. *Gardeners' Chronicle & Agricultural Gazette*, August 23, 1862, 789–790; September 13, 1862, 863; and September 27, 1862, 910.

Hunter, Cornelius G. *Darwin's God: Evolution and the Problem of Evil.* Eugene, OR: Wipf & Stock, 2019.

Huxley, Thomas Henry. *Darwiniana Essays.* [1893] New York: Appleton, 1896.

Irvine, William. *Apes, Angels, and Victorians: The Story of Darwin, Huxley, and Evolution*. New York: McGraw Hill, 1955.

John Bull. Unsigned review of *The Different Forms of Flowers on Plants of the Same Species*, by Charles Darwin. September 29, 1877, 618.

Johnson, Paul. *Darwin: Portrait of a Genius.* New York: Penguin, 2012.

Kendi, Ibram X. "Reigning Assimilationists and Defiant Black Power: The Struggle to Define and Regulate Racist Ideas." In *New Perspectives on the Black Intellectual Tradition*, edited by Keisha N. Blain, Christopher Cameron, and Ashley D. Farmer, 157–174. Evanston, IL: Northwestern University Press, 2018.

Klinghoffer, David, ed. *Debating Darwin's Doubt: A Scientific Controversy that Can No Longer Be Denied.* Seattle, WA: Discovery Institute Press, 2015.

Leifchild, John R. Review of *On the Origin of Species,* by Charles Darwin. *Athenaeum* 1673 (November 19, 1859): 659–60.

Lessl, Thomas M. *Rhetorical Darwinism: Religion, Evolution, and the Scientific Identity.* Waco: Baylor University Press, 2012.

Literary Churchman. Unsigned review of *The Various Contrivances by which Orchids Are Fertilised by Insects*, by Charles Darwin. July 16, 1862.

Lyell, Charles. *The Antiquity of Man*. [1863] London: J. M. Dent & Sons, 1914.

Maclaren, Charles. Review of *Coral Reefs*, by Charles Darwin. *Scotsman,* October 29, 1842, 2; and November 9, 1842, 2.

Malthus, Thomas Robert. *An Essay on the Principle of Population.* [1798] New York: Norton, 1976.

Mayr, Ernst. "Evolution and God." *Nature* 248 (1974): 285–286.

Medawar, Peter B. "Darwin's Illness." *Annals of Internal Medicine* 61 (1964): 782–787.

Meyer, Stephen C. *Darwin's Doubt: The Explosive Origin of Animal Life and the Case for Intelligent Design*. New York: HarperOne, 2013.

———. "Evidence of Intelligent Design in the Origin of Life." In *The Mystery of Life's Origin: The Continuing Controversy*, edited by Charles Thaxton et al., 415–470. Seattle, WA: Discovery Institute Press, 2020.

———. *Return of the God Hypothesis: Three Scientific Discoveries That Reveal the Mind behind the Universe.* New York: HarperOne, 2021.

Morris, Simon Conway. *From Extraterrestrials to Animal Minds; Six Myths of Evolution*. Conshohocken, PA: Templeton Press, 2022.

———. *Life's Solution: Inevitable Humans in a Lonely Universe.* Cambridge, UK: Cambridge University Press, 2003.

Noble, Denis. *Dance to the Tune of Life: Biological Relativity.* Cambridge, UK: Cambridge University Press, 2016.

Oppenheimer, Jane. Review of *Charles Darwin's Natural Selection*, edited by R. C. Stauffer. *The Quarterly Review of Biology* 51 (1976): 93–94.

Ospovat, Dov. *The Development of Darwin's Theory: Natural History, Natural Theology, Natural Selection, 1838–1859*. Cambridge, UK: Cambridge University Press, 1981.

Owen, Richard. Review of *On the Origin of Species*, by Charles Darwin. *Edinburgh Review* 111, April 1860, 487–532.

Pigliucci, Massimo and Gerd Müller, eds. *Evolution: The Extended Synthesis*. Cambridge, MA: MIT Press, 2010.

Richards, Evelleen. *Darwin and the Making of Sexual Selection*. Chicago: University of Chicago Press, 2017.

Richards, Robert J. *Darwin and the Emergence of Evolutionary Theories of Mind and Behavior*. Chicago: University of Chicago Press, 1987.

Roughgarden, Joan. *Evolution's Rainbow: Diversity, Gender, and Sexuality in Nature and People*. Berkeley: University of California Press, 2004.

Rudwick, Martin. "Darwin and Glen Roy: A 'Great Failure' in Scientific Method?" *Studies in the History and Philosophy of Science* 5 (1974): 99–178.

Sahai, Nita. "The Origins of Life: From Geochemistry to Biochemistry," Case Western Reserve University, *YouTube*, October 28, 2014, video, 59:05.

Saturday Review. Unsigned review of *The Various Contrivances by which Orchids Are Fertilised by Insects*, by Charles Darwin. October 18, 1862, 486.

Schwartz, Jeffrey H. *Sudden Origins: Fossils, Genes, and the Emergence of Species*. New York: Wiley, 1999.

Shapiro, James A. *Evolution: A View from the 21st Century*. Upper Saddle River, NJ: FT Press Science, 2011.

Shapiro, James and Denis Noble, "What Prevents Mainstream Evolutionists Teaching the Whole Truth about How Genomes Evolve." *Progress in Biophysics and Molecular Biology* 165 (2021): 140–52.

Shedinger, Robert F. *The Mystery of Evolutionary Mechanisms; Darwinian Biology's Grand Narrative of Triumph and the Subversion of Religion*. Eugene, OR: Cascade, 2019.

Sheffield Daily Telegraph. Unsigned review of *The Various Contrivances by which Orchids Are Fertilised by Insects*, by Charles Darwin. August 5, 1862, 6.

Skell, Philip S. "Why Do We Invoke Darwin?" *The Scientist*, August 2005.

Smith, Sydney. Review of *Charles Darwin's Natural Selection*, edited by R. C. Stauffer. *The New Phytologist* 76 (1976): 183.

Snobelen, Stephen. "'God of Gods, and Lord of Lords:' The Theology of Isaac Newton's General Scholium to the Principia." *Osiris* 16 (2001): 169–208.

Spectator. Unsigned review of *On the Origin of Species*, by Charles Darwin. November 26, 1859, 1210–1211.

Spencer, Larry T. Review of *Charles Darwin's Natural Selection*, edited by R. C. Stauffer. *BioScience* 27 (1977): 361.

Stauffer, R. C., ed. *Charles Darwin's Natural Selection: Being the Second Part of His Big Book Written from 1856 to 1858.* Cambridge, UK: Cambridge University Press, 1975.

Sulloway, Frank J. "Darwin and His Finches: The Evolution of a Legend." *Journal of the History of Biology* 15 (1982): 1–53.

Tanghe, Koen B. "*On the Origin of Species*: The Story of Darwin's Title." *Notes and Records* 73 (2019): 83–100.

Tegetmeier, W. B. Review of *The Various Contrivances by which Orchids Are Fertilised by Insects*, by Charles Darwin. *Welda's Register of Facts and Occurrences* (August 1862): 38–39.

Tour, James. "We're Still Clueless about the Origin of Life." In *The Mystery of Life's Origin: The Continuing Controversy*, edited by Charles B. Thaxton et al., 323–358. Seattle, WA: Discovery Institute Press, 2020.

van Wyhe, John. "Mind the Gap: Did Darwin Avoid Publishing His Theory for Many Years?" *Notes & Records of the Royal Society* 61 (2007): 177–205.

Vaughan, R. Review of *The Various Contrivances by which Orchids Are Fertilised by Insects*, by Charles Darwin. *British Quarterly Review* 36 (July 1862): 243–244.

Wallace, Alfred Russel, *My Life: A Record of Events and Opinions, Vol. 1.* London: Chapman and Hall, 1905.

———. "On the Tendency of Varieties to Depart Indefinitely from the Original Type." *Journal of the Proceedings of the Linnean Society (Zoology)* 3 (1858): 53–62.

———. *The World of Life: A Manifestation of Creative Power, Directive Mind, and Ultimate Purpose.* London: Chapman and Hall, 1911.

Weikart, Richard. *Darwinian Racism: How Darwinism Influenced Hitler, Nazism, and White Nationalism*. Seattle, WA: Discovery Institute Press, 2022.

———. *From Darwin to Hitler: Evolutionary Ethics, Eugenics, and Racism in Germany*. New York: Palgrave Macmillan, 2004.

Wells, Jonathan. *Icons of Evolution: Science or Myth?* Washington DC: Regnery, 2000.

———. *Zombie Science: More Icons of Evolution*. Seattle, WA: Discovery Institute Press, 2017.

Wilberforce, Samuel. Review of *On the Origin of Species*, by Charles Darwin. *Quarterly Review* (1860): 225–264.

Wilson, W. C. Review of *On the Origin of Species*, by Charles Darwin. *Methodist Quarterly Review* 43 (1861): 605–627.

Wollaston, T. V. Review of *On the Origin of Species*, by Charles Darwin. *Annals and Magazine of Natural History* 5 (1860): 132–143.

Wrightsman, Bruce, "The Legitimation of Scientific Belief: Theory Justification by Copernicus." In *Scientific Discovery: Case Studies*, edited by T. Nickles, 51–66. Dordrecht: Reidel, 1980.

Index

S

T

U

V

W

Printed in the USA
CPSIA information can be obtained
at www.ICGtesting.com
CBHW021736050124
3163CB00004B/11